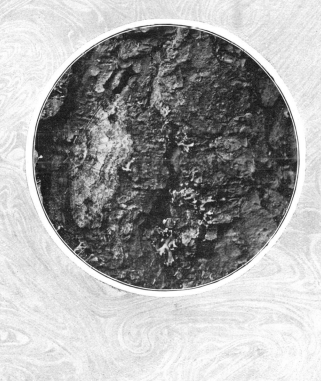

J. Wenward

The Rosaire

13/12/41

THE MOTHS
OF
THE BRITISH ISLES

THE MOTHS

OF THE

BRITISH ISLES

BY

RICHARD SOUTH, F.E.S.

AUTHOR OF
"THE BUTTERFLIES OF THE BRITISH ISLES"
EDITOR OF "THE ENTOMOLOGIST," ETC.

SECOND SERIES
COMPRISING
THE FAMILIES NOCTUIDÆ TO HEPIALIDÆ

WITH

ACCURATELY COLOURED FIGURES
OF EVERY SPECIES AND MANY VARIETIES
ALSO DRAWINGS OF EGGS, CATERPILLARS
CHRYSALIDS AND FOOD-PLANTS

LONDON
FREDERICK WARNE & CO. LTD.
AND NEW YORK

PREFACE.

———◦∘◦———

In the present and previous series of "The Moths of the British Isles," over 750 species have been portrayed on the plates and described in the text—a number that includes all those insects formerly grouped under the now obsolete term "Macro-Lepidoptera." The task of dealing with so many species in two volumes has necessarily imposed brevity in their treatment; but it is hoped that nothing has been omitted that could be legitimately regarded as falling within the scope of volumes especially designed for the votaries of Nature Study.

To have comprised in this scheme the large contingent of our moths known as "Micro-Lepidoptera" would have reduced further the space available for those species which experience shows appeal to the majority of nature students in a way that the minuter forms may not do. Even then, only a few general remarks on each group would have been possible, with, perhaps, a portrait or two of representative species. Such a course seemed hardly likely to prove of practical utility. The "Small Fry," as they have been called, exceedingly interesting though they may be to a limited number of students, have therefore been left for separate treatment at some more convenient season.

Both classification and nomenclature are always under revision, and we are probably a long way from hearing the last word concerning either. These are, however, matters that

cannot be ignored even in a popular work ; consequently I
have ventured to adopt sundry changes in arrangement and in
names which, although not departing from the old style in any
very large way, still approach pretty closely to the new.

I have again to tender my sincere thanks to Mr. Robert
Adkin, F.E.S., for kindly lending specimens of rare species and
varieties for figuring ; and also to Mr. B. Adkin, F.E.S., Mr. G.
T. Porritt, F.E.S., and Mr. A. J. Scollick, F.E.S. I desire also
to gratefully acknowledge the loan of further beautiful coloured
drawings by Mr. Alfred Sich, F.E S. These figures have been
most accurately reproduced in black and white by Mr. Horace
Knight, to whom I am greatly indebted for his able assistance
in connection with the numerous drawings of ova, larvæ, and
pupæ. In some cases the preserved skin of a caterpillar had
to serve as a model, and where this occurs the fact is
mentioned. A few figures of larvæ have been copied from
Dr. G. Hofmann's *Die Raupen der Schmetterlinge Europas*, 2nd
edit., by Professor Dr. Arnold Spuler. All such reproductions
are duly noted in the text.

Mr. Knight is also responsible for the coloured drawings for
Plates 1, 13, 36, 61, 96, 98, 100, 104, 134, and 148 ; the figures
on which, except that of *Zygæna filipendulæ ab. chrysanthemi*,
are from specimens.

"A Forester," Mr. H. Main, F.E.S., and Mr. W. J. Lucas,
B.A., F.E.S., were good enough to furnish prints of some of
their excellent photographs depicting life-history details of
moths and caterpillars in repose, as met with in nature.

RICHARD SOUTH.

PREFACE TO THE PRESENT EDITION.

———◆◇◆———

A NEW edition of this volume having become necessary, it was deemed a fitting opportunity to bring the subject matter somewhat in line with our present knowledge of the Nomenclature, Habits, and Distribution of the Species considered therein. With this end in view, the new facts have been incorporated in the text so far as this was possible. Matter that could not be accommodated in this way has been presented in the form of an Appendix.

The changes in the names of genera are not numerous, and in every case where such change has been made, the name used in the first edition has been placed in brackets—*i.e. Dyschorista fissipuncta* of the 1st edit on becomes in the present one *Dyschorista (Sidemia) fissipuncta.*

By this treatment it has been found convenient to utilise the old Index and, at the same time, to provide a Specific Index for those who prefer to consult the volume by its aid.

its known haunts nearest to London are Bromley and Chisle-
hurst in Kent, Richmond Park and Norbury in Surrey. At
Palmer's Green, Middlesex, a specimen was found on an oak
trunk, July 27, 1902, and a female example came to light in
West London in 1906. In 1888 it was plentiful at sugar in the
Bromley district. The New Forest in Hampshire is a noted
locality for the species, but although it may abound there in
some years, in other years it is scarce or entirely absent. It is
rather more constant in Epping, Romford, and some other of the
Essex woodlands, and occurs also in Berkshire, Huntingdonshire,
Northamptonshire, Gloucestershire, and Devon. Odd specimens
have been recorded from Tarrington, Herefordshire ; St. Albans,
Hertfordshire ; and from Tuddenham, Suffolk. The var. *renago*,
and its modifications, has been chiefly obtained in Essex and
Huntingdonshire, but it has been found also in the Reading
district, and elsewhere.

The Lunar-spotted Pinion (*Calymnia pyralina*).

There are two colour forms of this species ; var. *corusca*, Esp.,
is rather brighter in colour than the female specimen shown on
Plate 2, Fig. 3, which approaches more nearly the duller
coloration of the type as described by Vieweg. The latter is
perhaps the least frequent in England generally, but it occurs
sparingly in Middlesex.

The caterpillar is green, with whitish warts emitting fine hairs,
and has three lines along the back, the central one white and
stripe-like ; a yellow stripe low down along the sides is edged
above with black. It feeds in April and May on elm, oak,
apple, plum, etc., among the leaves of which it hides by day,
and may be dislodged therefrom by jarring the boughs. (Plate
3, Fig. 2, after Hofmann.)

The moth is out from about mid-July to mid-August. On
some nights it will come freely to sugar and on others it seems

THE MOTHS
OF THE BRITISH ISLES.

——◆◆——

NOCTUIDÆ.

TRIFINÆ (*continued*).

The Heart Moth (*Dicycla oo*).

A male specimen of the ordinary form of this moth is shown on Plate 2, Fig. 1. Ab. *renago*, Haworth has the space between the central shade and the submarginal line more or less suffused with dusky or reddish grey. An intermediate form (Fig. 2) has a transverse band of darker colour between the second and submarginal lines of the fore wings (ab. *ferruginago*, Hübn.). The ground colour varies from a whitish or straw-yellow to reddish yellow (ab. *rufescens*, Tutt), and the markings are more distinct in some specimens than in others.

The caterpillar, which feeds from April to early June on the foliage of the oak, is black above and brownish beneath; there are three white lines on the back, the central one widest and more or less interrupted; the stripe along the black-outlined reddish spiracles is yellowish-white; head, and plate on first ring of the body, black and shining.

The moth appears about the end of June or early July, and has been noted, in good condition, as late as August 17. It seems to be of very local occurrence in England, but some of

1. Heart Moth.
2.   ,,   ,,   var. renago.
3. Lunar-spotted Pinion.

4, 5. Lesser-spotted Pinion.
6, 7. White-spotted Pinion.
8-11. Dun-bar.

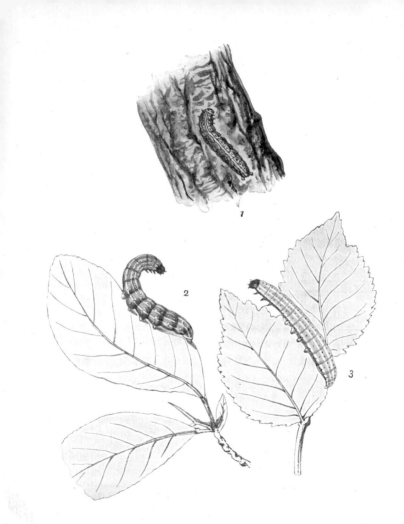

1. **Dingy Shears**: *caterpillar.*
2. **Lunar-spotted Pinion**: *caterpillar.*
3. **White-spotted Pinion**: *caterpillar.*

more partial to honeydew. It is obtained most frequently perhaps in Berkshire, Middlesex, Surrey, and Hampshire, but it is
also known to occur in Devon, Dorset, Sussex, Essex, Suffolk,
Cambs., Hunts, Hertfordshire, Oxfordshire, Gloucestershire,
Herefordshire, and South Wales. Two specimens have been
taken at light in Chester.

Abroad, the range extends to Japan.

The Lesser-spotted Pinion (*Calymnia affinis*).

This species varies in the ground colour of the forewings
from reddish (typical) to greyish brown (var. *suffusa*, Tutt). A
pale ochreous-brown form has been named *ochrea*, Tutt. The
cross markings and stigmata are sometimes all well defined,
but often the latter are hardly traceable, the cross lines only
distinct on the front margin, and the outer one frequently is
conspicuously widened. One example of each sex is shown on
Plate 2, Figs. 4 ♂ and 5 ♀.

The caterpillar, which feeds on elm from April to June, is of
a pale green, inclining to whitish green above, the raised dots
white ; there are three white lines on the back, the central one
broader and clearer white than the others ; the lines along the
area of the black spiracles are whitish ; head green and glossy,
legs black, pro-legs greenish marked with reddish. It feeds at
night, and conceals itself between leaves during the day.

The moth appears in July and August, is very partial to
sugar and " honeydew," and has been taken at light. It lurks
among the foliage of trees and bushes in the daytime, and may
occasionally be dislodged therefrom when the boughs are jarred.
Although its range extends northwards into Durham, where it
is local and scarce, the species seems to be chiefly obtained in
the eastern and southern counties of England. No doubt it
flourishes best where the elm (*Ulmus campestris*) is most plentiful.
In Wales it has been noted from Glamorganshire and Flint.

Kane states that it is very rare in Ireland, and I fail to find any record from Scotland.

The range abroad extends to Japan.

The White-spotted Pinion (*Calymnia diffinis*).

This pretty species is shown on Plate 2, Figs. 6 ♂ and 7 ♀. Its colour and marking are little prone to variation. Sometimes the ground colour has less red and rather more purple in its composition, and in some specimens the white marks on the front margin are larger than in others.

The caterpillar is pale green, with three whitish lines along the back ; the central of these is rather yellowish, agreeing in tint with the usual raised dots, and the outer ones are edged above with bluish green ; head, brownish, inclining to black below. It feeds at night, in April, May, and early June, on the common elm, and rests during the day on the undersides of the foliage or between leaves. (Plate 3, Fig. 3.)

The moth is out in July and August, and is obtained at sugar or at light, in almost all parts of England where its favourite tree grows freely. It seems to be more local in the Midlands, and appears to be but little known in the northern counties, although a specimen was taken at sugar in Hazleden Dene, Durham, in the autumn of 1898.

The Dun-bar (*Calymnia trapezina*).

On Plate 2 will be found portraits of four specimens of this variable species. Figs. 8 and 9 represent a male and a female of the more ordinary forms. Specimens of the typical whitish or greyish buff colour vary in the matter of cross lines, which are well defined in the type, but absent in ab. *pallida*, Tutt. Some examples have a reddish central band, and in others the band is blackish or black ; the latter are referable to ab. *badiofasciata*,

Teich. Ab. *ochrea*, Tutt, is of a reddish-tinged ochreous colour with clearly defined cross lines ; and ab. *rufa*, Tutt, is red with distinct cross lines. Perhaps the rarest form of all is ab. *nigra*, Tutt, which in ground colour is deep blackish grey, with the cross lines faint.

The caterpillar is green with black, glossy, raised dots, each encircled with white ; there are three whitish lines along the back, the central one rather wider than the other two ; a pale yellowish line along the area of the black spiracles ; head, green, tinged with dark brown or black about the jaws. It feeds, from April to June, on the foliage of elm, oak, sallow, and other trees and shrubs ; also, be it noted, on other caterpillars. The larvæ hunter should therefore get to know this cannibal on sight, so that he may exclude it from the common receptacle.

The moth, which frequents woods and woody country generally, is out in July and August.

The species appears to be common throughout England and Wales, the south of Scotland, and more or less frequent north-wards up to Moray. It is widely spread in Ireland.

Angle-striped Sallow (*Cosmia paleacea*).

From the typical pale yellowish ochre, the fore wings range in tint to a deeper buff, inclining to orange. The transverse lines are brown, or sometimes reddish, but are not always distinct, especially in the male. The stigmata are not infrequently obscure, but the blackish spot of the reniform is generally present. In some examples, chiefly of the female sex, there is an angulated dark shade crossing the central area, and some dark clouds or dashes on the outer area. (Plate 4, Fig. 1 ♂.)

The caterpillar is pale dingy green, dusted with whitish, and yellow between the rings ; three white lines along the back, and a double white line along the region of the purplish-edged white spiracles ; head, pale yellow, the jaws black, and a small red spot on each side above them. (Adapted from Porritt.) It feeds, from April to June, on the foliage of birch and aspen, and may be found in the daytime between the lower leaves.

The moth flies in August and September, and at night will visit the sugar patch and also heather blossom. It has but few fixed localities in England, and these are chiefly in Nottinghamshire (Sherwood Forest), and Yorkshire (woods near Doncaster, Huddersfield, and Sheffield). There are, however, records of its occurrence in the south of England. Stainton obtained one at Lewisham in 1846, and Barrett notes one at Highgate in 1870. One or two specimens have occurred in Essex, Somersetshire, and Gloucestershire. From its headquarters in Notts and Yorks. it seems to find its way occasionally into some of the adjoining and other counties. Forsythe states that he bred the moth from larvæ obtained from oak at Methop, Lancs., and it has been reared from a caterpillar taken in North Shropshire. It has occurred on Cannock Chase, Staffs., and rarely in Worcestershire.

From Porritt's *List of the Lepidoptera of Yorkshire* we learn that the occurrence of this species in Yorkshire was not noted until 1880 (Doncaster), but it seems to have since extended its range in the county, as in 1900 it was found in the Huddersfield district, and a few specimens occurred near York in 1903. As stated, it has been bred at Methop, Lancs., and, according to Barrett, it is not scarce in Cumberland. Southwards from its Yorkshire and Nottinghamshire headquarters it has been noted, more or less rarely, in Staffordshire, Shropshire, Worcestershire, Gloucestershire, and Somerset; and on the east side in Lincoln, Norfolk, Essex, and Kent. In Scotland it appears to be not uncommon in Moray, and it is occasionally recorded from Inverness and Perth. The range abroad extends to Amurland and to North America.

1. Angle-striped Sallow.   2, 3. The Suspected.   4, 5. Dingy Shears.
6. The Olive.   7. Double Kidney.   8. Centre-barred Sallow.
9. Centre-barred Sallow, var. unicolor.

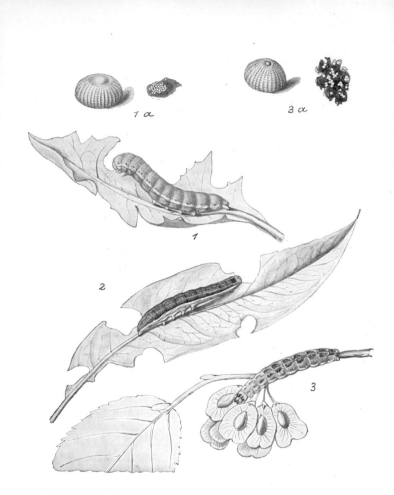

1, 1*a*. **Beaded Chestnut** : *eggs and caterpillar.*
2. **Red-line Quaker** : *caterpillar.*
3, 3*a*. **The Brick** : *eggs and caterpillar.*

The Suspected (*Dyschorista suspecta*).

Of this species (Plate 4, Figs. 2 and 3) there are two groups of forms—plain and variegated. To the first belongs the type with reddish-brown fore wings ; a dark modification of this form is ab. *nigrescens*, Tutt, which has the fore wings blackish red; a brighter red form is ab. *rufa*, Tutt. Of the variegated sections three forms have been named, but the most important of these is var. *congener*, Hübn., with the inner and the outer marginal areas of the reddish fore wings ochreous ; two other modifications have the ground colour redder or dark purplish inclining to blackish.

The caterpillar, which feeds on birch and sallow in April and May, is purplish brown above, and obscure greenish beneath ; there are three lines along the back, the central one white and distinct, the others less defined but noticeable on the black plate on ring nearest the head ; on each side of the central line are blackish marks ; head, ochreous brown, streaked with black.

The moth flies in July and August, and is partial to sugar and to the flowers of heather and ragwort. Its chief British quarters appear to be in Yorkshire, in which county it was first noted in 1841 ; thence it extends into Lancashire, Cumberland, and Durham, but is local and scarce in the latter county. Southwards it is found in the counties of Cheshire (locally not uncommon on moors and mosses), Derby, Nottingham, Stafford, Shropshire, Warwick, Gloucester (rarely) ; more locally in Norfolk, Suffolk, Essex, Surrey, and Kent (once at West Wickham). In 1896 it occurred in numbers in the New Forest, Hants, and I believe that a solitary specimen was secured in Hayling Island in 1901. In Scotland it occurs up to Inverness and Aberdeen ; and Kane states that in Ireland it is doubtfully recorded from Londonderry, but that he has seen lovely forms of the species from Killarney. It also occurs in Co. Wicklow. The range abroad extends to Siberia, Amurland, and Mongolia.

Dingy Shears (*Dyschorista* (*Sidemia*) *fissipuncta*).

In its typical form this species (Plate 4, Fig. 4) has the fore wings pale greyish brown, but occasionally they assume a reddish tinge. Var. *corticea*, Esp., is of the latter colour, and has the black edges of the claviform extended to beyond the middle of the wing. In another form the fore wings are dark grey brown (Fig. 5), leading up to var. *nigrescens*, Tutt, with blackish fore wings and the hind wings darker than usual. Besides the forms just mentioned, I have a bred specimen from Canterbury in which the fore wings are of a pale whity brown, with very faint markings, and the hind wings are almost white ; it is rather below the average size, and possibly is an abnormal aberration. This species is the *ypsilon* of Borkhausen, and the *upsilon* of other authors.

The caterpillar is brown, sometimes inclining to reddish marked with black above, and the under surface is paler ; there are three pale lines along the back, and one low down along each side ; head, pale brown freckled with darker brown. It feeds in April and May on willows, chiefly the narrow-leaved kind, and also, although less frequently perhaps, on poplar. These caterpillars may often be found in the daytime under loose bark of the willow, or lurking among grass roots or *débris* around the trunk. (Fig. 1 on Plate 3 is from a coloured drawing by Mr. A. Sich.)

The moth is out from late June through July. It is a constant visitor to the sugar patch, and will put in an appearance even when other species refuse to be drawn thereto. It appears to be pretty well distributed over England, and in the southern half at least is not uncommon, wherever there are old-established willows. In the northern counties it seems to be much less frequent, but it is recorded as common or plentiful in one or two Cheshire localities, and is said to be taken by all the Newcastle collectors. In Scotland it has been noted in only a few localities. Abroad, the range extends to Amurland.

Mesogona acetosellæ, Fabricius.—Mr. R. Adkin has a specimen of this Central and South European species. It was taken at sugar on the evening of October 26th, 1895, by Mr. T. Salvage, in his garden at Arlington, Sussex (*Entomologist*, xxviii. p. 316).

The Double Kidney (*Plastenis retusa*).

This olive-brown species, shown on Plate 4, Fig. 7, has a reddish-tinged form—ab. *gracilis*, Haw.—but otherwise there is little to be noted in the way of variation. The caterpillar is pale green with three whitish lines on the back, and a narrower and more irregular whitish line low down along the sides; head, yellowish green, or dark brown. Sometimes the body has a yellowish tinge at each end. It feeds on the foliage of sallow and willow, from April to June, drawing together the terminal leaves of a shoot as a retreat.

The moth is on the wing in July and August, and is more frequently attracted at night to the aphis secretion known as "honeydew" than to the sugar patch, although it does not ignore the latter altogether, and occasionally enters the illuminated moth trap. Barrett states that he has found it at the flowers of figwort (*Scrophularia aquatica*). Apparently a local species, but found more or less frequently in most of the southern and eastern counties of England, and through the Midlands to Cheshire, Lancashire, and Yorkshire; it is, however, rarely seen in the three last-named counties.

The range abroad extends to Amurland and Japan.

The Olive (*Plastenis subtusa*).

This moth is shown on Plate 4, Fig. 6. It is somewhat similar in general appearance to the last mentioned, but the colour of the fore wings is greyer; the cross lines are not parallel, and the outer margins of these wings are less irregular. The caterpillar is greenish, with black dots, and white lines along the back and sides; the head and plate on the first ring of the body black. It feeds, on poplar and aspen, in April and May. By day these caterpillars may be found spun up between two leaves or in a folded leaf. The moth is out in July and August, but is rarely noticed in the daytime, although at night, when it becomes active, it may be obtained, sometimes not altogether uncommonly, at honeydew, or in much fewer numbers at sugar or light. The best way to obtain the species is to search for the caterpillars, which are not at all difficult to rear. Most of them, however, prefer the higher foliage of well-grown aspen or poplar, where they may be seen but not readily secured; but I have generally found as many as I wanted within reach.

The species seems to have a wide distribution throughout England, and Scotland up to Moray, its occurrence in any locality depending on the presence of the poplar or aspen. The range abroad extends to Eastern Siberia.

The Centre-barred Sallow (*Cirrhœdia* (*Atethmia*) *xerampelina*).

The typical form of this pretty species has the fore wings yellow, with a purplish-red central band. The band, which fills up the space between the first and second lines, is rarely carried through to the front margins of the wing, but usually is only fragmentary above the reniform stigma, which forms part of it; it also varies in the intensity of the purple tint. In most British specimens the band varies as indicated above, but the general colour of the fore wings is orange-yellow (Plate 4, Fig. 8) —ab. *centrago*, Haw.—the hind marginal band agreeing in colour with that of the central band. Or the fore wings may assume the colour of Fig. 9, var. *unicolor*, Staud., but this form is rare

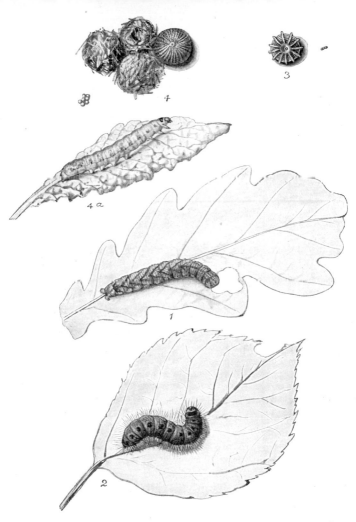

1. **Orange Upper-wing**: *caterpillar.*   2. **Dotted Chestnut**: *caterpillar.*
3. **Pink-barred Sallow**: *eggs, natural size and enlarged.*
4, 4a. **Sallow**: *eggs, natural size and enlarged, and caterpillar.*

1-4. **Lunar Underwing.**
7, 8. **Yellow-line Quaker.**
5, 6. **Red-line Quaker.**
9, 10 **The Brick.**

in Britain, although it is known to occur in the Isle of Man, and has been recorded from Ripon, Skipworth, and York, also from Derbyshire, Staffordshire, Notts, Lincoln, and Gloucestershire. The caterpillar is brownish, inclining to greyish above and to greenish grey beneath, freckled with darker brown; of the three whitish lines along the back, the central one is widest, but is only really distinct on the middle part of each ring; the lines are margined with black, the edging of the central one irregular, but of the others more complete; the spiracles are whitish, and the area above them is dark grey-brown enclosing paler spaces on each ring; head, shining grey-brown freckled with blackish. It feeds, in April, May, and June, on ash, and until the leaves expand it is content with the buds. After dark it may be beaten from saplings in the hedgerow, as well as from full-grown trees. By day it hides among moss or litter, or in the crevices of bark, and at dark may be found crawling up the trunks of ash trees.

The moths are out in August and September, and in the late afternoon may be seen, newly emerged from the chrysalis, on ash trunks, or on twigs and herbage immediately around the tree stems. When on the wing at night it is attracted by light, especially electric, and by sugar. Now that the habits of the species are better known than formerly, it has been ascertained to occur in most English counties. In Scotland it is widely distributed up to Argyll and Perthshire; it has been recorded from several parts of Wales, and in Ireland is found in counties Antrim, Tyrone, Fermanagh, Down, Armagh, Louth, West-meath, Wicklow, Sligo, Galway, Tipperary, and Cork.

The Lunar Underwing (*Omphaloscelis (Anchocelis) lunosa*).

In the general colour of the fore wings, this species, of which four figures will be found on Plate 7, ranges from pale ochreous brown to dark blackish grey. The typical form (*lunosa*, Haworth) has the ground colour pale, or bright, reddish (Figs. 1 and 3); the markings are well defined, and the wing rays are sometimes pale ochreous, or whitish. Four modifications of this form have been named; one of these has pale veins, but the general colour is red brown (ab. *brunnea*, Tutt); in another (Fig. 2) the colour is ochreous brown, the veins pale, and the other markings distinct (ab. *humilis*, Humph. and Westw.). Of the greyish forms, var. *agrotoïdes*, Guenée, is the darkest (Fig. 4).

The caterpillar is brownish, inclining to greenish beneath; there are three whitish lines along the back, the outer edged below with blackish; a thin whitish line along the sides is shaded above with blackish. It feeds on meadow grass (*Poa annua*), and other kinds of grass, from October to May. The moth appears in September and October, sometimes at the end of August. It is partial to light and to sugar, and where the latter is smeared over the foliage of trees and bushes it seems better attended by this, and other autumnal moths, than when painted on tree-trunks in the usual manner.

The species seems to be pretty generally distributed throughout Southern and Western England, and in some seasons it is very common. Eastward and through the Midlands it is perhaps less frequent; in the northern counties it is scarce on the east, but locally common on the west. It occurs in Wales; also in Scotland up to Perthshire. According to Kane, it is widely distributed in Ireland, but most common on the coast.

Abroad, it appears to be confined to France and Spain, although it has been recorded from North-west Africa.

The Red-line Quaker (*Amathes (Orthosia) lota*).

In its typical form this species is of a leaden-grey coloration on the fore wings, but these wings sometimes have a reddish tinge (ab. *rufa*, Tutt). In others the ground colour is blackish (ab. *suffusa*, Tutt), and a rarer form (ab. *pallida*, Tutt) has the fore wings whitish grey with a distinct black reniform stigma, and red submarginal line. (Plate 7, Figs. 5, 6.)

The caterpillar is ochreous brown, sometimes tinged with reddish or purplish brown on the sides ; of three whitish lines along the back, the central one is composed of spots, and the outer ones are not well defined, except on the dark first and last rings ; the line along the sides is reddish. Head, glossy, pale reddish brown, marked with darker brown. It feeds on willow and sallow, and may be found among the foliage from April to June, and especially the topmost leaves of a twig, which it spins together with silk to form a retreat during the day. (Plate 5, Fig. 2.)

The moth comes freely to sugar in September and October, sometimes even later. It may be found pretty freely also at ivy bloom, and at the flowers of *Tritoma*. Although apparently commoner in the south, it is generally distributed throughout England, Wales, and Scotland up to Perthshire and Aberdeen. In Ireland it is widely distributed, but local.

The Yellow-line Quaker (*Amathes* (*Orthosia*) *macilenta*).

The typical coloration of this species (Plate 7, Figs. 7 and 8) is pale ochreous brown, inclining to reddish in some specimens ; the lower part of the reniform stigma black. Sometimes, the black spot is absent (ab. *obsoleta*, Tutt). Another form has the ground colour pale yellowish brown, and this, with the black lower portion of the reniform present, is ab. *straminea*, Tutt, while specimens of the same tint, but minus the black spot, are referable to ab. *obsoleta-straminea* of the same author.

The caterpillar is reddish brown with white dots, and three white lines on the back ; the line along the spiracles is whitish

with a dusky edge above.   Head, ochreous brown ; plate on
first ring blackish lined with white.   It feeds on beech, oak, and
heather.   When approaching full growth it probably feeds on
low-growing plants, and it may be found from April to June.

The moth flies in September and October, sometimes in
November.   Decaying apples seem to have a stronger attractive
influence at times than either sugar or ivy bloom.   Except that
it appears to be local or scarce in the Midlands, the species
occurs, in many parts commonly, throughout England, Wales,
and Scotland to Moray.   In Ireland it is generally distributed
and abundant in some localities.

The Brick (*Amathes* (*Orthosia*) *circellaris*).

Yellow or ochreous is the typical coloration, but the most
frequent form of this common species in Britain is ab. *ferruginea*,
Hübn., which is ochreous tinged with rust colour.   Sometimes,
the fore wings are more or less suffused with blackish, and with
the markings black, such specimens are referable to *macilenta*
as figured by Hübner, Noct., Fig. 688.   The more usual form
is shown on Plate 7, Figs. 9, 10.

At the time it is freshly laid, the egg (Plate 5, Fig. 3*a*) is
yellowish, but changes in about a week to purplish with a more
or less distinct pearly sheen.

The caterpillar is brown inclining to yellowish, the head is
reddish, and the plate on first ring blackish ; there are three
pale lines along the back, the central one more or less interrupted by dusky V-shaped marks, the others with an interrupted
edging above ; the stripe along the region of the blackish
spiracles is yellowish grey.   It lives on wych-elm and ash,
eating the flowers, seeds, and leaves, but has a decided preference for the first two.   It may be beaten in May and early
June, sometimes in numbers, from the seeds (Plate 5, Fig. 3).

1. **Conformist:** *caterpillar.*　　　2. **Early Grey:** *caterpillar.*
3. **Red Sword-grass:** *caterpillar.*

1, 2. **Flounced Rustic.**   3-6. **Beaded Chestnut.**   7-9. **Brown-spot Pinion.**

The moth is out from late August well on into October, and is to be found, wherever its favourite trees are established, throughout the British Isles.

The Flounced Chestnut (*Amathes* (*Orthosia*) *helvola*).

On Plate 9 is shown a male specimen of the typical form (Fig. 1). In ab. *ochrea*, Tutt, the general colour of the fore wings is ochreous with a greenish tinge, and so it differs from the type, in which the ground colour is reddish. In another ochreous form the cross bands are of a purplish tint (ab. *punica*, Borkhausen), and in ab. *rufina*, Hübner, the bands are also purplish, but the ground colour is of a somewhat brighter red than in the type. Ab. *unicolor*, Tutt, is dull reddish with indistinct cross markings, and seems to be a modification of the almost unicolorous form of a bright red colour, ab. *rufa*, Tutt. (Fig. 2.)

The full-grown caterpillar feeds, in April and May, on the foliage of the oak, the elm, and some other trees ; also on sallow, hawthorn, and, according to Barrett, on bilberry and heather. In general colour it is brownish, often tinged with red, and more or less flecked with dark brown ; a fine whitish line along the middle of the back is only clearly traceable on the front rings, but there is a very distinct white stripe along the region of the black spiracles. In an earlier stage it is green with three whitish lines on the back, and another on the sides.

The moth is out in September and October, rather earlier in Scotland. Though much commoner in some districts than in others, this species is found in woodlands throughout the greater part of England, Wales, and the mainland of Scotland. In Ireland it appears to be rare, and has only been recorded, chiefly in single specimens, from Waterford, Wicklow, Galway, Armagh, and Derry.

The Beaded Chestnut (*Amathes* (*Orthosia*) *lychnidis*).

The name of this variable species (Plate 9, Figs. 3-6), long known as *pistacina*, is now recognised as the *lychnidis* of Schiffermiller, so, as the latter name has page priority over the former, it has to be adopted. Fig. 3 on the plate represents a well-marked reddish specimen of the typical form. A great many forms have been named, but only a few of the more distinct of these can be referred to here. Fig. 4 shows the greyish ochreous aberration known as *serrina*, Fab. Ab. *ferrea*, Haworth (Fig. 5) has almost uniform reddish fore wings, and ab. *venosa*, Haworth has the fore wings greyish brown with the veins whitish.

When newly laid the egg (Plate 5, Fig. 1*a*) is yellowish, but changes to olive-brown. The caterpillar (Plate 5, Fig. 1) is green inclining to yellowish, freckled with greyish, and dotted with whitish ; there are three fine whitish lines along the back, and a broad white stripe along the sides. It is found from March to June, and feeds on grasses, dandelion, groundsel, buttercup, and a variety of low plants; it will also eat sallow.

The moth is out from September to November, and is often abundant at sugar and ivy bloom, and not uncommon on gas lamps or around electric lights. Generally distributed and plentiful over the greater part of England and Wales, but from Yorkshire northwards and through Scotland to Perthshire it is very local, and apparently not at all frequent. In Ireland it is widely spread and common.

The Brown-spot Pinion (*Amathes* (*Orthosia*) *litura*).

On Plate 9 are shown specimens from Scotland (Figs. 8 ♂, 9 ♀). The male, which has the basal area of the fore wings pale, is referable to ab. *borealis*, Sparre-Schneider, whilst the female is more nearly typical. In England the majority of the specimens belong to ab. *rufa*, Tutt, which is reddish in the coloration of fore wing (Fig. 7). Sometimes the basal area in this colour form is pale also.

The caterpillar is green, sometimes tinged with olive and freckled with darker green; there are three dark-edged pale-green lines along the back; the under surface is tinged with yellowish, and is separated from the green colour of the upper surface by a whitish stripe, edged above with black; head, brownish, with darker freckles. It occurs in April and May, when it feeds on bramble, rose, oak, sallow, and some low-growing plants.

The moth is found in September and October throughout England, and Scotland up to Moray.

The Orange Sallow (*Cirrhia* (*Xanthia*) *citrago*).

The ground colour of the fore wings is generally yellow, but in some districts the specimens exhibit a tendency towards orange-red. The latter tint is very decided in var. *aurantiago*, Tutt. There is but little variation in marking, but the central cross line is broader in some specimens than in others. (Plate 10, Fig. 1.)

The caterpillar is dark olive-grey above, with white dots, and obscure greenish beneath; of the three whitish lines along the back, the central one is rather wider than the other two, which are edged above with black; along the region of the spiracles the colour is whitish grey. Head, brown, shining, and darker on the mouth; a black mark on ring of body next the head. (Adapted from Porritt.) It feeds on lime (*Tilia vulgaris*) in April and May, and conceals itself between two spun-together leaves during the daytime. In such retreats I have frequently detected them by simply standing under the branches and looking upwards and outwards from the trunk. When nearly full grown they more often descend the tree, and hide by day

Series II.   C among the undergrowth, etc., at the base of the trunk, whence they return to their feeding quarters by crawling up the tree at dusk.

The moth is out in August and September, and although it does not seem to care much about the collector's sugar when spread on tree trunks in the usual way, it seems to accept it freely enough when daubed on the foliage. The leaves of the lime are, however, generally well coated with a sweet substance proceeding from *Aphides*, and commonly known as honeydew. This in itself is very attractive to the moths. The species seems to be widely distributed over England, and will perhaps be found in most districts where limes flourish. In Wales it has occurred in Flintshire, Denbighshire, and Carnarvon. McArthur obtained a specimen in the Isle of Lewis in 1887, and Renton records it as found in Roxburghshire. Little is known of it from Ireland, but it has been noted from Wicklow and Galway.

The Barred Sallow (*Ochria* (*Xanthia*) *aurago*).

The ground colour of the fore wings, which in the type is pale yellow, ranges through various shades of yellow to deep orange. The basal and outer marginal bands are pale purplish, in the type, but in the more orange forms the bands are rather more reddish purple. In ab. *fucata*, Esper, the purplish colour of the bands spreads over the orange central area, and in ab. *unicolor*, Tutt, the orange invades the basal and outer marginal regions, so that the bands are pretty well obliterated, and the fore wings assume a more or less uniform orange coloration. The latter form is uncommon, but a rarer one in this country is ab. *lutea*, Tutt, which has the fore wings almost entirely orange-yellow. (Plate 10, Figs. 2 and 3, the latter inclining to ab. *unicolor*.)

The caterpillar is reddish brown with pale dots, and with

three whitish lines along the back ; a pale stripe along the sides. Head, pale brown, shining. May be found from April to June on beech, or on maple where this occurs around beech woods. At first it feeds on the buds, but later on the leaves ; for protection during the day it spins together two of the leaves, and so forms a suitable resting place. Sycamore, it may be mentioned, is acceptable to this caterpillar when reared in captivity.

The moth is out in September and early October, and is chiefly found in the neighbourhood of beech woods, especially those in chalky districts in Oxford and adjoining counties, Hertfordshire, Middlesex, Essex, Suffolk, Norfolk, Kent, Surrey, Sussex, Wilts, Somerset, Dorset, and Devon. It also occurs in the counties of Hereford, Worcester, and Cheshire ; it has been found in Yorkshire since 1890 in several localities, including Barnsley, Doncaster, Huddersfield, and Rotherham. At least one specimen has been recorded from Pembrokeshire, and others from Flint and Denbighshire, in Wales.

The Pink-barred Sallow (*Xanthia lutea* (*flavago*)).

In some examples of this species (Plate 10, Figs. 4, 5) the oblique band of the fore wings is purplish, and in others red or reddish ; the former are typical, and the latter are referable to ab. *ochreago*, Borkhausen. Often the band is incomplete, and sometimes it is only indicated by three more or less regular series of reddish dots (ab. *togata*, Esper). I have one example of this form from the Isle of Hoy, and another specimen from the same locality is somewhat similar, but the spots are not so well separated, and are purplish in colour.

The eggs (Plate 6, Fig. 3) are yellowish when laid, but become purplish later, and the ribs then appear whitish.

The caterpillar when young lives on catkins of the sallow, and when these fall it feeds on low-growing plants, but it will eat the leaves of sallow and the seeds of wych-elm. It may be found from March to June.

The moth appears in September and October. It is widely distributed, and often common at the sugar patch, over the whole of England, Wales, Scotland up to Moray, and Ireland.

The range abroad extends to Amurland, Japan, Kamtschatka, and North America.

The Sallow (*Xanthia fulvago*).

A typical male and female of this species are shown on Plate 10, Figs. 7, 8 ; Fig. 6 on the same plate represents ab. *flavescens*, Esper. Sometimes the fore wings are orange-tinged, and such examples having the typical markings well defined are referable to ab. *aurantia*, Tutt. In *cerago*, Hübner, the markings are fainter than in the type, and the orange-yellow modification of this form has been named *imperfecta*, Tutt.

The caterpillar is brown above with a tinge of red or purple, and freckled with darker ; there are three pale lines along the back, but only the central one is distinct, and this is more or less interrupted by clusters of darker freckles ; there is a darker stripe composed of freckles on the sides, and below this is a pale brownish stripe ; head, brown, plate on the first ring of the body blackish with pale lines upon it. It feeds when young in sallow catkins, and later on low-growing plants, also leaves of sallow and seeds of wych-elm. Early stages are figured on Plate 6. The moth is out in September and early October. It is widely distributed, and generally common, throughout England and Wales, Scotland to Moray, and Ireland. Its range abroad extends to Amurland and Japan.

NOTE.—It may be stated here that the present species, together with *aurago*, *lutea*, *fulvago*, *gilvago*, and *ocellaris*, are referred to *Cosmia*, Ochs. and Treit., by Hampson (*Cat. Lep. Phal.* vi. 497).

1. **Orange Sallow.**
6-8. **The Sallow.**
2, 3. **Barred Sallow.**
9, 10. **Dusky-lemon Sallow.**
4, 5. **Pink-barred Sallow.**
11. **Pale-lemon Sallow.**
12. **Orange Upper-wing.**

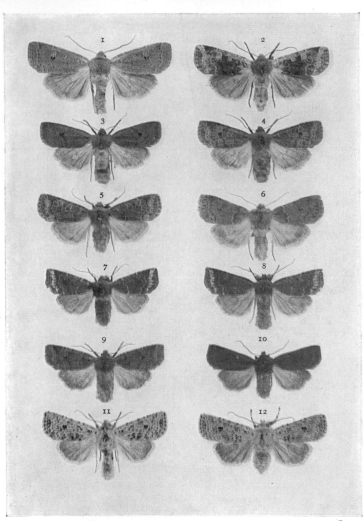

1, 2. Red-headed Chestnut Moth.   7-10. Dark Chestnut.
3-6. Chestnut Moth,   11, 12. Dotted Chestnut.

The Dusky-lemon Sallow (*Mellinia* (*Xanthia*) *gilvago*).

Two examples of this species are shown on Plate 10, Figs. 9 and 10. The purplish-brown mottling or clouding and greyish suffusion of the fore wings is much denser in some specimens than in others. Often the suffusion is quite absent, and the purplish brown is only seen as spots. Again, in an almost unicolorous form the ground colour is of a pale orange tint, the cross markings and outlines of the reniform are as in the type, and the series of blackish points on the submarginal line, usually present in the type, are more conspicuous, owing to absence of the other usual dark markings; this seems to be the *palleago* of Hübner, which has been considered a distinct species; I think, however, that it is only a form of *gilvago*. The earliest recorded British specimen of this form was taken at Brighton in 1856, and it and others captured in the same district were then thought to be examples of *M. ocellaris*, but their true identity was established by Doubleday in 1859. Very few specimens of this form have been reported from other parts of England, but I have recently seen one that was taken at light in the Canterbury district, Kent, on October 3, 1907. In its typical form this species has an extensive range in England, spreading from Durham to Surrrey and Sussex. The earliest known British specimens were captured in the neighbourhood of Doncaster over sixty years ago, but its occurrence in Surrey seems not to have been noted until comparatively recent times.

The caterpillar is pinkish grey-brown, with three paler lines and a series of purplish diamonds along the back; the sides are mottled with purplish brown above the black spiracles, and striped with ochreous grey below them. According to Buckler, whose description is here adapted, the four pale raised dots circled with dark brown, placed within the dark marks on the back of each ring, serve to distinguish this caterpillar from its allies. It feeds on the seeds of wych-elm, and may be beaten or jarred from the branches in April and May. The moth is out in the autumn.

The Pale-lemon Sallow (*Mellinia* (*Xanthia*) *ocellaris*).

Although sparsely marked yellowish examples of the last species have been mistaken for the present one, the true *M. ocellaris* was not known to occur in Britain until 1893, when three specimens were taken at Wimbledon and Twickenham. In 1894 a specimen was recorded from Bognor in Sussex, and another in West Dulwich. The following year one specimen was taken at Richmond, Surrey, and one at Ipswich, Suffolk. Three specimens were obtained at sugar in 1899, and five others in 1900, in a locality in North Kent. Odd specimens have also been noted as follows:—Suffolk, Beccles (1898), Woodbridge (1899) ; West Norfolk (1904 and 1906) ; Cambridge (1907). For further records, see Appendix. The caterpillar, which is ochreous grey with black dots, feeds on poplar, and is stated by one continental author to live in the buds and catkins when young, and afterwards on low plants. So far, it has not been detected in England.

The moth is depicted on Plate 10, Fig. 11. From the last species this one is easily separated by the more pointed fore wings, by the white dot at lower end of the reniform stigma, and by the different shaped cross lines.

The moth has been taken at sugar or light in September and October.

The Orange Upper-wing (*Xantholeuca* (*Hoporina*) *croceago*).

This species is shown in its typical form on Plate 10, Fig. 12. Occasionally a dull reddish-brown form (ab. *latericolor*, Raynor) occurs, of which I some years ago reared several examples, from eggs laid by a female taken at sallow in Darenth Wood, Kent.

The caterpillar (Plate 6, Fig. 1) is pale ochreous brown, inclining to orange, finely freckled with brown, and with brown V-marks on the back of rings 4 to 11 ; the line along the middle of the back is pale yellow, and there are two pale yellow spots on ring 11 ; head, pale brown, freckled with darker brown, and sometimes rosy tinged. It feeds on oak, and may be found in May and June.

The moth flies in September and October, and then visits ivy bloom and sugar at night ; after hibernation it comes to sallow bloom. It has been found during the winter between dry leaves on oak twigs in the hedgerows. Females taken late in the spring and enclosed in a chip box will probably deposit a good supply of eggs ; caterpillars hatching from them are not difficult to rear.

The species does not appear to have been noticed in the eastern or northern counties of England, but it occurs from Worcester southwards to Somerset, Dorset, Devon, and Cornwall. From Herefordshire it spreads into Wales. North of London it is found in Hertfordshire, Middlesex, and to the south in Kent, Surrey, Sussex, and Hampshire.

It is represented in Japan by *sericea*, Butler, which is considered a distinct species by some authors.

The Red-headed Chestnut (*Orrhodia* (*Conistra*) *erythrocephala*).

The portraits of this species on Plate 11 are from Austrian specimens. Fig. 1 is typical and Fig. 2 is ab. *glabra*, Hübner.

A specimen was captured at Marlow, Bucks, in October, 1859, by Mr. A. H. Clarke, who presented it to the British Museum in 1903; but perhaps the earliest-known British specimen was one taken near Brighton in 1847. Between the last-named Sussex locality and Eastbourne in one direction, and Lewes in the other, one or more specimens of the type or of ab. *glabra* have occurred from time to time. Mr. E. P. Sharp took a specimen of *glabra* at Eastbourne on Nov. 30, 1913. The species has also been noted from Hampshire (New Forest and Bournemouth), Somerset, Devon, Kent (Darenth), and Hertfordshire (St. Albans). The most recent records from Hants refer to two captures at Bournemouth in 1902.

The Chestnut (*Orrhodia* (*Conistra*) *vaccinii*).

Figure 3 on Plate 11 represents this species in its typical form, which is of a dark chestnut colour, and almost without markings. The brighter red modification of this form has been named ab. *rufa*, Tutt ; while another assuming the blacker hue of *O. ligula* has been described as ab. *unicolor*, Tutt. In some of the redder forms the cross lines are dark and conspicuous, thus approaching ab. *spadicea*, Hübner, which has distinct black lines as seen in Fig. 6. It should be noted that the figure just referred to is from a German specimen, as I was unable to obtain a suitable British example of the form. Another far more frequent form of this variable species is ab. *mixta*, Staud. (Fig. 4), in which the ground colour is ochreous, more or less tinged with red ; the more yellow-coloured examples of this form have been separated under the name *ochrea*, Tutt. Figure 5 shows a form that is rather less common than either of those just adverted to ; the specimen is one of a short series from Kent that I have labelled ab. *suffusa*, Tutt ; as will be noticed, the band on the outer area is in strong contrast to the rest of the fore wings. Apart from the above and other named forms, there is considerable aberration in the markings, and more especially as regards the stigmata. The lower extremity of the reniform is usually black or blackish, but it may be very faint or entirely absent, and as a contrast to this, the orbicular sometimes has a blackish dot at its lower end.

The caterpillar feeds, in May and June, on oak, elm, etc., and also upon low-growing plants. It is reddish brown above, and greenish beneath, sometimes the upper surface is tinged with green also ; the back is freckled with pale brown, and the three lines along it are faintly paler, the raised dots are whitish ; head, glossy pale brown, freckled with reddish-brown, and lined with darker brown.

The moth occurs at sugar, ivy bloom, etc., in the autumn and early winter, also at sallow catkins in the spring, in probably almost all wooded localities throughout the British Isles.

Its range abroad extends to Japan.

The Dark Chestnut (*Orrhodia (Conistra) ligula*).

Four examples of this species are shown on Plate 11. The typical form has a white band on the outer area of the fore wings (Fig. 7); sometimes this band is ochreous (ab. *subnigra*, Haworth), and a modification of this, in which the outlines of the stigmata and the veins are pale, is var. *ochrea*, Tutt. Ab. *polita*, Hübner (Fig. 9), has a whitish-grey submarginal band and greyish cross lines, and ab. *spadicea*, Haworth (Fig. 10), is a dark form without any distinct markings. This species has long been incorrectly known as *spadicea*, Hübner, which, as noted above, is a form of *vaccinii*, L. Staudinger, probably to prevent confusion, deposed *spadicea*, Haworth, and set up *subspadicea* in its place.

Fig. 8 represents a specimen from North Kent that somewhat suggests ab. *suffusa*, Tutt, of the previous species. On comparing the outer marginal contour of the fore wings of these closely allied species, it will be noted that in all forms of *ligula* the margin below the tip is always slightly concave, thus giving

the wings a decidedly pointed tip, a character which will serve
to distinguish *ligula* from *vaccinii* in nearly every instance.

The caterpillar is reddish brown, freckled with paler ; the
three pale lines along the back are distinctly white on the plate
on ring 1, the outer lines edged below with brownish ; spiracles
outlined in black, and the stripe along them is reddish
ochreous. It feeds in spring and early summer, at first on oak,
sallow, and hawthorn, and afterwards on low-growing weeds.

The moth flies in October and November, and as it lives
through the winter is seen at sugar on any mild night, but it
does not seem to turn up at the sallow catkins in the spring.
The species is rather less generally distributed than the last,
but it is not uncommon in the southern and eastern counties,
and is found throughout England to the Tyne. Recorded from
very few localities in Ireland, and apparently not noticed in
Scotland.

The Dotted Chestnut (*Orrhodia (Dasycampa) rubiginea*).

A pair of typical specimens are represented on Plate 11,
Figs. 11 and 12. A form of the species occurring in Somersetshire has the fore wings reddish brown, and the usual black
dots are largely absent (ab. *unicolor*, Tutt).

The caterpillar (Plate 6, Fig. 2) is purplish brown freckled
with blackish ; there are three obscure paler lines along the
back from ring 3, and a central series of black spots ; the head
is black, and the fine hairs of the body are yellowish brown.
It feeds, in May and June, on apple, plum, dandelion, etc. The
fact has been noted that, if supplied with apple until about half
grown, and afterwards with dandelion, it attains full size more
quickly than when kept to one kind of food only.

The moth appears in October and November, retires during
the cold weather, and comes forth again in the spring. When

reared in confinement, it emerges from the chrysalis about a month earlier. Ivy bloom, ripe yew berries, and also sugar attract it in the autumn, and in the spring it visits the blossoms of sallow, damson, and sloe. There are several records of its having been taken at light, perhaps the latest of these being that of a specimen captured at Exeter on April 11, 1906.

Except in Devonshire, where it is of more regular occurrence, the species is far from common in England, but is taken in, or has been recorded from, the counties of Dorset, Wilts, Gloucester, Hereford, Monmouth (S. Wales), Hants and Isle of Wight, Sussex, Surrey, Berks, Bucks, and Cambridge. In Ireland it is noted from Dublin, King's County, Kerry, Wicklow, and Galway.

It is represented in Japan by the larger ab. *fornax*, Butler.

The Satellite (*Eupsilia* (*Scopelosoma*) *satellitia*).

An example of each sex of this species is shown on Plate 12, together with a less common form. Although specimens vary in the amount of red in the colour of the fore wings, there is more striking aberration in the colour of the lunular marks representing the reniform stigma; these are frequently white, but may be yellow (typical), or reddish orange in either sex. The dull brownish specimen (Fig. 3) is from Yorkshire, and appears to be referable to var. *brunnea*, Lampa.

The caterpillar is dark brown, with indistinct paler lines on the back; the line along the spiracles is white or whitish, but often reduced to a series of spots on rings 1, 2, 5, and 11. Head, ochreous-brown, darker about the mouth. It feeds, in May and June, on the leaves of oak, beech, elm, and other trees, also on low plants; and has a keen appetite, it is said, for other caterpillars when the opportunity offers.

The moth is out in September, and may be seen at ivy bloom or sugar during that month, and also in October and November if the weather is favourable ; it is early on the wing again in the spring.

Although apparently uncommon in some few parts, the species seems to be generally distributed and plentiful throughout England, Wales, Scotland up to Ross (recorded from Stromma, Orkney), and Ireland.

In Japan, a greyish form with larger spots (ab. *tripuncta*, Butler) occurs.

The Tawny Pinion (*Lithophane (Xylina) semibrunnea*).

An example of this species is represented on Plate 12, Fig. 4. The black streak from above the middle of the inner margin towards the hind margin should be noted, as this character distinguishes *semibrunnea* from dark forms of the following species—*L. socia*.

The caterpillar is yellowish green, with a broad creamy stripe along the middle of the back, and two indistinct fine lines on each side ; below the black-outlined white spiracles is a yellow stripe. Head, bluish green, freckled with darker green. It feeds on ash in May and June.

The moth appears on the wing, and may be seen at ivy bloom and sugar, from September to November, and is sometimes captured at sallow, after hibernation, in March or April.

It is on record that two specimens taken in November were kept in confinement, and three other captives were added in February. All continued to live until June, and two were still alive on the 23rd of that month.

Although this species is found more or less regularly in most of the English counties south of Worcester on the west, and Huntingdon on the east, it is always very local, and never plentiful. It has been reported from Carmarthenshire in South Wales ; and Kane states that in Ireland it has been taken in Galway and Kerry.

1-3. The Satellite.   6. Grey Shoulder-knot.
4. Tawny Pinion.   7. Early Grey.
5. Pale Pinion.   8, 9. Golden-rod Brindle.

1, 2. The Conformist. 3. The Nonconformist. 4, 5. The Cudweed.

The Pale Pinion (*Lithophane* (*Xylina*) *socia*).

The pale ochreous-brown insect shown on Plate 12, Fig. 5, is without the dark, sometimes blackish suffusion on the inner area which is characteristic of the type of this species. Var. *rufescens*, Tutt, is a reddish form.

The caterpillar is pale green with three white lines, the central one broad and stripe-like; the line along the spiracles is yellow. Head, pale green, variegated with white. (Adapted from Porritt.)

The moth comes to ivy bloom, sugar, etc., in September and October, and even later if the weather is mild. After hibernation it reappears as early as February, and visits the sallows as soon as the catkins open.

Although it seems to be absent from the eastern counties, except Cambridge—where, however, it is scarce—this species is found in most of the other counties mentioned for the last species. It is generally more plentiful, especially in the west. Occasionally specimens have been taken in Cumberland, and single examples have been recorded from the Liverpool and Hartlepool districts. It seems to be not uncommon in South Wales, and has been reported from Capel Curig, in Carnarvonshire, and from Anglesea. As regards Ireland, Kane says that there are few Irish localities where this species is not found.

The Conformist (*Graptolitha* (*Xylina*) *furcifera*).

The typical form of this species has the fore wings of a pale slaty grey colour; this, however, does not seem to occur in Britain. Our form, var. *suffusa*, Tutt (shown on Plate 13, Figs. 1 and 2), is much darker grey with blackish mottling, a yellowish mark at the base and a reddish cloud in the reniform stigma; the outer area is more or less tinged with violet, and this tint sometimes spreads over the whole of the fore wings;

the inner margin is tinged with reddish orange at the base, or along the basal half, and there are some clouds of the same colour on the black submarginal line.   This is *conformis* of British authors.

The caterpillar (drawn from a skin, Plate 8, Fig. 1) is olive brown, tinged with green above, and paler brown, tinged with pink beneath ; the dots are yellowish in black circles, and there is a dark olive-brown mark on ring 1 ; there are three yellow lines along the back, the central one interrupted by darker brown freckles, clustered so as to form a series of diamond-shaped patches, and the others are edged above with dark olive. It feeds on alder, from April to June.

The moth is out in September and October, and, after hibernation, in March and April.   Ivy bloom and sugar attract it in the autumn, and it has been taken at sallow catkins as well as at sugar in the spring.

Since 1861, when its occurrence in Wales was first announced, it has been found more or less regularly in Glamorganshire, South Wales, or the adjoining English county of Monmouth. The latest record is that by Mr. P. J. Barraud, who took a male specimen at sallow bloom in the Wye Valley on March 31, 1907.   The capture of a specimen at sugar, near Brighton, September 13, 1898, has been reported.   One specimen has been recorded from Yorks., another from Westmoreland ; and in 1902, two from near Lancaster.   Wales, however, appears to be the home of this species in the British Isles.

The Nonconformist (*Graptolitha* (*Xylina*) *lamda*).

The example of this species shown on Plate 13, Fig. 3, is of the typical form, and hails from the Continent.   Of the six specimens observed in England the majority have been recorded as *zinckenii*, Treitschke, a form having the fore wings more variegated with white.   Another form, ab. *somniculosa*, Hering, has most of the typical markings, especially on the outer area, absent.

The earliest occurrence of this species in Britain appears to have been that of a specimen on the trunk of a poplar tree in the northern environs of London, October, 1865. Then on September 30, 1866, one was detected on the bole of a willow tree in a locality not indicated more definitely than " near New Cross " ; another specimen was taken in the same year in the Guildford district, at sugar. On October 3, 1870, a fourth was found on the reverse side of a tree that had been sugared, at Dartford, Kent ; and a specimen, labelled Erith, September, 1875, was in the collection of the late Mr. Bond. Lastly, a specimen came to sugar at Copdock, Ipswich, in late September, 1895.

The range of this species abroad extends through Scandinavia, Belgium, North Germany, and North Russia, to East Siberia, and Amurland. It is found in North America, where it is known as *thaxteri*, Grote.

The Grey Shoulder-knot (*Graptolitha* (*Xylina*) *ornithopus*).

The moth, of which a portrait will be found on Plate 12, Fig. 6, emerges from the chrysalis in the autumn, and may then be found at night on ivy bloom or at the sugar patch ; and in the daytime it may frequently be seen on tree trunks, palings, etc. After hibernation, it is again seen in the spring, on fences, pales, etc., and visits the sallow catkins at night. Females of this species, and other hibernating kinds, taken in the spring generally deposit fertile eggs pretty freely ; often such specimens are not in the best condition, but one female, if she has not already parted with most of her eggs, will as a rule deposit quite as many as the collector is likely to need.

The caterpillar is of a blue-green colour with whitish freckles ;

three broken whitish lines along the back; head, green, with a paler mark on each cheek. It is to be found in May and early June on the leaves of oak.

The species is widely distributed throughout England and Wales, but is more frequently met with in the south than in the north. It is found in Scotland, but only rarely, and the same remark applies to Ireland generally, although the species is not uncommon in some parts of Wicklow, Cork, and Kerry.

Its range abroad extends to Amurland and Japan.

Golden-rod Brindle (*Cloantha* (*Lithomoia*) *solidaginis*).

On Plate 12, Fig. 8 represents a Lancashire specimen, whilst Fig. 9 is taken from an Aberdeen example. The first, having the central area suffused with brown, is more nearly typical, and the other varies in the direction of ab. *virgata*, Tutt, in which form the central shade is black. Other named forms are—ab. *cinerascens*, Staud. = *pallida*, Tutt (pale ashy-grey, central shade almost or quite obsolete), ab. *suffusa*, Tutt (similar to *virgata*, but the basal area also black or blackish).

The caterpillar is brown, with a purplish or violet tinge, and freckled with grey; an indistinct line along the middle of the back and a creamy stripe along the sides, the latter is edged above with black; head, shining reddish-brown, freckled with darker brown. It feeds on bilberry, bearberry (*Arctostaphylos uva-ursi*), heather, sallow, birch, and hawthorn, and is to be found from May to July.

The moth is out in August and September, and in its woodland and moorland haunts is to be seen sitting about on the dead stems of bracken, charred twigs and stems of heather, or on birch trunks, rocks, walls, etc. When thus resting, however, they very closely resemble twisted birch bark, grouse droppings, and other common objects occurring in the haunts of the species, so that its detection is not easy at first.

In England this species is found from Shropshire and Staffordshire northwards to Cumberland; thence through Scotland to Aberdeen and Sutherland. In Wales it has been obtained commonly near Rhos in the north.

Abroad its range spreads to Amurland; and it occurs in North America, where it is known as *germana*, Morrison.

The Early Grey (*Xylocampa areola*).

A typical specimen of this widely distributed and, at least in the southern half of England, rather common species, is shown on Plate 12, Fig. 7. A dark form has been named ab. *suffusa*, Tutt, and one with the fore wings of the typical grey colour, but with a pinkish flush, is ab. *rosea*, Tutt.

The caterpillar (figured from a skin, on Plate 8, Fig. 2) is yellowish-brown, with a fine pale central line along the back, often only distinct on rings 1, 11, and 12, and always obscured by dark brown patches on 7 and 8; a blackish line low down along the sides. The body tapers towards each end, and especially so towards the small head. It lives

FIG. 1.
Early Grey at rest.
(Photo by W. J. Lucas.)

upon honey-suckle, and feeds on the leaves at night, during May and June, or sometimes later.

The moth appears in March and April, and, in the daytime, is often met with at rest on posts, fences, and the trunks of trees; also upon stone walls, but seemingly less frequently, probably owing to the moth being then less easy to detect. At night it flies around sallow bushes and sometimes settles on the catkins, but is always on the alert.

Series II.

The Sword-grass (*Calocampa exoleta*).

Except that the pale grey brown fore wings are more clouded with blackish in some specimens than in others, there is little of importance to note. Usually there are two black wedges pointing inwards from the indistinct submarginal line, but occasionally one, or more rarely both, may be absent. (Plate 14, Figs. 3 ♂ and 4 ♀.)

The caterpillar is green, with two series of white-spotted black marks, the line below these is yellow, and that lower down on the side is bright red ; the spots between the lines are white, encircled with black. From April to May it feeds, often in the sunshine, as well as at night, on restharrow, thistles, stonecrop, groundsel, dock, in fact on almost all low-growing plants, as well as the foliage of some trees. The caterpillars of this and the next species are exceedingly pretty creatures, and are sure to attract attention whenever met with. Dr. Chapman notes that the caterpillar will feed on stale leaves.

The moth emerges in the autumn, and seems to be on the wing until quite late in the year, and is seen again as early as March, and thence on until May. One male and two females captured at sugar, March 12 and 13, were placed in a glass cylinder with various food plants, and a sprig of sallow catkins, moistened occasionally with syrup, afforded nourishment for the moths every evening. On April 13, two batches of eggs were noted on nettle, but these were not fertile. On April 15 and 20 pairing took place ; and by May 3 over three thousand eggs had been deposited. On May 13 the two females, being still alive, were set at liberty (Goodwin).

Although it certainly appears to be less frequently seen in the south than northwards, the species is known to occur pretty well all over England and Wales. In Scotland, where it is generally commoner than in England, except perhaps in the northern counties of the latter, its range extends to the Orkneys.

Abroad, it is found throughout Europe (except the most northern parts) ; Asia to Japan ; and the Canaries.

The Red Sword-grass (*Calocampa vetusta*).

In this species the ground colour of the fore wings varies from whity brown to ochreous brown with a slight reddish tinge. A greyish shade spreads from the base along the median vein to below the reniform stigma in the paler and more typical specimens ; the inner area is dark brown, but widely broken below the reniform by the grey suffusion. The specimens figured on Plate 14 (Figs. 1 ♂, 2 ♀) are from Sligo, Ireland, and are referable to var. *brunnea*, Tutt. The inner area in this form is red-brown, or inclining to blackish brown.

The caterpillar is green, with three yellow lines along the back, and a reddish orange stripe along the area of the spiracles ; a series of black-circled white dots on each side of the central line ; in the form figured (from a skin) on Plate 8, Fig. 3, the lines on the back are white, and the spaces between them black, dotted with white ; the stripe along the reddish spiracles also white, edged above with black ; head, shining light reddish brown. It feeds, from May to July, on various low herbage, such as dock, persicaria, knotgrass, etc., also sedges and yellow flag.

The moth appears in September and October, and again in March and April, but seems to have been noted at various times both earlier and later. Mathew records that a female captured at sugar on June 11, deposited 36 eggs during the following week. These were laid in a chip box, and the caterpillars hatched out on June 24, fed up quickly on knotgrass-attained full growth by July 24, and pupated about that date.

One moth emerged September 29, and five others, including three cripples, later.

This species is most frequent in Ireland and Scotland, being distributed throughout the latter country to Orkney and Shetland. It has been noted from Wales and almost every part of England, but does not seem to be plentiful generally in either country.

The distribution abroad ranges to East Siberia and to North America.

The Mullein (*Cucullia verbasci*).

Two specimens, representing both sexes, of this species are shown on Plate 15, Figs. 1 ♂, 2 ♀. Sometimes the darker colour on the marginal areas, especially the inner, inclines to blackish ; while in some specimens the whole of the fore wings is suffused with brownish.

The caterpillar is white with a greenish tinge, each ring of the body is banded with yellow, has four black spots on the back, and some black dots and lines on the sides ; the head is yellowish, dotted with black. It may be found in June and July quite exposed on mullein (*Verbascum thapsus*, and *V. pulverulentum*); also figwort (*Scrophularia nodosa*, and *S. aquatica*). Barrett states that it has been noted on *Buddlœa globosa*, an American plant sometimes grown in gardens. These caterpillars are certainly attacked by parasitical flies, but do not seem to be quite so frequently "stung" as those of some other species of the "Sharks." The caterpillar figured on Plate 18, Fig. 1, was obtained at Box Hill by Mr. Norman Riley.

The moth is out in late April and in May, and, except an occasional capture at light, is rarely seen in the open. The caterpillars are probably obtainable in most English and Welsh counties, especially the southern ones of both countries, wherever there is an abundance of its food plants. Except that McArthur found the species in the Isle of Lewis, in 1901, there

1 2. **Red Sword-grass**, *male and female*.
3, 4. **The Sword-grass**,   ,,

1, 2. **The Mullein Moth.**
3. **The Water Betony.**
4, 5. **The Striped Lychnis.**
6. **The Starwort.**

is no record from Scotland. In Ireland it has been recorded from Dublin by Birchall; and in 1901 three moths were taken at Timoleague, Co. Cork, and caterpillars later on were plentiful in the district.

The Water Betony (*Cucullia scrophulariæ*).

A good deal of confusion exists both in Britain and on the Continent as to the identity of the *Cucullia* figured and described by Capieux in 1789, and by most authors since that time. I have received over twenty specimens from Austria, Germany, and other parts of Europe, sent to me as *scrophulariæ*. As I have been unable to separate the majority of these specimens from *C. lychnitis*, and the others from *C. verbasci*, Mr. F. N. Pierce has been good enough to examine the genitalia of six of the males, and of these he reports four are *C. lychnitis*, and two are *C. verbasci*.

In England we certainly have a *Cucullia* sometimes appearing in the moth state rather later than *C. verbasci* and always earlier than *C. lychnitis;* the caterpillar producing it feeds on *Scrophularia nodosa* in July. It is, however, very local, and is found chiefly in North Kent, and occasionally in the Eastern Counties. Mr. Pierce finds that the male genitalia of a North Kent *scrophulariæ* sent to him do not differ from these parts in *C. verbasci*, but Dr. Chapman informs me that he detects a slight difference in one that he examined.

It must be admitted that the identity of the North Kent and East Anglian *Cucullia* with the *scrophulariæ* of Capieux is very doubtful, but we evidently shall not be greatly opposed to Continental methods if we continue to allow April and May moths resulting from *Scrophularia nodosa* caterpillars to do duty for *C. scrophulariæ*. I have therefore figured as this species a specimen that was reared, with others, in April and May, 1877, from larvæ obtained in the Dartford marshes. (Plate 15, Fig. 3.)

The caterpillar is of a whitish-grey colour ; along the middle of the back is a series of broad deep yellow triangles pointing backwards, each edged on both sides by large confluent deep black spots, usually forming a somewhat C-shaped marking, which encloses another yellow spot, and below is followed by several black spots ; behind all these, on each segment, is a deep green transverse spotless band. The forms of the black markings, composed of united spots, vary in the degree of union of these spots ; each anterior spot is confluent with the posterior one below it, but does not unite transversely with the others ; in one variety they resemble tadpole forms united by the tails, in another these tails are as thick as the spots and form blotched curves ; and in still another they are so thick and confluent as to include some of the side spots, thus completely edging two sides of the yellow triangle with a blotched black border. (Adapted from Buckler.)

The Striped Lychnis (*Cucullia lychnitis*).

An example of each sex of this species is shown on Plate 15, Figs. 4 and 5. The general colour of the fore wings is paler, and the streaks along the front and inner margins are darker than in *C. verbasci ;* and the outer margins of the wings are less jagged.

The caterpillar (figured on Plate 18, Fig. 2, from a photo by Mr. H. Main) is greenish white or yellow ; the rings are cross banded with yellow and spotted with black ; usually the spots are united as in the figure, sometimes they are smaller and well separated, and occasionally all but those low down along the sides are absent. Coupled with decrease in size and number of the black spots, there is variation in the width of the yellow bands. *Verbascum nigrum* is the more usual food plant in Britain, but it will also eat *V. lychnitis.* It feeds, in July and August, on the flowers and unripe seed capsules in preference to the foliage.

Between sixty and seventy years ago, the late Mr. Samuel Stevens obtained the caterpillars on mullein growing in a chalk pit at Arundel in Sussex, and this seems to be the earliest notice of the species occurring in Britain. It is now known also to inhabit Hampshire, Surrey, and Oxfordshire ; has been reported from Norfolk, Suffolk, and Gloucestershire.

The Star-wort (*Cucullia asteris*).

The silvery-grey fore wings of this moth (Plate 15, Fig. 6) are broadly suffused with reddish brown along the front margin, and more narrowly with purplish brown inclining to blackish along the inner margin ; the latter is separated from a purplish brown blotch at the outer angle by a whitish edged black curved mark.

The caterpillar (figured on Plate 18, Fig. 3, from a photo by Mr. Main) is green with a black-edged yellow stripe along the back, and another along the white spiracles; between these stripes are two pale greenish lines ; head, green, sprinkled with blackish. In another form the body is suffused with reddish, inclining to purplish on the back ; yellow markings pretty much as in the green form. It feeds chiefly on goldenrod (*Solidago virgaurea*) and sea star-wort (*Aster tripolium*), showing a decided preference for the flowers, but will eat the foliage of the plants mentioned. In confinement it can be reared on garden asters and Michaelmas daisy. It may be obtained on its food plants from July well into September.

The moth emerges in June and July as a rule, sometimes in early August, but has been known to come from the chrysalis during September up to the 23rd of that month. The species is found often abundantly in the caterpillar state in the seaboard counties of Norfolk, Suffolk, Essex, Kent, Sussex, Hants, and Dorset. In Surrey it has occurred at Haslemere, and in the Croydon district (?) ; and it has been recorded from Here-fordshire and North Lancashire.

The range abroad extends to East Siberia, Amurland, and Japan.

The Shark (*Cucullia umbratica*).

On the fore wings of this greyish species (Plate 16, Figs. 5 ♂ and 6 ♀) there is some variation in the short black streaks on the basal and outer areas, and in the dots around the stigma ; the front margin is sometimes brownish tinged. The hind wings of the female are always darker than those of the male.

The caterpillar feeds on plants of the sowthistle (*Sonchus*) kind, also on garden lettuce and the wild species. It may be found in August and early September, but, as it feeds only at night, it should be searched for in the daytime on the under-sides of the lower leaves. In general colour it is ochreous inclining to greyish, with an intricate raised pattern in blackish on the upper surface ; the head is black, and there is a yellow spotted sooty brown plate on the first ring of the body.

The moth is to be seen in June and July, sitting on the upper parts of palings, and other kinds of wooden fencing ; also on tent pegs, etc. ; but it is not easy to detect even when its whereabouts is indicated. At night it visits flowers of campion, sweet william, honeysuckle, etc.

Widely distributed throughout the British Isles to the Orkneys, but seemingly more plentiful and regular in occur-rence in the south of England than in the north.

The Chamomile Shark (*Cucullia chamomillæ*).

Although somewhat similar to the last species, this moth may be distinguished by the more brownish tinge of its grey fore wings. The hind wings are also brown-grey in both sexes, but darkest in the female.

Sometimes the central area of the fore wings is clouded with blackish from the front to the inner margin ; such specimens are referable to ab. *chrysanthemi*, Hübn. (Plate 16, Figs. 1 typical, 2 ab.)

The caterpillar, which may be found in the summer months, is greenish white with zigzag olive markings, the lines on the back meeting in the middle of each ring, where there is a small pinkish blotch ; head, pale yellowish, striped with brown on the face. It feeds on wild chamomile (*Matricaria*), stinking mayweed (*Anthemis*), and *Pyrethrum* (Plate 18, Fig. 4, pupa). The Rev. Miles Moss, writing his experience of this species at Rossall, near Fleetwood, Lancashire, notes that until half-grown the caterpillars live exposed, and are then found lying in a half-circle on the crowns of unexpanded flower heads. At this time they are green with dark and also white markings. He adds that caterpillars measuring about an inch in length when collected, were preparing for pupation a week later.

The moth is out in April and May, and has been captured even in July. When chrysalids are kept indoors, but not dry, the moths sometimes emerge in March, and occasionally in the earlier months of the year. A habit more or less general among the species of this genus is to remain in the chrysalis state for two or more winters ; the present species has been known to emerge during March of the first, second, and third years following that in which the caterpillars were found.

Widely distributed over England and Wales, but apparently most frequent in the seaboard counties. In Scotland it occurs up to Perthshire, and it is found on various parts of the Irish coast.

The Cudweed (*Cucullia gnaphalii*).

Portraits of two specimens of this very local species, kindly lent by Mr. R. Adkin, will be found on Plate 13, Figs. 4 and 5.

The general coloration is usually silvery grey, but occasionally it inclines to yellowish. The moth has rarely been noted by day, and only one specimen seems to have been captured on the wing. Even caterpillars are by no means common in their best-known localities, and of those obtained after much labour a large proportion may frequently prove to have been the victims of parasitic flies.

The caterpillar is green, inclining to olive green, thickly freckled with pale yellow atoms ; a purplish-brown stripe along the middle of the back and two faint purplish lines along the sides ; a pale yellow line along the region of the black-edged spiracles, which are set in purplish-brown blotches. (Adapted from Buckler.)

Its food plant is golden-rod (*Solidago*), and it feeds at night and hides by day, low down on the stems or under the leaves : July to September. In confinement the caterpillars will eat garden aster and Michaelmas daisy.

The British haunts of the species are chiefly in Kent (Sevenoaks, Tunbridge Wells, etc.), and Sussex (Tilgate Forest, etc.) ; but according to Barrett it is also known from Hampshire, Surrey, and Essex. Abroad, the range extends through Central Europe to Southern Scandinavia, Livonia, Southern Russia, the Altai Mountains, Italy, and Armenia ; but the species is nowhere plentiful.

It may be mentioned here that a very closely allied, and on the Continent common, species—*C. xeranthemi*, Boisduval—might easily be mistaken for *C. gnaphalii.*

The Wormwood (*Cucullia absinthii*).

This moth is shown on Plate 16, Fig. 4. The fore wings are usually tinged with purplish over the greyish ground colour ; black dots on the stigmata give to each of these marks some resemblance to the figure 8.

The caterpillar, which feeds on the flowers and seeds of wormwood (*Artemisia absinthium*) and will eat mugwort (*A. vulgaris*), is best found on sunny days. It is yellowish green, suffused with purplish grey on the back of each ring; there are three pale green lines along the back, and an ochreous grey plate on ring 1. To be found in August and early September, but on dull days it must be sought for among the lower leaves, or on the ground. When resting among the flowers it so closely harmonises with them that it might easily escape detection.

The moth is out in July.

The species is perhaps most abundant on the South Devonshire coast, but its range extends into Cornwall, and eastward to the Isle of Portland and the Isle of Wight; it is not uncommon along the coasts of North Devon (Lee and Croyde), Somerset (Minehead), and South Wales. It has also been recorded from North Wales, and from parts of the Suffolk coast. In Ireland, a specimen was taken in a garden at Cromlyn, Westmeath, in 1873, and more recently two specimens of the moth, and also some caterpillars, were obtained at Timoleague, Cork.

Cucullia artemisiæ (*abrotani*).

This species, of which a Continental example is represented on Plate 16, Fig. 3, is apparently exceedingly rare in this country, and most probably is not a native.

In the collection of the late Dr. Mason, which was dispersed at Stevens' in 1905, there were three specimens, each of which had seemingly been included among series of *C. absinthii* purchased at three separate sales. A fourth specimen, also mixed with *C. absinthii*, was in the collection of the late Rev. H. Burney. Two other specimens have been reported from Devonshire, where, it is said, they were found sitting on a fence.

The caterpillar feeds, in August and September, on worm-wood and other kinds of *Artemisia*. It is green with red raised spots, a white line along the middle of the back, and a yellow stripe low down along the sides; head, brown inclining to blackish above. The moth is out in June and July.

The Beautiful Yellow Underwing (*Anarta myrtilli*).

In its typical form (Plate 17, Figs. 1, 2) this species has the fore wings purplish brown or blackish brown, whilst in var. *rufescens*, Tutt, the general colour of the fore wings is reddish inclining to crimson, and the white markings are clearly defined. In some dark specimens the markings are more or less obscure, and in others only the central white dot is distinct.

The caterpillar is green, dotted and marked with white; there are three rows of yellowish bars along the back, those forming the outer series slightly curved. It is to be found on ling (*Calluna vulgaris*), also on heath (*Erica*), from July to October, but it seems to be more frequently obtained in early autumn. Occasionally it has been found in the spring. Hawthorn has been mentioned as a food-plant (Plate 20, Fig. 1).

The moth has been taken in each month from April to August, but it is perhaps most plentiful from May to July. The species occurs on heath and moorlands throughout the British Isles, but so far it has not been recorded from the Shetlands. It flies on sunny days and is very active on the wing, but when the sun is obscured, or towards evening, it may be found at rest on the heather sprays, usually at their tips.

The Small Dark Yellow Underwing (*Anarta cordigera*).

The pretty moth represented on Plate 17, Fig. 7, is only found in the British Isles, on the mountains of Scotland, chiefly in Perthshire and Aberdeenshire. Sometimes the basal area of

1, 2. **Chamomile Shark.**   4 **The Wormwood.**
3. *Cucullia artemisiæ.*   5, 6. **The Shark.**

1, 2. Beautiful Yellow Underwing.   3, 4. Small Yellow Underwing.
5, 6. Broad-bordered White Underwing.   7. Small Dark Yellow Underwing.
8, 9. The Pease Blossom.   10, 11. Bordered Sallow.

the fore wings is suffused with black, and to a lesser extent the outer area also (var. *æthiops*, Hoffm. = *suffusa*, Tutt); on the other hand, typical examples have both basal and outer areas silvery grey, and the central area black. A form, which I have not seen, is described as having the black central area broken by an ashy cross band passing between the stigmata (var. *variegata*, Tutt).

The caterpillar is reddish brown, with three white lines along the back, and a reddish-freckled ochreous stripe low down on the sides. Sometimes the general colour is blackish. It feeds on bearberry (*Arctostaphylos*) in June and July; also said to eat *Vaccinium uliginosum;* in confinement it will thrive on *Arbutus unedo*, commonly known as the " strawberry tree."

The moth is out in May, when it flies in the sunshine, and in dull weather sits about on the rocks, stones, lichen, etc. Mr. Cockayne notes that at Rannoch he met with it from May 17 in numbers, but always in isolated spots where bearberry was plentiful. Here the moths were either feeding on the flowers or settled on the ground. He further remarks that this species occurs at the comparatively low elevation of 800 to 900 feet, whereas the next species ascends to 2000 feet.

The distribution abroad extends to Amurland and Labrador.

The Broad-bordered White Underwing (*Anarta melanopa*).

This species has the ground colour of the fore wings greyish in the type and brownish in var. *wiströmi*, Lampa. Specimens with the fore wings more or less typical, but with the normally white area of hind wings dark greyish, are referable to ab. *rupestralis*. I remember seeing a specimen of the last-named form in the collection of the late Mr. S. Stevens, but I believe that it is very rare in the British Isles. In all forms there is variation in the stigmata, and in the orbicular especially. (Plate 17, Figs. 5 ♂ and 6 ♀.)

The caterpillar is of a purplish pink colour, with a black-edged ochreous-brown line along the middle of the back, broken up by reddish-brown triangles ; the stripe along the region of the black spiracles is yellowish white flecked with red ; the sides of the body above the stripe are flecked with reddish, and above them is a yellowish-white line and some black marks. Head, brownish, freckled with darker. It feeds at night, in July, on bilberry (*Vaccinium myrtillus*), cowberry (*V. vitis-idæa*), and can also be reared on strawberry tree, sallow, knotgrass, etc. In the daytime it must be searched for under the leaves.

The moth is out in May and the early part of June, and is most active in the sunshine, but flies on dull days when the weather is warm. It seems confined to the higher level of the mountains, and its habits are similar to those of the last species, but its range extends to the Shetland Isles. The species was not recognised as British until about 1830, and the same remark applies to *A. cordigera*.

The Small Yellow Underwing (*Heliaca tenebrata*).

The fore wings are a little more reddish in some specimens than in others, and occasionally the yellow of the hind wings is much reduced in area by the expansion of the black border, or it may be suffused with blackish. (Plate 17, Figs. 3 and 4.)

The caterpillar is green, with three lines along the back, the central one dark green and the others whitish, bordered below with dark green ; the stripe low down along the sides is yellowish white, edged above with dark green. It feeds, in June and July, on mouse-ear chickweed (*Cerastium*), devouring the blossom and seeds, when young boring into the unripe capsule.

The moth flies on sunny days in May and early June, and is more or less common in grass-bordered lanes, hay meadows, etc., in most counties throughout the southern part of England.

In the midland counties it appears to be far more local, thence to Durham (its northern limit in England) it is generally scarce. It has been recorded from Pembrokeshire and Flintshire, in Wales. A specimen has been reported from Robroyston, near Glasgow, in Scotland. As the species has been obtained in Kerry and Sligo, the probability is that it occurs in other parts of Ireland.

The Pease-blossom (*Chariclea delphinii*).

The beautifully tinted moth represented by Figs. 8 and 9 on Plate 17 was known as British to Haworth (1802), but it had been figured by Wilkes in 1773, and by Moses Harris in 1775. In 1829 Stephens remarked that there were then but few native specimens in British cabinets, among which were examples from the Windsor district "caught about fifteen years since, in June." He adds, the interest and value of these, and older specimens, was lessened by "the execrable practice of introducing Continental insects into collections." Stainton (1857) refers to the Windsor specimens only, and Newman (1869) ignores the species altogether. In 1902 two specimens were presented to the British Museum by Mr. J. F. Bennett, and are now in the National Collection of British Lepidoptera. These were obtained at Brighton in 1876 by the donor's father, but whether captured or reared is not known.

The Bordered Sallow (*Pyrrhia umbra*).

The fore wings of this species (Plate 17, Figs. 10, 11) in its typical form are yellow inclining to orange, with the outer area more or less tinted with purplish. In a paler form, ab. *marginata*, Fab., the fore wings are without the orange tint, and the outer area is rather greyish brown.

The caterpillar (Plate 20, Fig. 4) is grey or greenish, speckled with white, and with raised black dots ; there are three lines along the back, the central one white edged, broader and darker than the outer ones, which are sometimes white ; a white-edged pale yellow stripe low down along the sides. In some examples the general colour is pinkish brown.

It feeds on restharrow (*Ononis*) in July and August, but can be reared on knotgrass, and has been known to thrive on the green pods of the scarlet runner bean (*Phaseolus vulgaris*). The moth flies at dusk in June, sometimes earlier or later. It visits the flowers of various plants, especially those of *Silene* and *Lychnis;* also comes to the sugar patch and may be attracted by light. Although not generally common, it seems to be widely distributed over England and Wales, but is most frequent in the seaboard counties, and this is more particularly the case in the north. In Scotland it appears to occur from Berwick northwards to Moray, and in Ireland it has been noted from several of the littoral counties, chiefly southern, but also from Sligo.

The range abroad extends to the North-west Himalayas, Amurland, Corea, and Japan ; the species also occurs in North America from the Atlantic to the Rocky Mountains.

The Marbled Clover (*Heliothis dipsacea*).

The ground colour of this species (Plate 19, Figs. 1, 2) ranges from yellowish to ochreous with a greyish, or olive, tinge; the central band including the reniform stigma is olive, or reddish brown, terminating on the inner margin in a cloud extending towards the hind margin ; submarginal line preceded by a shade-like band similar in colour to the central one, but often only well defined on costal and inner margins ; the whitish area of the hind wings is sometimes much reduced. The darker specimens are typical of the species, whilst those with the paler

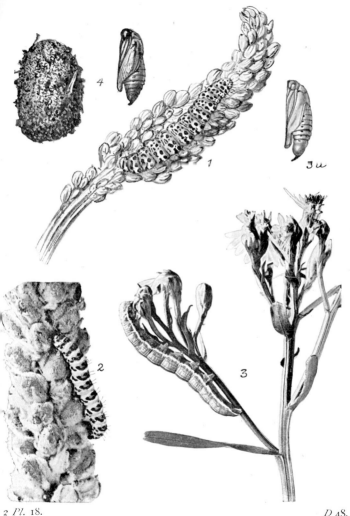

1. **Mullein :** *caterpillar.*   2. **Striped Lychnis :** *caterpillar.*
3, 3*a.* **Starwort :** *caterpillar and chrysalis.*   4. **Chamomile Shark :** *chrysalis and cocoon.*

1, 2. **Marbled Clover.**
4, 5. **Bordered Straw.**
9. **Pale Shoulder.**

3. **Spotted Clover.**
6-8. **Scarce Bordered Straw.**
10 **The Four-spotted.**

ground colour and brighter cross bands are referable to var. *maritima*, Grasl.

The caterpillar varies in colour, green of various shades, pinkish, or purplish brown ; three lines along the back, the central one with dark edges, and the outer ones whitish, with dark lower edge ; the line low down along the sides is often whitish ; but this, and also the other white lines, may be replaced by greenish or yellowish. It feeds on various low-growing plants such as restharrow, scabious, toadflax, white campion, bladder campion, clover, etc., preferring the flowers and seeds. It has been found from July to September. Sometimes it has been reared on the pods of the scarlet-runner bean.

The moth, which is out in June and July, dashes about rapidly in the daytime, and as it is partial to the flowers of the bugloss, or those of clover, etc., it may be netted when feasting on the blossoms. It occurs in meadows, on heaths, and on sandhills by the sea, in most of the southern and eastern counties of England, but is only rarely seen northwards, and has not been recorded from other parts of the British Isles.

Distribution abroad : the whole Palæarctic region less the extreme north ; also represented in North America by *phlogophagus*, Grote and Robinson.

The Spotted Clover Moth (*Heliothis scutosa*).

The very distinct-looking moth shown on Plate 19, Fig. 3, is exceedingly rare in Britain, only about eleven specimens being authenticated. The earliest-known British specimen was captured in a locality near Dalston, in Cumberland, July, 1835. The next record is of three examples near Skinburnness, also in Cumberland. Then, in 1875, one occurred in Norfolk, at the Cromer lighthouse, and this was followed by another in 1876. In 1877 one was captured as it flew over clover at Weston-super-Mare. On September 19, 1878, a specimen was netted at the flowers of ragwort on the shore of Lough Swilly, near Buncrana, Ireland, and one is recorded as taken near Aberdeen, Scotland, in July of that year. The late Dr. Mason had a specimen said to have been taken at Attleborough, in Norfolk, June, 1880. The latest recorded capture is that of a specimen taken by Mr. F. Capel Hanbury in a clover field near Dartmouth, South Devon, September 4, 1900.

The range abroad extends through Central and Southern Europe eastward to North India, North China ; and southwards to North-west Africa. It occurs also in the Western United States of America.

The Bordered Straw (*Heliothis peltigera*).

Two examples of this species are shown on Plate 19, Figs. 4, 5. The fore wings are pale ochreous brown, with a more or less reddish tinge ; the cross lines are not always distinct, but there is generally a dark dot on the costal end of the first line, and a large olive-brown spot between the second and submarginal lines ; following the submarginal line is a pale band of variable width, but always with a black dot (sometimes double) towards its lower end. Very pale specimens are referable to ab. *pallida*, Cockerell.

The caterpillar (Plate 20, Fig. 3, figured from a coloured drawing by Mr. A. Sich) is green, with three darker green or reddish stripes along the back ; the stripe along the area of the spiracles is dark green, edged below with white, but when the other stripes are reddish this is also marked with that colour. Several other forms have been described, and the caterpillar seems to be a most variable one. It feeds, from June to August, and again in September and October, on many kinds of low-growing herbage, such as restharrow (*Ononis*), clover (*Trifolium*), *Matricaria inodora*, etc. ; also on furze or gorse (*Ulex*), and thorn apple (*Datura*). The blossoms and unripe

seeds are preferred in almost all cases, and flowers of the
garden marigold will be found useful when these caterpillars
are reared in confinement.

From eggs deposited by a female moth taken at Deal in the
evening of June 17, 1904, the caterpillars hatched out in due
course, fed up on wild convolvulus, pupated at the end of July,
and the moths emerged during the last week of August and the
first week of September.   In another case, moths were developed
in about forty-seven days from eggs laid in mid-July.   In 1907
six caterpillars were found in South Devon during the second
week in August, and one of these attained the moth state on
September 3.   Previous to 1906, which was a notable one for
the species, the moth seems not to have been observed earlier
than June, but in the year mentioned several were taken at the
flowers of valerian during May, at Torquay.   Caterpillars were
plentiful on restharrow in the same district during June and
July, and an example, presumably, of a second generation was
captured at bramble blossom on August 11.   In the same
year and on the 15th of the month just noted, a specimen
was reared from a caterpillar found on *Ononis*, July 18, and
another specimen captured, August 24, as it flew in the
sunshine on a slope of the South Downs.   In Clarendon Wood,
near Salisbury, Wilts, one example was taken at sugar, September 2, 1906.   The species seems to be of fairly regular
occurrence in Devonshire and Cornwall, but it has also been
observed, more or less rarely, in many other English counties,
chiefly those on the coast; in Pembrokeshire and Glamorganshire, South Wales; a few specimens have occurred in Co.
Cork, and one in Co. Wicklow, Ireland.   All that appears to be
known of this species in Scotland is that one specimen has
been recorded from Markton, Ayrshire.

Abroad, its distribution is extensive, ranging from Africa, the
Canaries, and Madeira to Central and Southern Europe, and
through Asia to India.

The Scarce Bordered Straw (*Heliothis armigera*).

This species (Plate 19, Figs. 6–8) has an almost universal distribution.   It is found in Europe, Asia, Africa, America, and Australia.   As regards the British Isles, it was first recorded by Mr. Edleston, who noted a specimen taken at Salford, Lancashire, by Mr. John Thomas, in September, 1840.   This specimen, also one captured at Mickleham, Surrey, and others "taken in various localities," are referred to in the *Entomologist's Annual* for 1855.   The following year one was reported from Exeter and one from the Isle of Wight.   The summer of 1859 was a hot one (as were the two previous summers), and the species was recorded from the following localities : Brighton, Bristol, Cambridge, Edmonton, Isle of Wight, Ramsgate, Torquay, Weston-super-Mare, Worthing, and other places.   Apart from the captures on the Devonshire coast, chiefly at Torquay, where the moth seems to occur pretty nearly every year, the records since 1859 are : 1866 (Scarborough) ; 1871 (Wakefield) ; 1876 (Hartlepool, and Kentish Coast) ; 1877 and 1881 (Gloucester); 1890 (Chatham) ; 1895 (Tunbridge Wells) ; 1901 (Isle of Wight) ; 1902 (Chester and Harwich); 1903 (Lewes).   In all cases only single specimens.   The species has been noted once in South Wales, and twice in North Wales ; several specimens were secured in 1898 near Berwick-on-Tweed, and odd specimens have been recorded from Ireland.

The caterpillar is variable in colour ; in one form it is green with a yellowish stripe along the sides, and in another the colour is purplish brown.   The form figured (Plate 20, Fig. 2) is pinkish brown with a black-edged whitish line along the back, and a pinkish freckled and brownish edged yellowish stripe along the sides ; the raised dots are white as a rule, but sometimes in the darker forms they are blackish.   In some examples of the green form the dots and lines are black.

In 1869 two specimens of the moth were reared from caterpillars imported with tomatoes from Spain ; twenty-three years later Mr. Arkle referred to the arrival here of *H. armigera* in the larval state with consignments of tomatoes, from Valencia, landed at Liverpool in the months of June and July. The late Mr. Tugwell reared larvæ, from eggs deposited by a captured female moth, on scarlet geranium ; and there is a record of the finding of caterpillars on such plants, in the autumn of 1876, in the Isle of Wight. Specimens of the moth found at large in Britain occur in the autumn.

In the United States of America, where it is known as the " Cotton Boll worm," " Corn-ear worm," and " Tomato fruit worm," this caterpillar is chiefly destructive to corn crops, as of the five generations stated to occur during the year in the States three occur in cornfields. It also attacks beans, tobacco, pumpkins, melons, oranges, garden flowering-plants, and many kinds of wild plants. The British nurserymen and farmers are perhaps to be congratulated on the fact that this moth is only an accidental visitor and not a native.

The Pale Shoulder (*Acontia* (*Tarache*) *lucida*, var. *albicollis*).

Only eight specimens of this species seem to have been noted in Britain, and all these are apparently referable to the summer form, var. *albicollis*, Fabricius. (Plate 19, Fig. 9.) Stephens, who figured it as *solaris*, Wien Verz. (Haustellata iii., Plate 29, Fig. 3), states that the specimen was in Marsham's collection, but that nothing farther was known about it. He, however, mentions two other specimens " taken within the Metropolitan area about ten years ago [that would be 1820] and four others near Dover above six years ago." Dale fixes the date of Dover captures as June, 1825. On August 25, 1859, a specimen was taken in a clover field at Brighton.

The species has an extensive range abroad, being found in Southern Europe and North-west Africa to Madeira and the Canaries ; also in Central Europe, through Western and Central Asia to North India and East Siberia.

The Four-spotted (*Acontia* (*Tarache*) *luctuosa*).

The fore wings of this species (Plate 19, Fig. 10) are sometimes finely powdered with white, but more often the outer marginal area is distinctly flecked with white. The conspicuous central spot is usually white, but occasionally it has a pinkish ochreous tinge ; very rarely it is reduced to a narrow streak with a short spur from its outer edge. The white band on the hind wings is sometimes narrowed and contracted below the middle.

The eggs are shown on Plate 23, Fig. 2. They were, when laid on June 17, whity brown marked with reddish brown.

The caterpillar is ochreous greyish inclining to reddish or brownish ; three dark-edged stripes along the back, a dark-brown line along the black spiracles, with two finer wavy lines above it ; lower down there is a broad stripe of reddish brown ; head marked with four lines of black dots. It feeds, at night, during June, July, and August (later in some seasons), on the small bindweed (*Convolvulus arvensis*), and although it will eat the leaves when nearly full grown it prefers the flowers and seeds in its infancy.

The moth appears in May and June, and a second generation in August and September. In the sunshine it is active on the wing, but in dull weather it hides under herbage, in clover fields, chalky slopes, and rough places where its food plant occurs.

The female will often lay her eggs in a chip-box when she is thus secured after capture ; the caterpillars are not difficult to rear if flower buds of the bindweed can be obtained to start them upon.

1. **Beautiful Yellow Underwing :** *caterpillars.*
2. **Scarce-bordered Straw :** *caterpillar.*
3. **Bordered Straw :** *caterpillar.*
4. **Bordered Sallow :** *caterpillar.*

1, 2. Purple Marbled.   3. Small Marbled.   4. Silver-barred.
5. Silver Hook.   6. *Thalpochares paula.*   7. Marbled White-spot.
8. Straw Dot.   9. Rosy Marbled.   10, 11. Small Purple Barred.
12. Spotted Sulphur.

The species is especially common in the south-west of England, chiefly on the coast, but it seems to occur in most suitable localities in nearly all the southern counties, and its range extends to Gloucestershire on the west and to Norfolk on the east. About seventy-five years ago Stephens used to obtain specimens on a chalky ridge near Hertford, and recently the moth has been found at Hitchin in North Hertfordshire.

The Purple Marbled (*Thalpochares ostrina*).

Two Continental specimens of this little moth are shown on Plate 21, Figs. 1 typical, 2 ab. *carthami*. An example of this species was obtained in June, 1825, in a lane near Bideford, Devonshire, and Stephens refers to this as the only specimen of the species that up to that time (1830) had been noted in England. Nothing more was heard of *T. ostrina* until 1858, when another Devonshire specimen was taken, this time near Torquay, on June 8, and during the month several others were captured on the coast; two were also secured in the Isle of Wight, and one in Ayrshire, Scotland. In 1865, a specimen was recorded as taken in July a few years previously at Pembrey, South Wales; 1880, one at Dover in September, and one near Swanage; Barrett mentions specimens taken on the Culver Cliffs, Isle of Wight, in 1859.

It seems unquestionable that examples of this species captured in Britain, and also of the other two *Thalpochares* to be presently referred to, are immigrants, and it is quite conceivable that besides the specimens captured here, others which have escaped detection may also have arrived with them.

The distribution abroad is extensive, embracing South Europe, Turkey, Asia Minor, Egypt, North-west Africa, Madeira, and the Canary Isles. It has also been found in France and Germany, but its occurrence in the latter country has been even less frequent than in England.

The Small Marbled (*Thalpochares parva*).

This species, of which a foreign example is represented on
Plate 21, Fig. 3, has a similar distribution to that of *T. ostrina*,
only it does not seem to occur in Madeira or the Canaries, and
its eastward range extends to Central and Southern India.

The fore wings are pale reddish ochreous ; first line, oblique,
dusky, slightly waved on lower half, bordered inwardly with
brownish and outwardly with white; second line, dusky and
irregular.

The earliest specimen noted in Britain was captured at
Teignmouth, South Devon, in July, 1844; another was said to
have been captured at Weston-super-Mare, Somerset, but it
has been suggested that this specimen might probably be
referable to *T. ostrina*. Mr. E. Bankes has a specimen, taken
by himself on a salt marsh in the Isle of Purbeck, Dorset,
June 8, 1892. This seems to be all that is definitely known
of this species in Britain, but others have been noted from the
Isle of Wight and the Isle of Man.

Thalpochares paula.

The fore wings are white, clouded with pale brownish grey
beyond the almost straight and rather oblique first line, and
also beyond the angulated second line.

Of this species (Plate 21, Fig. 6) a specimen, now in the
collection of Mr. E. R. Bankes, was taken at Freshwater, Isle
of Wight, in June, 1872. Two other specimens, one of which
seems to have been captured by a boy who was collecting on
the south coast, were recorded in 1873 ; these insects were at
that time in the collection of the Rev. H. Burney, and had been
caught several years earlier.

The range abroad extends through Europe and Asia to South
Siberia. The specimen figured is from Dresden.

Marbled White Spot (*Lithacodia (Erastria) fasciana*).

The ground colour of the fore wings of this species (Plate 21, Fig. 7) is brownish grey, more or less clouded and sometimes suffused with blackish; the white patch on the outer marginal area is, in some examples, much obscured by dark-grey markings, and in occasional specimens the only trace of white on this part of the wing is a thin edging to the second line (ab. *albilinea*, Haworth). Has been referred to *Hapalitis*.

The caterpillar is pale yellowish, with a greenish, sometimes red, tinged line along the middle of the back, and a brown one on each side; a reddish line under the black spiracles; head, brownish; the raised dots of the body are dusky edged with reddish. It feeds from July to September. A reddish form of this caterpillar has been noted. Buckler, from whose description the above has been condensed, states that the food-plant is blue moor-grass, or purple melic-grass (*Molinia cærulea*), and this is confirmed by Bignell, who remarks that in Devonshire he easily finds the caterpillars "feeding about half way up the blades" of this grass.

The moth is out in June and July, or in forward seasons in late May. It is partial to pine and larch trunks as a resting place during the day, and is local and more or less frequent in most of the southern counties, from Kent to Cornwall, through Somerset and Gloucester (extending into Oxford), to Hereford and Worcester, on the west, and from Essex to Norfolk on the east. A specimen was taken at light in Chester in June, 1901.

The range abroad extends to Japan.

The Silver Barred (*Bankia (Erastria) argentula*).

In its typical form this species (Plate 21, Fig. 4) has the colour of the fore wings olive brown, but occasionally it is tinged with reddish in some English, and more generally in Irish, specimens. The silvery oblique lines, or bands, vary in width, and sometimes there is a distinct spur from the lower outer edge of the first band.

The caterpillar is yellowish green, with a rather darker green line along the middle of the back, and a yellow one on each side of it. It feeds on grasses, such as *Poa aquatica* and *P. pratensis*, etc., in July and early August.

The moth is out in June, and may be found during the day sitting about on the herbage in its marshy haunts, or flying over the vegetation towards the evening.

The species is exceedingly local in Britain. In ancient times it occurred in Norfolk, but in the present day it seems to be confined to Cambridgeshire, in which county it was first noted rarely in Wicken fen about thirty years ago, but in 1882 it was found plentifully in Chippenham fen, and in that locality (which is a private one) the species still flourishes. In Ireland it is well distributed over co. Kerry, and is especially abundant on the bogs of Killarney.

The range abroad extends to Amurland, where the brownish form var. *amurula*, Staud., is found.

The Silver Hook (*Hydrelia (Erastria) uncula*).

The usually olive brown central area of the fore wings is sometimes reddish tinged, and in fresh specimens the whitish front marginal streak is distinctly rosy ; the reniform stigma, which appears to be a spur of the costal streak, is also white or rosy tinged, and sometimes encloses a greyish mark. This stigma is the so-called "hook" to which both the English name and the Latin specific name refer. (Plate 21, Fig. 5.)

The caterpillar feeds in July and early August on sedges (*Carex*) and coarse grasses. It is green, with three lines along the back, the central one rather darker green, and the other

1. The Herald.   2. The Dark Spectacle.
3. The Spectacle.   4. Golden Plusia.
5, 6. Burnished Brass.

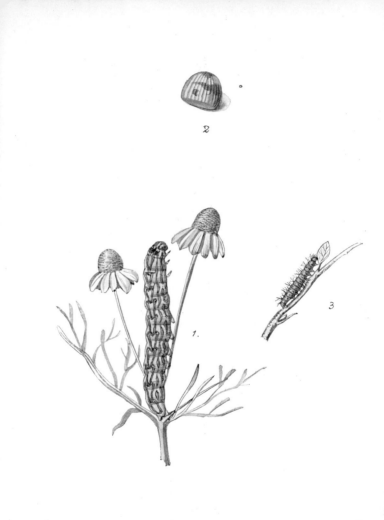

1. **Chamomile Shark :** *caterpillar.*   2. **The Four-spotted :** *eggs.*
3. **Straw Dot :** *caterpillar.*

two whitish ; low down along the sides is a broader yellowish line ; the head is green with a yellowish tinge.

The moth is out from late May to early July, sometimes later.

This is also a marsh-loving species, and is generally plentiful in the fens of Norfolk, Suffolk, and Cambridgeshire ; in the Southern counties it is either very local or, owing to its small size, has escaped detection, but has been noted as occurring in Surrey (Wisley and Richmond Park), Kent (Deal), Hants (New Forest), Dorset, Devon, Cornwall, and Somersetshire ; also in Yorkshire (Askham bog), and in Cumberland. The Welsh counties in which it has been found are Pembroke, Glamorgan and Carnarvon (Abersoch). It is locally common in Clydesdale, and has also been reported from Kirkcudbrightshire, and Perthshire. In Ireland it abounds in the boggy parts of Kerry, and is more or less frequent in several other parts of Ireland. Near Castle Bellingham, co. Louth, where it is common, a second brood was observed on Aug. 1st, 1894.

Its range abroad extends to Amurland and Japan.

Rosy Marbled (*Monodes* (*Erastria*) *venustula*).

Another local species, but a frequenter of drier localities than the last two. This delicate rosy-flushed whitish moth first became known as a native of Britain by the capture of a few specimens in Essex. Stephens, writing in 1830, remarks, " I have hitherto seen four examples only—a pair in my own cabinet ; one of the latter taken, I believe, in Epping forest by the late Mr. Honey, the other by the late Mr. Bentley." No other British specimens seem to have been recorded until 1845, when the late Mr. H. Doubleday, in July, noted several of the moths disporting themselves over, or settling upon, bracken in Epping Forest. For many years Loughton and some other parts of the forest remained the only known English haunts of the species, but in 1874 it was found commonly in

St. Leonard's Forest, Sussex; later still, it was discovered in the Brentwood district, Essex. It still occurs in all these localities, but appears to be now less frequently noticed in the original one than formerly (Plate 21, Fig. 9).

The caterpillar feeds in July and August on the flowers of cinquefoil (*Potentilla*), and is said to eat bramble blossoms also. Hellins describes it as rich brown, with a row of eight dusky-red diamonds down the back, enclosing the dorsal line of brighter red. The moth is out from the end of May and in June; it may be put up from herbage during the day, but its proper time of flight is in the early evening, and then only when the weather is favourable. If cold or damp the insects will not get on the wing. (Plate 25, Fig. 3; after Hofmann.)

The range abroad extends to Amurland.

The Straw Dot (*Rivula sericealis*).

This pale ochreous species, an example of which is represented on Plate 21, Fig. 8, varies in the amount of darker shading or suffusion on the outer marginal area of the fore wing; sometimes this is grey-brown or pale reddish brown, but often there is no shading whatever, and in such specimens the ground colour is usually very pale. The dark brown reniform mark is always present, but the cross lines are more often absent than present.

The caterpillar is green, with a darker green line along the middle of the back, and a white stripe on each side of it, the inner edge of each of the latter irregular; head, greenish grey, and the bristle-bearing raised dots are shining green with a dusky cap. It feeds on *Brachypodium sylvaticum*, but seems to accommodate itself to a diet of *Phalaris arundinacea*, and would perhaps eat other grasses: August to May. (Plate 23, Fig. 3; after Hofmann.)

The moth is out all through the summer months, and

frequents marshes, damp rides and borders of woods, heaths, and where there is plenty of tall grass.

The species is widely distributed over England and Wales, although it appears to be rather scarce in the midlands and northwards. In Ireland it is generally abundant, but in Scotland it has only been noted from the south, and is there local and rare.

The distribution abroad includes Amurland, Corea, and Japan.

The Small Purple Barred (*Prothymnia viridaria*).

The fore wings of this species (Plate 21, Figs. 10 ♂, 11 ♀) range in colour from olive grey to olive brown, and are frequently adorned with two rosy-red (typical) or purplish bands (*aenea*, Haw.). In some specimens the bands are of a dusky hue and not very distinct, whilst in others the wings are of a uniform dingy brown tint (ab. *fusca*, Tutt).

The caterpillar (Plate 25, Fig. 2) is velvety-green above and paler beneath, yellowish between the rings, with a dark green slender line bordered by paler lines along the back, and three pale lines along the sides; below the yellowish spiracles there is a broader pale line becoming whitish on rings 9–12; head, green mottled with brown (adapted from Hellins).

It is to be found in August and September on the common milkwort (*Polygala vulgaris*). On May 31, 1906, I met with the moth in some numbers on a marshy bit of heath in Surrey, where there was a plentiful growth of lousewort (*Pedicularis*), but, so far as I know, no *Polygala*. All the moths were much below the average size, the bands were mainly purple, but in no case rosy. The moth flies in May and June, and specimens have been captured both earlier and later. Except that it does not appear to occur in the extreme north of Scotland, the species seems to be pretty generally distributed over the British Isles, and is often very common in many parts.

The eastern distribution extends to E. Siberia.

The Spotted Sulphur (*Emmelia trabealis*).

Although this pretty black and yellow moth (Plate 21, Fig. 12) was noted by Stephens (1830) as being occasionally captured in Battersea fields, and as occurring near Margate, and elsewhere in Kent, it was not until 1847 that the Breck-sand district of Norfolk, adjoining parts of Suffolk, and Cambridge, became known as being inhabited by The Spotted Sulphur. The vicinity of Brandon and Tuddenham is especially favoured by the species, but it occurs in several other parts of the area. Occasionally, specimens have been captured in various Kentish localities, and between thirty and forty years ago single examples were taken in Hackney Marshes, Lower Clapton (August 2), also in Wandsworth (at light, July 26). From these facts it would appear possible that the species occasionally strays from its haunts in the eastern counties and sometimes to a considerable distance. Once, indeed, a specimen was found on a gas lamp at Exeter. On the other hand, it is quite conceivable that such wanderers may have come from abroad.

Some specimens are of a paler yellow than others, but there is rather more noticeable aberration in the number and intensity of the black markings.

The caterpillar is reddish brown, with three darker lines along the back, the central one pale edged ; a pale yellow stripe runs along the region of the spiracles, and has a fine brownish line running through it from end to end. Another form is green with white lines. It feeds on the bindweed (*Convolvulus arvensis*) in July, and has a second brood in September. The moth, which rests among herbage by day, and flies towards evening, is found in June, July, and August.

The species is found throughout Central and Southern Europe, its range extending to Denmark and South Sweden ; eastward it occurs in Asia Minor, Syria, and through Asia to Japan.

GONOPTERINÆ.

The Herald (*Scoliopteryx libatrix*).

Haworth (1802) gave this attractive species the English name of " Furbelow Moth," but Harris (1782) had named it Herald Moth (Plate 22, Fig. 1).

In the majority of specimens the purplish, or grey-brown fore wings, are more or less reddish tinged throughout, but occasionally the outer marginal area is free of this tint ; the orange red marks on the central and basal areas are brighter in some specimens than in others.

The caterpillar, which feeds on sallow, osier, willow, and probably poplar (a chrysalis having been found in a curled leaf of black poplar), is a long, rather thin, greenish creature without any distinct markings, except that when full grown the front rings have two black spots. It may be found reposing on the upper leaves of its foodplant, from June to August. (Plate 25, Fig. 1, from a coloured drawing by Mr. A. Sich.)

The moth may be obtained at sugar, ivy-blossom, etc., from August to October, and it seems that the earliest to emerge are those that first take up hibernating quarters in barns, outhouses, roofs, belfries, and under arches. In the spring it reappears, and may be met with even in June. A specimen was taken at sugar on July 20, 1899, but whether this is to be regarded as a very late date or an unusually early one, I cannot say. Generally distributed throughout Great Britain and Ireland, but of the Scottish Isles only recorded from Shetland. Abroad it ranges through Europe to North-West Africa, and through Asia to Amurland and Japan ; also in temperate North America.

NOTE.—Stephens (1829) referred this species to the genus *Calyptra*, Ochs., but in 1831 he adopted *Scoliopteryx*, Germar (1811). *Gonoptera*, Latr., which has been frequently used, only dates from 1825.

QUADRIFINÆ.

The Golden Plusia (*Plusia moneta*).

The British history of the grey tinged pale golden species, shown on Plate 22, Fig. 4, dates back only to 1890. In that

year, on July 2, Mr. Christy, of Watergate, Emsworth, found a specimen in his illuminated moth trap ; this was noted in the *Entomologist* for August, 1890. From subsequent records it appears that a specimen had been taken on the same date at a gas lamp near Reading, by Mr. W. Holland ; whilst one was captured, at a light, near Tunbridge Wells on July 1. The earliest British specimen, however, was one netted whilst hovering over flowers of *Delphinium* at Dover, on June 25 of the same year, but this was not announced until October. Since

FIG. 2.
Golden Plusia at rest.
(Photo by H. Main.)

its arrival here the species seems to have spread over England at a great rate, and it has been reported from

1. Scarce Burnished Brass.   2. Gold Spangle.
3, 4. Gold Spot.   5, 6. Beautiful Golden Y.
7, 8. Plain Golden Y.

1. **Herald :** *caterpillar.*   2. **Small Purple-barred :** *caterpillar.*
3. **Rosy-marbled :** *caterpillar.*

Cheshire. Larvæ were found at Hart, Co. Durham, in May, 1919. In some southern gardens the caterpillars abound. On the continent it is said to feed on sunflower, artichoke, burdock, and cucumber.

The caterpillar is green, dotted with white ; a dark line along the back and a white one along the sides. In the early stage it is black or sooty brown, and hides itself among the spun together flower buds, or in a turned down tender leaf. It feeds in May and June, occasionally found in late April, after hiberna-tion, and a second generation sometimes occurs in July and August. Monkshood (*Aconitum*) and larkspur (*Delphinium*) are the usual food plants, and it is curious to note that whilst some observers state that larkspur alone is eaten, others say that monkshood is the only food. The moth flies in June and July, and sometimes there is an emergence in August and September. It visits the blossoms of various garden plants, and is also attracted by light.

The caterpillar, represented on Plate 27, Fig. 1, was found with others on larkspur in Mr. Herbert Smith's garden at Wal-lington, Surrey. The cocoon and chrysalis is from a photo by Mr. H. Main. Another photo by Mr. Main shows the young caterpillar constructing its retreat.

According to Duponchel this species occurred in Normandy, Central and Northern Europe, as far back as 1829. A much paler form inclining to silvery, var. *esmeralda*, Oberthür, is found in Ussuri, North China, and other parts of East Asia.

The Burnished Brass (*Plusia chrysitis*).

Two forms of this metallic-looking species are represented (Plate 22) ; 5 is typical and 6 shows the ab. *juncta*, Tutt. Between these are various intermediate stages leading to the complete division of the central band. The broken central band is a character of var. *nadeja*, Oberthür, from Amurland and

Series II.   F

Japan, but that form has also a more or less complete series of ochreous-brown dots on the outer area. The metallic colour is sometimes greenish in all forms.

The caterpillar is pale green, with a darker green line along the middle of the back, bordered on each side by an irregular white line ; an oblique white streak on the sides of each ring from 4–11 ; a stripe low down along the sides is white ; head, yellowish tinged. It feeds on stinging nettle, probably on other plants, and after hibernation attains full growth about May. In favourable seasons caterpillars also occur in July and August. The moth is out in June, July, and August, less frequently in September, and may be found flying along the sides of hedges and ditches, especially where flowering weeds are plentiful, throughout the British Isles ; so far, however, it has not been recorded from the Hebrides, Orkneys, or Shetlands.

The Scarce Burnished Brass (*Plusia chryson*).

The more or less square golden (sometimes green-tinged) patch on the velvety purplish brown fore wings, distinguish this species (Plate 24, Fig. 1) from any other British *Plusia*.

The caterpillar is green, with a darker line along the middle of the back, and a fine white line on each side of it ; there is a dark green stripe low down along the sides, edged below with white, and oblique white lines run from it to the central line on rings 3–11. It feeds on hemp-agrimony (*Eupatorium cannabinum*), hibernates when small, and completes its growth in May or early June.

The moth is out in July and August, and is said to be occasionally seen, on sunny days, flying about, or resting on, the flowers of the hemp-agrimony and other plants. Night, however, is its more usual time of activity, and it may also be found at the blossoms of the larval food plant, and at those of honeysuckle, etc.

The species has been found, chiefly in the past in most of the southern counties of England from Kent (Deal district) to Cornwall, also in Gloucestershire, and in South Wales. Chippenham fen in Cambridgeshire is the most noted locality for it in the present day, and it has been found in Norfolk and Suffolk. There is even a record of a specimen having been beaten out of honeysuckle near Preston, Lancs., but this happened nearly forty years ago.

The range abroad extends to Amurland and Japan.

The Gold Spangle (*Plusia bractea*).

The purplish brown fore wings of this moth have a bright solid-looking golden mark on the upper edge of a velvety, deep brown patch. This metallic " spangle " varies a little in size and in shape, but not to any noteworthy extent (Plate 24, Fig. 2).

The caterpillar is bright green, dotted with white, above, and dull darker green below ; there is a fine dark green line along the middle of the back, some indistinct and irregular white lines followed by a whitish stripe lower down, along the sides. It seems to feed upon a variety of low-growing plants, among which are groundsel, dandelion, white dead-nettle (*Lamium album*), and stinging nettle, also on honeysuckle, from August to May. In a state of nature, it hibernates when small, and becomes full grown in May or early June, but when reared from the egg it can be induced, by keeping it in a warm place, to continue feeding, grow up quickly, pupate, and assume the winged state in the late autumn. Under such artificial conditions it is said to eat lettuce and plantain.

Normally, the moth is out in June and July, and has been met with in August. Like all members of this group it is partial to flowers, and has been frequently taken at those of the honeysuckle, although all sorts of blossoms, down to the lowly *Viola cornuta*, have attraction for it.

The species is more especially a denizen of Ireland and Scotland, but it occurs in most of the northern counties of England, and has been recorded from Worcestershire and Herefordshire ; also from Carmarthenshire in South Wales.

Abroad, its range extends to Central Asia; and in Amurland and Japan it is represented by *P. excelsa*, Kretschmar.

The Gold Spot (*Plusia festucæ*).

In this species (Plate 24, Figs. 3 and 4) the fore wings are golden brown, clouded with purplish brown ; sometimes the purplish brown is confined almost entirely to the broad area. Besides the large central metallic marks, there are more or less conspicuous patches of metallic colour at the base of the costa, on the middle of the inner margin, and towards the tips of the wings. Usually the central spots are clearly apart, but I have one example from Bishop Auckland, Durham, in which they are only separated one from the other by a slender brown line.

The caterpillar is green, with a white-edged dark-green line along the middle of the back, and some slender yellowish lines on each side of it ; a whitish or yellow tinged stripe low down along the sides ; head, tinged with brown.

It feeds on sedge, coarse grasses, bur-reed (*Sparganium ramosum*), and yellow-flag (*Iris pseudacorus*) ; also said by Collins to eat water plantain (*Alisma plantago*) : April to June, and in some localities and seasons, again in July and August. The black chrysalis is enclosed in a rather long greyish cocoon, spun up on the undersides of the leaves of sedge or reed ; usually placed towards the tip of the leaf, which droops over and so hides it.

The moth is out in June and July, and in some years there seems to be an emergence in August and September ; this has been more particularly noted in Cheshire, where Arkle has had moths emerge in June, July, August, and September. A second

1, 2. **Silver Y.** 3. **Ni Moth.**
4, 5. **Scarce Silver Y.** 6, 7. **Mother Shipton.**
8, 9. **Burnet Companion.**

1, 1*a*, 1*b*. **Golden Plusia :** *caterpillars and chrysalis.*
2. **Dark Spectacle :** *caterpillar.*

flight has been noted in Ireland by Kane and others ; and late
examples have also been recorded from Scotland.

Although it has been recorded from some of the southern
counties, it is most frequent in the eastern and northern parts of
England, and in South Wales.   Occurs throughout Scotland up
to Moray ; and in Ireland it is found in most localities, though
not often common, except by the sea in Co. Kerry, and in
Connamara, Co. Galway.

Abroad, it extends to East Siberia, Amurland, and Japan.

The Plain Golden Y (*Plusia iota*).

In typical specimens the metallic mark is V-shaped, with a
dot below and a little to one side (Plate 24, Fig. 8).   In ab.
percontationis, Treit. (Fig. 7), these spots are united and form a
Y-like mark.   Sometimes the spot is absent and the V-mark
much reduced, and more rarely the V also disappears (ab.
inscripta, Esp.).

The larva is yellowish green, white dotted, with a white-
edged darker line along the middle of the back ; a band composed of whitish irregular lines runs along the sides, and a thin
yellow line along the area of the spiracles.   It hatches from
the egg in the late summer, hibernates when quite small, and
feeds up in the spring.   The food plants comprise the dead
nettles (*Lamium*), woundwort (*Stachys*), mint, stinging nettle,
honeysuckle, hawthorn, etc.   There is a record of sixteen larvæ
which hibernated among dead leaves of *Lamium album*, re-
sumed feeding on February 18, spun up April 23–25, and
produced moths May 27—June 4.   Usually the moth is on the
wing in June and July.

The species seems to be pretty widely distributed throughout the British Isles to the Orkneys ; it was not known to occur
in the Hebrides until 1901, when McArthur obtained it in the
Isle of Lewis.

The Beautiful Golden Y (*Plusia pulchrina*).

This species (Plate 24, Figs. 5 and 6) so closely resembles the last that it has been considered a variety thereof; there is no question, however, that it is quite distinct. The fore wings in both species are somewhat similar in general tints, but the following points of difference distinguish *pulchrina*—the darker colour is less evenly displayed, and gives the wings a more mottled or marbled appearance; the cross lines, especially those on the basal area, are almost invariably golden edged; the second cross line is more acutely bent inwards above the inner margin, the reniform has a more or less complete golden outline, and it is placed in a dark cloud; the golden V-mark and dot below are generally thicker. As a rule, the fringes of all the wings are more distinctly chequered, but this feature cannot be relied on alone in separating one species from the other. In ab. *percontatrix*, Aurivillius (= *juncta*, Tutt), the golden V and dot are united and so form a Y-mark (Fig. 5). An aberration, probably unique, was taken in June, 1919, by Mr. C. G. Clutterbuck, of Gloucester. The Y-mark is here replaced by a large wedge-shaped golden blotch.

The caterpillar is green with a broad central white stripe and several finer white lines along the back; a yellowish-tinted white stripe low down along the sides; head shining, marked with black on each side of the mouth. It feeds on various low-growing plants, such as the dead nettles, groundsel, etc., also on honeysuckle and bilberry.

The moth occurs in June and July, and is found more or less frequently all over the British Isles to Orkney, but in England is more plentiful from the Midlands northwards than in the southern countries.

The Ni Moth (*Plusia ni*).

The present species (Plate 26, Fig. 3) bears a strong resemblance to a small pale specimen of *P. gamma*; but, as will be noted, the silvery central Y-mark is differently formed. Here it is made up of a curve somewhat like the letter U, and an oval or round spot, the latter very close to and sometimes, as in the example figured, united with the former.

The caterpillar, which feeds on cabbage and other Cruciferæ, also on lettuce, tomato, etc., is green, inclining to yellowish green and dotted with white; three white lines along the back, and a white stripe along the sides. It is said to be more slender in form than the caterpillar of *P. gamma*. (Plate 28, Fig. 1.)

The earliest British specimen was taken at flowers of red valerian in a garden at Exeter, August, 1868. The next year a specimen occurred, also in a garden, at Penzance. Then followed captures in Dorset, one 1885, and one (Isle of Portland) 1888. Two caterpillars were found in the Isle of Portland in 1894, and these produced moths in September of that year. At least eight moths were secured at Penzance in 1894, and specimens were subsequently reared from caterpillars found on cabbages in the gardens around Lynwood. In May, 1896, one example of the moth was taken by Mr. Percy Richards at Norbiton, Surrey. The last recorded capture appears to be that by Mr. Finzi of a female specimen at Tenby, South Wales, on June 9, 1906. She deposited a few eggs in the collecting-box, and the caterpillars that hatched from them were reared on broccoli and lettuce, and produced moths, July 24–30.

Plusia ni ranges through south-east and southern Europe, to Asia Minor, North Africa, and the Canaries. In the Isle of Capri it is said to be almost as common as *P. gamma*. *Brassicæ*, Riley (1870), is a well-known *Plusia* in America, where it is classed among noxious insects. It is somewhat larger and browner in colour than European *ni*, but in every other respect it seems to agree so exactly that it can hardly be considered specifically distinct.

The Silver Y (*Plusia gamma*).

This species, represented by portraits of two specimens on Plate 26, Figs. 1 and 2, varies somewhat in the ground colour of the fore wings, which ranges from a whitish grey through various tints of grey and brown to velvety black. The melanic form last referred to is very rare, but I caught one example of it at Eastbourne in the late summer of 1888, and I saw, but did not secure, another near Esher in the autumn of 1906; one taken at Dartmoor in September, 1894, is in Mr. F. J. Hanbury's collection.

Occasionally a purplish red tinge, often present below the silvery Y, spreads over a larger area of the fore wings. The Y-mark is well defined as a rule, but now and then specimens are found in which only the tail of the Y is distinct.

The caterpillar varies in general colour from pale green to a dark olive green approaching black. In the white dotted paler green forms there are several transverse whitish lines, some of them wavy, between the yellowish spiracular line and the dark green line along the middle of the back; head, marked with black on each cheek. It will eat almost every kind of low-growing vegetation, either wild or cultivated, and in some years may be found throughout the summer. Small larvæ were recorded as seen at the end of October, 1901. The blackish chrysalis is enclosed in a whitish cocoon, often placed under leaves of thistle, burdock, etc.

The moth is seen in the spring and early summer (most probably immigrants), and again in the autumn, when it is generally more abundant.

This well-known migrating species has been observed in greater or lesser numbers over the whole of the British Isles. Its distribution abroad embraces the Palæarctic Region, North Africa, and North America.

The Scarce Silver Y (*Plusia interrogationis*).

Portraits of two examples of this species will be found on Plate 26, Figs. 4 and 5. The metallic central marks on the fore wings vary a good deal in size and in form, and are sometimes almost absent; these wings have the general greyish colour more clouded or suffused with blackish in some specimens than in others. Kane states that Irish specimens, when freshly emerged, have a tinge of violet purple, and Tutt notes some British specimens as beautifully tinted with rose colour (ab. *rosea*).

The caterpillar, which feeds on heather (*Calluna*) and bilberry (*Vaccinium*), is green inclining to blackish on the sides and underparts, with six white lines along the back; two of which are irregular; the raised dots are white and the bristles therefrom dark; head, green dashed with purple, shining. (Fenn.) After hibernation it may be found without much difficulty in May and June on its food plants, either in the daytime, or by the aid of a lamp at night. Large numbers fall victims to parasitical flies. (Plate 28, Fig. 2.) The white cocoons enclosing the black chrysalids are spun up on or under the twigs of bilberry and heather. The moth is out in July and August, and may be found on moorlands, in the north of England from Shropshire (with Radnor) and Staffordshire on the west, and Lincolnshire on the east, through Scotland to Sutherland, and in all suitable localities in Ireland.

The Dark Spectacle (*Abrostola triplasia*).

The fore wings of this moth are blackish grey inclining to purplish and rather shining; the basal area is pale reddish brown, edged by a curved dark chocolate brown cross line; a reddish grey band on the outer area clouded with ground colour and edged above the inner margin by a dark chocolate brown curved line; raised scales on the central area and on the cross lines. Two oval reddish brown marks on the front of the collar have some resemblance to a pair of spectacles, hence the English name. (Plate 22, Fig. 2.)

The caterpillar is green, sprinkled with white dots; on rings 4, 5, and 11 are whitish-edged darker marks, and there is a dark line, also whitish-edged, along the middle of the back between rings 5 and 11; a white line on the back from ring 4 to the brownish head, and white-edged dark oblique lines on the sides of rings 6 to 11; the line low down along the sides is whitish with an ochreous tinge. A purplish brown form also occurs (Plate 27, Fig. 2), in which the pale markings are ochreous tinged. It is found from July to September on nettle and hops, the latter more especially. The earlier caterpillars, in some years, attain the moth state in August or early September, but the bulk of them remain in the chrysalis state during the winter, the moth emerging in June or July of the following year.

The species is not uncommon in most southern English counties, but becomes less frequent or more local northwards from the Midlands to Cumberland, Northumberland, and South Scotland. It occurs in Wales, and is widely spread in Ireland.

The range abroad extends to Amurland.

The Spectacle (*Abrostola tripartita*).

This species, known also as *urticæ*, Hübner, has the basal and outer marginal areas of the fore wings whitish grey, finely mottled with darker grey; the central area is greyish brown, mottled with darker brown. The spectacle mark in front of the thorax is whitish grey, ringed with black, and the raised scales on the cross lines and central area of the fore wings are more distinct in this species (Plate 22, Fig. 3). The caterpillar is pale green, with white-edged dark-green >-shaped marks along the back, most in evidence on rings 4–11 ; two slender whitish lines on each side, only distinct on rings 1–4 ; a white stripe low down along the sides, edged above with dark green and with whitish streaks from it to the white edging of the marks on the back. Head, green, rather shining, with dusky marks on each cheek (adapted from Fenn). It feeds in July, at night, on the common stinging nettle, from the foliage of which it may be beaten out, or, by searching, found on the undersides of the leaves. In some years there is a second brood in September.

The moth is out in June, sometimes late May, and, when there is a second emergence, in August. Occasionally it is seen on fences, etc., but at night it visits the blossoms of various plants, both wild and cultivated ; the flowers of spur-valerian (*Centranthus ruber*), honeysuckle, and woundwort (*Stachys*) being especially attractive, as also they are to the Dark Spectacle, and most of the species of *Plusia*.

Although apparently commoner in some counties than in others, this species ranges over the British Isles to the Orkneys.

The distribution abroad extends to Amurland.

The Mother Shipton (*Euclidia mi*).

The ancient fathers of British Entomology were sometimes happy in their selection of names in the vernacular for those of our moths that were known to them at the time, and the present species is a fair example of this. Moses Harris first dubbed it the Shipton Moth, but afterwards changed the name to the "Mask Moth." Both names refer to the peculiar shape of the markings which adorn the fore wings and bear a more or less fanciful resemblance to a grotesque mask, and even more closely to the profile of an historical dame yclept

Shipton. This character, also supposed to be like the letter M, hence the specific name *mi*, stands out very distinctly in the paler specimens, but in some of the darker individuals it is somewhat obscured. On the hind wings the spots are whitish or yellowish, and those composing the central series are sometimes united, and form a band. (Plate 26, Figs. 6 ♂, 7 ♀.)

The egg is greenish, and the caterpillar is pale ochreous-brown, with darker brown lines along the back and sides : head, ochreous, with brown lines. It feeds on clover and grasses, in July, August, and September, and the chrysalis, which is covered with a whitish powder, is enclosed in a brownish cocoon spun up in a blade of grass. All the early stages are figured on Plate 30. The enlarged chrysalis, Fig. 1, is from a photo by Mr. H. Main. The moth flies in May and June, and is often common in meadows, on railway banks, and other sloping banks and such-like places where wild flowers abound. The species is widely distributed over England, Wales, and South Scotland ; also Ireland.

The range abroad extends to Amurland.

The Burnet Companion (*Euclidia glyphica*).

The ground colour of the fore wings is purplish brown, sometimes becoming greyish on the outer area ; the space between the dark brown or blackish cross bands is sometimes filled up with the darker colour. Some specimens are much greyer than others, and all the examples in a series from the Lake district that I have seen were distinctly grey, with very dark bands. The yellow on the hind wings sometimes inclines to orange, and sometimes it is so pale as to be almost whitish ; there is also variation in the amount of black marking and shading on these wings. (Plate 26, Figs. 8 ♂, 9 ♀.)

The caterpillar is somewhat similar to that of the last species ;

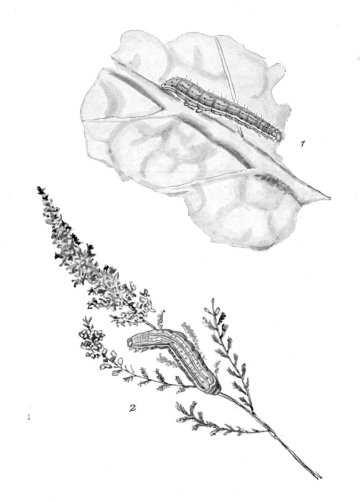

1. **The Ni Moth:** *caterpillar.* 2. **Scarce Silver Y:** *caterpillar*

Pl. 20.

it feeds on clovers and trefoils in July and August, but so far does not seem to have been noted to eat grasses.

The moth is on the wing at the end of May and in June, and inhabits similar kinds of places to those mentioned for the last species, often in company with it, and also with the Burnet moths. Widely distributed over the greater part of the British Isles ; common in some southern localities. Its distribution abroad extends to Amurland, and in Japan it is represented by the larger and paler form *consors*, Butler.

Leucanitis (Ophiusa) stolida, Fab.—An example of this species, which is a native of Africa and South Europe, was captured by Mr. J. Jäger in the neighbourhood of Dartmouth, S. Devon. It was in fine condition, and came to sugar on September 23, 1903.

Lunar Double Stripe (*Minucia (Pseudophia) lunaris*).

The portrait of this species on Plate 29, Fig. 1, is taken from a Spanish example. Exceedingly few British specimens have been recorded. The earliest seems to be the following : "Among my cabinet specimens there is one example of *Ophiodes lunaris*, captured at the Lowestoft Light in 1832. I conclude this is a great rarity, having seen many cabinets without it.— E. Chawner." *Entom.* vi. p. 147 (1872–73). Presumably this is the same specimen as that mentioned by Stainton (1857), Newman (1869), and later authors, as taken in Hants by Captain Chawner. In 1860 one example was obtained at sugar at West Wickham ; and in 1864 Bouchard caught two specimens at Killarney. On June 17, 1873, one came to sugar in Abbots Wood, Sussex ; one at Brighton in June, 1874, and another in Sussex, May, 1875. One specimen came to light in Norfolk, May, 1878 ; and one to sugar at Folkestone, May, 1892. In June, 1901, a specimen was secured in Delamere Forest, Cheshire, also at sugar. Dr. B. White's record of a capture at Perth makes a total of eleven specimens.

The caterpillar is ochreous brown, sprinkled and lined with reddish brown ; a stripe low down along the sides is reddish orange. It feeds, in July and August, on the leaves of oak and poplar, but it has not been found in our Isles.

The Alchymist (*Catephia alchymista*).

This moth seems to have been known as a British species to Haworth, but he, and subsequently Stephens (1830), referred it to *Noctua leucomelas*, Linn. At all events, Stephen's description of the specimen in Haworth's cabinet bearing this name applies exactly to *C. alchymista*. In the *Ent. Ann.* for 1860 there is a figure of a specimen that was taken at sugar in the Isle of Wight, September, 1868. Seven years later, one was captured in an oak wood near Horsham, Sussex (June 4), and another found on the trunk of an oak tree near Colchester (June 9). In 1882, a specimen was taken at sugar in a wood near Dover (June), and on June 24, 1888, one came to sugar at St. Leonards, Sussex. In the last-named year, two other specimens, said to have been taken in the Isle of Wight, July, 1867, were recorded.

Fig. 2, Plate 29, represents a specimen from Dalmatia.

The Clifden Nonpareil (*Catocala fraxini*).

This handsome species (Plate 29, Fig. 3) seems to have been known to quite the earliest writers on, and delineators of, British moths, and a specimen in the Dale collection, now in the Hope Museum, Oxford, was obtained in Dorset in 1740. Stephens (1830) mentions captures in the years 1821, 1827, and 1828. Since that time the occurrence of the species in the British Isles, chiefly in single specimens, may be tabulated as follows : England—London, 1842, 1870, 1872. Kent, 1889,

1893, 1895, 1900. Sussex, 1838, 1869, 1889, 1895, 1908. Isle of Wight, 1866, 1900. North Devon, 1895. Somerset, 1850. Shropshire, 1872. Suffolk, 1868, 1872, 1901, 1905. Norfolk, 1846, 1872, 1894, 1900. Lincoln, 1872. Durham, 1917. Yorkshire, five specimens in all, the most recent in 1896. Lancashire, six specimens, latest 1868. Cheshire, four specimens, latest 1868. Scotland—1876 (Berwick); 1896 (Aberdeen and Orkney); 1898 (Roxburghshire). Ireland—1845, 1896.

It may be noted that during a period of seven years—1866 to 1872 inclusive—1867 and 1871 were the only years in which a specimen was not recorded from some part of England.

The caterpillar is pale ochreous, tinged with greenish and freckled with brown ; head, pinkish, inclining to purplish above. It feeds on poplar in May, June, and July. From eggs (obtained from abroad) the caterpillars hatched April 27 till May 9, pupated between June 17 and 27, and the moths emerged July 20 to August 4.

The range abroad extends through Central Europe to Scandinavia, and eastward to Amurland.

Catocala electa.

Only two specimens of this moth are known to have occurred in Britain. One of these was taken at Shoreham, near Brighton, Sussex, September 24, 1875, and the other at Corfe Castle, Dorsetshire, September 12, 1892. The specimen shown on Plate 31, Fig. 1, is from Saxony.

In a general way this species is not unlike (*C. nupta*), but the fore wings are smoother looking, of a softer grey coloration, and the black cross lines are more irregular ; the black markings on the crimson hind wings are similar, but the inner edge of the marginal border is more even.

This Central European species ranges to Amurland and Corea, and is represented in Japan by a larger form, *zalmunna*, Butler.

The Red Underwing (*Catocala nupta*).

Both sexes of this species are shown on Plate 31, Figs. 2 and 3. The fore wings are darker in some specimens than in others, and very rarely, in connection with a change in the hind wings from red to brownish, there has been a purplish tinge over all

FIG. 3.
Red Underwing at rest.
Photo by H. Main.

the wings. Specimens with the hind wings of a brown tint have only so far been noted in the environs of London. In 1892 one was taken at Mitcham (warm brown), another at Wandsworth, 1895, a third at Chingford, 1896 (dusky black-brown), and a fourth at Brondesbury in 1897 At a meeting of

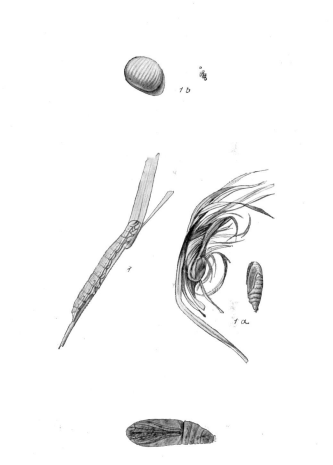

Mother Shipton : *eggs, natural size and enlarged, caterpillar, and chrysalis,*
natural size and enlarged.

1. *Catocala electa.*   2, 3. Red Underwing.

the South London Entomological and Natural History Society, held on January 10, 1889, a coloured sketch of a specimen with blue hind wings, taken at Colchester, was exhibited (ab. *cærulescens*, Cockerell). Sometimes the hind wings are a dingy red, or they may incline to an orange tint ; the central black band usually terminates just beyond the middle, but there is often a detached blackish cloud on the inner margin ; and I have two specimens in which the band unites with this cloud.

The eggs which are deposited on bark of poplar trees, as Fig. 2*a* on Plate 33, are deep purplish with a whitish bloom, and inclining to yellowish on the top. The caterpillar (Plate 33, Fig. 2) is whitish-grey clouded and mottled with darker brown ; the head is rather paler grey, marked with black. It feeds at night on willow and poplar, and, although rather difficult to detect, may be found in the chinks of the bark from April to July. The pupa is brownish, thickly powdered with bluish-white, and is enclosed in a strong, coarse, cocoon, spun up between leaves.

The moth is out in August and September, sometimes later, and in confinement has emerged in July. It is more abundant in some years than in others, and is fond of sitting on walls, pales, etc.; occasionally quite large numbers have been observed at rest on telegraph poles by the roadside, only one on a pole, as a rule, but sometimes in twos and threes. Mr. W. J. Lucas, when at Oxford in August, 1900, counted six on one post, and five on each of two other posts.

The species is found in suitable localities, that is, where poplars and willows grow, throughout the south and east of England. The only clear record from Ireland is that of a worn specimen at sugar, September 16, 1906, at Passage West, co. Cork ; but Kane mentions two others.

Represented in North India by var. *unicuba*, Walker, and in Amurland by var. *obscurata*, Oberthür.

Series II.

G

The Dark Crimson Underwing (*Catocala sponsa*).

The fore wings of this species vary in general colour from
ashy grey to an almost olive brown ; the dark clouding is much
in evidence in some specimens, but absent in others ; the white
or yellow marks in the vicinity of the white outlined reniform
are noticeable features. Hind wings, crimson, more or less
tinged with purple ; the upper half of the central black band is
acutely angled on its outer edge, and bluntly so on its inner
edge, thence curved to the inner margin. (Plate 32, Fig. 1.)

The caterpillar is greyish-brown with a greenish tinge, and
dusted with black ; paler on the fourth ring and between rings
7 and 8, and 10 and 11 ; the hump on ring 8 has an ochreous
tip ; raised spots, red, bearing black bristles ; head, pale brown.
(Fenn.) It feeds on oak in May and June.

The chrysalis is reddish, dusted with purplish grey, enclosed
in a rather open silken cocoon between leaves. (Plate 33,
Fig. 1 larva, 1a pupa.) The moth is out in July and August.
Its chief home is the New Forest, Hants, where it abounds,
in some years, and in others is so scarce that few specimens
can be found. It has been taken occasionally in one or other
of the southern English counties adjoining Hants, and has been
noted in Oxfordshire and Suffolk ; but such occurrences seem
to be exceptional.

The Light Crimson Underwing (*Catocala promissa*).

Generally smaller, and the fore wings are usually greyer, than
the last species; the first black cross line is inwardly shaded with
blackish ; on the hind wings the central black band is straighter,
and the upper half, although sometimes slightly expanded, is
not angled ; in some examples the band does not quite reach
the inner margin, and such specimens have been referred to ab.
mneste, Hübner. (Plate 32, Fig. 2.)

The caterpillar is of a greenish-tinged greyish coloration, freckled with darker grey, and with yellowish brown patches on rings 4, 8, and 9. It feeds, at night, on oak, boring into the buds at first, but afterwards attacking the foliage: May and June. The moth occurs in oak woods in July and August, but it does not seem to be met with anywhere in England so frequently as in the New Forest, Hampshire. Even in that favourite locality it is seen but rarely in some seasons. It is, or has been, found in several other southern and eastern counties, but, as a rule, only in a casual way.

The Blackneck (*Toxocampa pastinum*).

In some examples of this species (Plate 32, Fig. 3) the ground colour of the fore wings, usually pale grey sprinkled with brown, is inclined to whitish, and but little powdered with brown, except the outer fourth, upon which there is generally some brown shading. The reniform stigma varies in shape; in some specimens it is lunular, and in others triangular, with the apex directed inwards; the orbicular, represented by a black dot, is occasionally absent; the cross lines are usually traceable, but the central shade is not often distinct.

The caterpillar is rather long, and tapers slightly from the middle towards each end. In colour it is greyish, inclining to ochreous on the back, and dusted with black; there are three reddish lines along the back, the outer ones edged below with white; the spiracles are black, and the line along their area is white. It feeds at night on the tufted vetch (*Vicia cracca*), and after hibernation attains full growth about May, when it pupates in a cocoon among leaves on the plant, or on the ground. The moth comes out in June and July, and in its haunts, which are the borders of woods or the clearings therein, it flutters about at early dusk, when it can be easily netted. Unlike the species next referred to, it does not seem to have any great partiality for flowers, but it has been taken at sugar, and the females are found at night upon the food plant. It is known to occur in Berkshire and most of the southern counties from Kent to Devon, and eastward from Essex to Norfolk, Cambs., and Hunts.; has also been recorded from Yorks., Hereford, and South Wales.

The range abroad extends to Amurland.

The Scarce Blackneck (*Toxocampa craccæ*).

This species (Plate 32, Fig. 4) is similar to the last, but the wings are rather less ample, the tint is slightly more brownish, and the veins are paler, especially on the outer area. Distinguishing features are the heavier and deeper black collar, and four blackish dots on the front edge of the fore wings. Var. *plumbea*, Bankes, the usual form in Cornwall, is darker than the type, having the fore wings bluish-grey mixed with chocolate, instead of pale ash-grey mixed with light walnut brown; hind wings brownish grey, instead of pale greyish brown. The caterpillar, which in shape is similar to that of the last species, is ochreous brown, with darker brown lines along the back and sides. It feeds at night on the wood vetch (*Vicia sylvatica*), but is said to eat other kinds of vetch in confinement. It may be found resting on stems of the food plant by day, or, when feeding at night, by the aid of a lantern, but it quickly falls off when disturbed. The moth flies at dusk in July and August, and has a strong liking for the flowers of the wood-sage, but visits golden-red and other flowers also, and will sometimes turn up at the sugar patch. It is not uncommon in some parts of the rocky coast of North Devon, as near Lynmouth, where it was first met with by the late Rev. E. Horton in 1861. It has since been found commonly on the Cornish coast. From what I know of its habits, I should say that the species would be found all along the North Devon

1. Dark Crimson Underwing.   2. Light Crimson Underwing.
3. The Black Neck.   4. Scarce Black Neck.

2 *Pl.* 33.   *G* 85.

1, 1a. **Dark Crimson Underwing:** *caterpillar and chrysalis.*

2, 2a. **Red Underwing:** *eggs: natural size and enlarged, and caterpillar.*

and Cornish coasts, wherever the food plant occurs ; but it does not seem to inhabit any other part of Britain. Abroad, its range extends to East Siberia and Amurland.

HYPENINÆ.

The Beautiful Hook-tip (*Laspeyria flexula*).

Some specimens are browner and others greyer than that shown on Plate 36, Fig. 1 ; the pale even lines are generally edged with reddish brown, and the notch under the tip of the. wing is margined with the same colour.

The caterpillar has the first and second pairs of prolegs very short, and below the brown-ringed spiracles there is a projecting ridge, fringed with a row of fleshy greenish-white filaments, some of which are forked. Bluish-green, sometimes tinged with ochreous ; raised dots, black at the tips, on a base of whitish green ; along the middle of the back is a series of darker green spear-points, and beyond this on each side a pale line, edged above by a fine wavy black line, and below by a darker green line ; the eighth and eleventh rings of the body darker than the others. (Abridged from description by Buckler.) It feeds on lichens growing upon larch, spruce, hawthorn, sloe, fruit trees, etc., from September to May. The moth is out in June, July, and August, and may be beaten from the branches of trees, and from hedges, but the flushing of a specimen in this way is always a more or less casual event. It has been taken on several occasions at street lamps, and also in illuminated moth traps.

In England the species seems to be widely distributed over the southern counties to Oxfordshire and Gloucestershire; and in the east to Norfolk. It has also been recorded from Derbyshire (one), and Yorkshire (two).

The range abroad extends to Amurland.

The Waved Black (*Parascotia fuliginaria*).

In the shape of its wings and general appearance the dingy insect represented on Plate 36, Fig. 2, would seem to belong to the Geometridæ rather than to the present group, and, indeed, has been mistaken for a dark form of *Ematurga atomaria*. However, the long, projecting palpi are evidence of its being a member of this sub-family.

The caterpillar, which is moderately stout, and tapers slightly towards each end, has only twelve feet. Ground colour, sooty black, with orange-coloured raised dots, from which arise long recurved hairs. The late Mr. W. H. Tugwell (from whose description of the larva that given above has been adapted), in 1884, was shown caterpillars upon a black sooty-looking fungus (determined by Dr. M. C. Cooke as an effused *Muscedine*), growing in masses on rotten wood in an old wooden building in Bermondsey, near the river. He afterwards reared the moths.

The caterpillar hatches from the egg in August, but it is not full grown until May or June, when it spins a fairly compact cocoon of greyish silk, which is coated with particles of decayed wood and dried fungus.

The moth is out in June and July, and most of the known British specimens have been captured in London, or reared from caterpillars found therein.   Stephens (1831) mentions three or four examples taken during the previous thirty years, and gives as localities—Blackfriars bridge, and Little Chelsea ; Stainton (1859) adds, Fleet Street. Other specimens have been taken in the City in 1855, 1859, 1862, 1870, 1879, and 1881. One occurred at Clapham in 1864, and one has been reported from Crome in Worcestershire. More recent records are—one specimen flying around a sugared post at Walthamstow, July 29, 1901 ; eight, chiefly at light, at Camberley, 1904-5 ; one at St. Katharine's Docks, July, 1906, and one in Surrey, July, 1917.

The Fan-foot (*Zanclognatha tarsipennalis*).

This species is shown in both sexes on Plate 35, Figs. 1 ♂, 2 ♀; it is the *Pyralis tentaculalis* of Haworth, and also that author's *tarsicrinatus*, and the *tarsicrinalis* of Stephens. The general colour is brownish, sometimes inclining to ochreous, and occasionally with a greyish cast. The submarginal line starts from the front edge, before the tip, of the fore wing.

The caterpillar is greyish brown, darker freckled, and dotted with black, downy; three broken darker lines along the back, the central one broad and inclining to black, and lower down along the sides is a series of blackish streaks; head, darker. It feeds in July and August, and hibernates when nearly or quite full grown. Among various foods that have been mentioned for it are raspberry, ivy, and knotgrass. Some years ago I had some moths emerge in the autumn; these resulted from caterpillars that I had reared from the egg on blackberry, and I remember that they showed a decided preference for the withered leaves left in the cage for them to pupate among. (Plate 34, Fig. 2.)

The moth is out in June and July, but individuals of a second generation seldom occur in the open. Although it occurs in woods, it is far more frequent in lanes and hedgerows. Common and generally distributed, from Worcester southwards, and to the east and west; northwards its range extends to Yorkshire, but it is local and uncommon.

In Scotland it is not scarce in some parts of Ayrshire, and has been recorded from Kircudbrightshire. Kane mentions it as fairly common in Ireland.

The range abroad extends to Amurland, Corea, and Japan.

The Small Fan-foot (*Zanclognatha grisealis*).

This species (Plate 35, Fig. 3) is somewhat similar to the last in colour, but it is smaller, and the submarginal line is rather curved, and runs to the tip of the fore wing. The caterpillar is obscurely greyish, with a pinkish tinge; three darker lines along the back, the central one broadest, but not distinct on the first three rings; head, brown, freckled with darker brown, plate of first ring of the body, blackish brown. It feeds on oak, and may be beaten from the foliage in August and September. Buckler states that this species passes the winter in the chrysalis state, and this has been confirmed by Plum. (Plate 34, Fig. 1; after Hofmann.)

The moths emerge in June and July, and may frequently be dislodged from trees, hedges, and undergrowth in the daytime. Pretty generally distributed over the southern half of England, plentiful in many parts, and widely spread over the northern half of the country. It is not scarce in some parts of Wales, but seems to be uncommon in Scotland, and has been recorded from the south only. In Ireland it has a wide range, but does not appear to be noted as common in any locality.

The Olive Crescent (*Zanclognatha* (*Sophronia*) *emortualis*).

The species depicted on Plate 36, Fig. 8, from a continental specimen, is exceedingly rare in England, in fact, apart from the specimens mentioned by early authors, only three authentic British examples appear to be known. These are—one captured at Brighton, Sussex, in June, 1858; one in June, 1859, in Epping Forest, Essex; and one taken at sugar by the Rev. B. H. Binks, of Stonor, Henley-on-Thames, in July of the year last mentioned.

Stephens (1834), who gives a very unsatisfactory description of the species, refers to two specimens, of which one was in his collection, from Devonshire. Wood's figure (768) of *emortualis*, in the Westwood edition of the *Index Entomologicus*, does not represent this species, but is far more like *Herminia derivalis*, Hübner.

Abroad, the range extends to Amurland.

The Lesser Belle (*Madopa salicalis*).

A portrait of this uncommon British moth will be found on Plate 35, Fig. 4. The greyish fore wings are crossed by three paler edged reddish-brown lines, the outer one running to the tip of the wing, and the inner one is sometimes faint or absent.

The caterpillar is said to feed in July and August on sallow and aspen, and is described by Hofmann as having only fourteen feet; green, inclining to greyish, in colour, with black spiracles, and the ring divisions yellowish. (Plate 39, Fig. 3; after Hofmann.)

The moth is out in May and June, and in its few known localities in England it is found in moist woods, hiding among grass and varied undergrowth.

Stephens (1834) wrote, "A very rare and local insect : I have specimens taken many years since in the neighbourhood of Bexley, in which vicinity I believe my friend Mr. Newman has captured it within these few years ; it has also been found at Charlton." Since that time other localities in Kent have been mentioned, among which were Darenth Wood and West Wickham ; the species was also noted from Birch wood, Surrey. A specimen was found in a gas lamp at Dulwich in 1858 by the late Mr. C. G. Barrett, and one was taken in Shooter's Hill wood, Kent, in June, 1859.

Between 1862 and 1868 specimens were obtained at Hasle-mere, Surrey, and near Sevenoaks, Kent. According to Barrett it occurred at Petersfield, on the borders of Sussex and Hampshire, in 1877.

It has also been recorded from Dunham, Cheshire.

Abroad, its distribution extends to Amurland, Corea, and Japan.

The Dotted Fan-foot (*Herminia cribrumalis* (*cribralis*)).

The fore wings of this species (Plate 35, Fig. 5) are whitish tinged with brown, inclining to purplish on the outer margins ; beyond the blackish central dot there are two series of blackish dots crossing the wings, but these are not always distinct.

The caterpillar, which feeds on various marsh grasses, *Carex*, *Luzula*, etc., hatches from the egg in late summer, hibernates when about half-grown, and feeds up in the spring. It is pale greyish brown with fine yellowish freckles ; there are three lines along the back ; the central one dark, finely edged on each side with pale greyish, the outer ones pale ; the usual dots are dusky and the spiracles are black.

The moth may be found in June and July in fens and marshes, where it hides among the herbage in the daytime, but is easily seen and netted when it takes wing at dusk, or sits on the sedges, etc., before or after flight.

It is most frequent in the fens of Cambridge and Norfolk, (Stalham), but occurs also in Suffolk ; Essex (Shoeburyness) ; Kent (Deal); Surrey (recorded from marshes near Redhill, Dorking and Guildford); Sussex; Hants (bogs near Lyndhurst), and, according to Barrett, Somerset.

The Clay Fan-foot (*Herminia derivalis*).

This local species has the wings pretty much of the same shape as those of *S. emortualis*, and has been mistaken for that species ; but the colour is ochreous-brown, and the cross lines are dark brown. Its favourite haunts appear to be woods in Kent and Sussex, and in the last-named county it is perhaps most frequently met with in Abbots wood, Guestling, and Lewes. It has also been recorded from Essex (Colchester). (Plate 35, Fig. 6.)

The caterpillar feeds on dead oak leaves, chiefly those that have fallen to the ground. After hibernation it becomes full grown about June, and is then brown with a downy appearance ; there are three faintly darker lines along the back, and the usual dots are dusky. (Plate 34, Fig. 3 ; after Hofmann.) The moth is out in June and July, and in the daytime may be put up from its lurking place among herbage in wood clearings, or netted as it flies in the gloaming. It is also attracted by sugar and light.

The species has been erroneously recorded from Chester and Barmouth (North Wales) ; and Mr. Carr informs me that he is not quite sure that a specimen he recorded from Dawlish, South Devon, was correctly identified. In the catalogue of Malvern Lepidoptera *H. derivalis* is stated to be rather common in that district, but the occurrence of the species in the Midlands requires confirmation.

Abroad, the range extends to Amurland.

The Common Fan-foot (*Pechipogon barbalis*).

The fore wings of the species shown on Plate 35, Fig. 7, are greyish brown, crossed by three darker lines, the outer one almost parallel with the hind margin, and edged with whitish.

The caterpillar feeds on the dead leaves of oak and birch, and has almost attained full growth when it retires for the winter. In the spring it has been known to eat birch catkins. The general colour is reddish ochreous, with diamond-shaped markings, forming a series along the back and two series along each side.

The moth, which is out from late May until early July, frequents the more open parts of woods, and in the daytime may be induced to show itself by tapping the lower branches of trees or brushing the bushes and undergrowth as we pass along.

The species is widely distributed over England, from Staffordshire southwards, but it is apparently most frequently met with in some of the woods of Kent, Surrey, and Sussex.

The distribution abroad extends to Amurland.

The Beautiful Snout (*Bomolocha fontis*).

The portraits of this species on Plate 35 show each sex in its most usual form : Fig. 8 representing the male, and Fig. 9 the female. The outer and inner areas of the fore wings are generally ashy grey, more or less brownish tinged, in the male ; and the same parts are whitish in the female. Although some examples of the male have the outer and inner areas whitish, as in the female, they can be distinguished by their darker hind wings and the blackish central crescent thereon. A form of the female in which the large central patch of the fore wings is reddish brown has been named *rufescens*, Tutt ; there may be males also of this form, but I have not seen any. In both sexes, the brown patch extends nearer to the inner margin in some specimens than in others, and not infrequently there is a spur from the lower edge of the patch to this margin.

The caterpillar is green, with darker green lines, one along the middle of the back, and two along each side ; the usual raised dots are green or brownish, and each emits a fine hair ; the head is green and rather glossy. It feeds on bilberry (*Vaccinium myrtillus*) in August and September. (Plate 37, Fig. 1 ; after Hofmann.) The moth, which is out in June and July, hides by day among heather, bilberry, etc., especially where these plants overhang the edges of banks or trenches. It may be found locally in most of the southern counties of

1. **Small Fanfoot**: *caterpillar.*
2. **Fanfoot**: *caterpillar.*
3. **Clay Fan-foot**: *caterpillar.*

1, 2. Fan-foot. 3. Small Fan-foot. 4. Lesser Belle.
5. Dotted Fan-foot. 6. Clay Fan-foot. 7. Common Fan-foot.
8, 9. Beautiful Snout. 10. The Snout. 11, 12. Buttoned Snout.

England from Kent to Cornwall; also in Berks, Stafford, and Leicester. It has been recorded from Suffolk, Worcester, Cheshire (one at electric light, Chester, July, 1900), and North Wales. In Ireland it is widely distributed, and is not uncommon in Co. Kerry.

The Snout (*Hypena proboscidalis*).

This species (Plate 35, Fig. 10) is more generally distributed and common than any other of the group. Wherever nettles grow in quantity there we may expect to find this moth in its season, that is, in June and July. In favourable years there is sometimes a second flight, on a small scale, in the autumn; this was the case in 1905.

The caterpillar is green, with raised dots, from each of which a brownish hair arises : the line along the middle of the back is dark, and those along the sides are yellowish ; the head is ochreous brown. It feeds on nettles in May and June. (Plate 37, Fig. 3 ; after Hofmann.)

In Amurland, and some other parts of eastern Asia, the species is represented by the brown-sprinkled yellowish form, var. *deleta*, Staudinger.

The Bloxworth Snout (*Hypena obsitalis*).

The fore wings of this species are brown, crossed by a number of darker lines and a thicker angulated line beyond the middle ; the latter is outwardly edged with pale brown, chiefly towards the costa ; some white dots on the veins represent the submarginal line, and below the tips of the wings there are some black streaks.

One example of this form of the species, which is a variable one, was taken by the Rev. O. Pickard Cambridge, in

September, 1884. He found it sitting on a door-jamb in his garden at Bloxworth, Dorset. A specimen has been recorded from Paignton, Devon, 1908.

The specimen shown on Plate 36, Fig. 9, hails from Mogador.

Abroad, the range of the species includes southern Europe, Asia Minor, Egypt, N. W. Africa, Madeira, and the Canaries.

The Buttoned Snout (*Hypena rostralis*).

Two forms of this species are shown on Plate 35. The typical one is represented by Fig. 12, and Fig. 11 shows ab. *palpalis*, Tutt (?), Fabr. and Stephens. The front margin of the fore wings is often streaked with a pale colour, and in ab. *radiatalis*, Hübner (134), which is otherwise similar to the last-named form, this is pale or ochreous brown. A uniform pale greyish form has been named ab. *unicolor*, Tutt, and one almost entirely ochreous or greyish-ochreous, ab. *ochrea*, Tutt.

The caterpillar is green, with blackish dots ; a darker line along the middle of the back, and white lines along the sides ; head, yellowish green dotted with black. It feeds on hop (*Humulus lupulus*) in June and early July, and in the daytime may be found on the undersides of the leaves. (Plate 37, Fig. 2 ; after Hofmann.) The moth is out in August and September, and after hibernation reappears in the spring, and may be met with until June. It may be obtained at sugar, or at ivy bloom. Given the food plant, the species will probably be found in most of the counties of England from Worcester southwards, but its occurrence northwards appears to have been very rarely noted.

The range abroad extends to East Siberia.

The White-line Snout (*Hypenodes tænialis* (*albistrigalis*)).

This species, and also the two immediately following, are so small in size, and so obscure in appearance, that they are probably more often neglected than secured when met with. The moth under consideration, and of which the sexes are figured on Plate 36 (Figs. 3 ♂ and 4 ♀) has brownish fore wings which are crossed by two rather irregular blackish lines, sometimes hardly traceable on the front margin ; the outer line is edged externally with whitish, and the space between the lines is often somewhat darker ; the black central mark is more or less X-shaped.

The caterpillar does not seem to have been noted in this country, and it is not well known on the continent. It is said to feed on the flowers, chiefly the withering ones, of heather and thyme, in August and September.

The moth is out in July and early August, sometimes in September. Its haunts are the edges of woods, hillsides, and sloping banks, where there is plenty of bushes and herbage to hide in. From such retreats it may be disturbed, but is more easily obtained at sugar, or honey dew, and sometimes at ivy bloom. It is widely distributed over the southern half of England ; occurs in South Wales, and has been recorded from Cheshire and Yorks.

Abroad, the species is found in Holland, Belgium, Germany, Austria, Armenia, and the Canaries ; also recorded from south Sweden and Corea.

The Pinion-streaked Snout (*Hypenodes costæstrigalis*).

Although somewhat similar in the general colour of the fore-wings, this species (Plate 36) may be distinguished from the preceding by the whitish dash from the tips of the wings and the black streak running inwards from it ; this black streak is to be seen clearly in Fig. 6 ♂, but owing to the darker ground colour is less distinct in Fig. 7 ♀.

The caterpillar is shining purplish-brown, inclining to yellowish-brown below, with three pale brownish lines along the back, the central one rather broad, and that on each side is edged below with dusky. What the food may be in a natural state has not been ascertained, but the caterpillars have been reared from the egg on a diet of thyme flowers, supplemented by the bodies of a few brothers or sisters. July and August.

The moth has been noted in June (end), July, August, September, and October; but whether there are two generations or only one in the year is not definitely known; the assumption is that there are two.

This species is partial to moist localities, and its favourite haunts are fens, mosses, or marshy heaths, and the outskirts of damp woods. It ranges over the greater part of England, and is found in Wales (Pembrokeshire). In Scotland it has been noted from Roxburghshire, and is locally common in Clydesdale. It is known to occur in Cork, Kerry, and Sligo, and probably is to be found in other parts of Ireland.

The Marsh Oblique-barred (*Tholomiges turfosalis*).

The species shown on Plate 36, Fig. 5, is much smaller than either of the last two. The narrow fore wings are whitish-ochreous, more or less thickly sprinkled with brown; the first of the three dark cross lines is often indistinct, the second is bent under the black central dot, and the third runs obliquely to the tip of the wing; the last two are each outwardly edged with whitish.

Nothing seems to be known of the early stages.

This species was first made known as an inhabitant of the British Isles by Doubleday, who described it as *Hypenodes humidalis*, in 1850, from specimens taken in Ireland by Weaver in 1848. In 1850 it was found plentifully on one of the Cheshire moors; and Harrison, in *The Zoologist* for 1851, writes: "From the middle of July up to the 8th of August, it might be seen any fine evening, between the hours of six and eight, flying

1. **Beautiful Hook-tip.**   2. **Waved Black.**   3, 4. **White-line Snout.**
5. **Marsh Oblique Barred.** 6, 7. **Pinion-streaked Snout.** 8. **Olive Crescent.**
9. **Bloxworth Snout.**

1. **Beautiful Snout** : *caterpillar*.
2. **Buttoned Snout** : *caterpillar*.
3. **The Snout** : *caterpillar*.

on most of our swamps [Keswick] in plenty." He goes on to state that the moths were so common that he boxed forty in less than an hour, and could have secured as many dozens. At the present day the species is to be found on boggy heaths and moors in Surrey, Hampshire, Dorset, and from Somerset through Gloucestershire into Berkshire, and thence northwards through Warwick and Staffordshire to Cheshire, Lancashire, and Cumberland. Barrett mentions Perthshire as a Scottish locality, and Kane states that it is common at Killarney in Ireland. When this species and its allies receive more of the collector's attention they may probably be found in many localities from which there are no records at present.

The range abroad extends to Amurland.

BREPHIDÆ.

By some systematists this small group of moths is treated as a subfamily of the Geometridæ. *Brephos*, however, which is typical of the family, does not seem to have any close affinities with the Noctuidæ or with the Geometers, and is therefore better considered as apart from both those families. Meyrick includes *Brephos* with *Aplasta, Erannis*, and *Baptria*, in his family Monocteniadæ.

Only five species are known to inhabit the Palæarctic Region, and two of these occur in Britain.

The Orange Underwing (*Brephos parthenias*).

The white markings of the fore wings vary a good deal in size ; in some specimens, chiefly males, they are very small and confined to the front margin ; in others, mainly females, they are much enlarged, and the central one is continued as a band across the wings. On the orange hind wings the blackish

H

central band is usually more or less complete, but sometimes
it is nearly or quite absent above the blackish triangular patch
on the inner margin. Occasionally, there is a yellow blotch at
the anal angle, and frequently another on the costal area.
Still more rarely the whole ground colour is yellow. (Figured on
Plate 38, Figs. 1 ♂ and 2 ♀.) The caterpillar is green, with six
white lines along the back, and white stripes along the sides.
When young it feeds on the catkins of birch, and afterwards on
the foliage. April to early June. (Plate 39, Fig. 1.)

The moth is out in March and April, and on sunny days the
males may be seen flying, generally pretty high up, on the lee
side of the birch trees growing on heaths ; also in open spaces
in or around birch woods. The females rest on the twigs, as
also do the males when the sun is obscured. Both sexes have
been found sitting on the ground in sunny glades.

The species is widely distributed over the southern and
eastern counties, common in many parts ; but its range extends
through England to Durham, and it has been recorded from
Wales. Although it does not seem to have been noted in
Scotland south of Kincardineshire, it occurs on the east to
Moray. Westmeath is the only Irish locality that has so far
been mentioned.

Its distribution abroad extends to East Siberia and Amurland.

The Light Orange Underwing (*Brephos notha*).

Very similar to the last species, but rather smaller in size, and
the fore wings are much less variegated. The antennæ of the
male of this species are bipectinated, whilst those of *parthenias*
are finely serrated. (Plate 38, Figs. 4 ♂ and 5 ♀.)

The caterpillar feeds in May and June on aspen, eating the
foliage and hiding between two leaves drawn together. The
head is greenish or greenish-brown, with three conspicuous
black spots. Body, green, olive-green, or reddish ; line along

1, 2. **Orange Underwing.**
3. **The Rest Harrow.**
4, 5. **Light Orange Underwing.**
6-8. **Grass Emerald.**

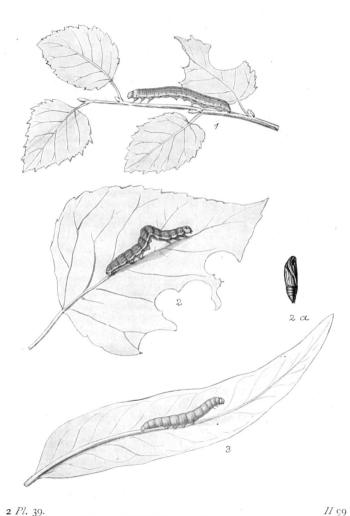

1. **Orange Underwing**: *caterpillar.*
2, 2a. **Light Orange Underwing**: *caterpillar and chrysalis.*
3. **Lesser Belle**: *caterpillar.*

middle of the back darker green edged with white ; two thin white lines on each side, and a whitish stripe along the spiracles. When mature it burrows into decayed bark or wood (virgin cork in confinement), and before changing to a reddish-brown chrysalis, it spins a thin covering of silk and woody particles over the mouth of the chamber. The caterpillar and the chrysalis are shown on Plate 39, Figs. 2 and 2a. Although the bulk of the moths emerge the following April, some have been known to remain until the following or even the third year. The males fly about aspen, but only in the sunshine ; in other respects its habits are pretty much those of the last species.

The distribution of the species in England seems confined to two areas : a western one represented by Worcester, Gloucester, with Monmouth, Wales, Wilts, and Dorset ; and an eastern one by Norfolk, Cambridgeshire, Suffolk, Essex, Middlesex, Kent, Surrey, and Sussex. In Scotland only recorded from Moray.

The range abroad extends to Amurland.

GEOMETRIDÆ.

Caterpillars of this family of moths, with very few exceptions, have only two pairs of claspers or prolegs ; when there are more than four claspers, the extra ones are only rudimentary and therefore useless. In moving from place to place the caterpillar stretches out to its full length, first to one side and then to the other, as though measuring the distance. When a hold is secured with the true legs the body is arched and the claspers are brought up almost to the point held by the true legs ; the latter are then thrust forward and the measuring business proceeds as before. Some kinds perform the looping manœuvre very deliberately, but others at a quick rate. In common parlance among British entomologists the caterpillars are called "geometers" or "loopers," but to our American confrères they are known as "measuring-worms" or "span-worms."

Most of the caterpillars feed openly on the foliage of trees, shrubs, or low-growing herbs, and the majority remain upon their respective plants during the day.

A large proportion of the moths may be obtained in the day-time, either by beating or otherwise disturbing the foliage or herbage among which they hide ; several kinds rest on tree trunks, palings, rocks, walls, etc., where they are sometimes conspicuous, but more frequently not easy to distinguish from their surroundings. On the whole, members of this family are more available to the day collector than are those of the Noctuidæ. Although several species occasionally visit the sugar patch, such species are, as a rule, obtained more readily and in larger numbers by other methods. Brilliant light has a great attraction for many of the moths, some are more often captured at gas or electric lamps than in any other way, and among these are the migratory species.

The family is here divided into the following subfamilies :—

Geometrinæ (= Geometridæ, Meyrick).
Acidaliinæ (= Sterrhidæ, Meyrick).
Hydriomeninæ (= Hydriomenidæ, Meyrick).
Boarmiinæ (Selidosemidæ, Meyrick).

The typical genus of Larentiinæ of authors would be *Larentia*, Treit, to which something over two hundred species have been referred, among which are upwards of sixty that occur in the British Isles. Following some of the later generic changes, I find that none of our species are left in *Larentia*, but a few fall into *Hydriomena*, Hübner, and therefore Hydriomeninæ has been adopted for this subfamily.

GEOMETRINÆ.

The Rest Harrow (*Aplasta ononaria*).

This greyish-brown moth has two darker, sometimes reddish, cross lines on the fore wings, and one such line on the hind wings. It is presumably only to be regarded as an accidental visitor to England. The first record was of a specimen captured in the Warren at Folkestone in July, 1866, and since that year others were obtained in the same locality, but apparently not more than about half a dozen altogether. None seems to have been recorded for over thirty-five years. The specimen, whose portrait is shown on Plate 38, Fig. 3, was obtained from Dresden.

Abroad, the range includes Central and Southern Europe Asia Minor, Syria, and Armenia.

The Grass Emerald (*Pseudoterpna pruinata*).

When freshly emerged from the chrysalis, the species represented by Figs. 6 to 8 on Plate 38 is of a beautiful blue-green colour, but in course of time a greyish shade creeps over the wings. The dark cross lines vary in intensity; in some specimens well defined and blackish, in others very faint, and hardly discernible; occasionally, the space between the lines on the fore wings is dark shaded; the whitish sub-marginal line is not always present. This species is the *cythisaria* of Schiffermiller, and the *cytisaria* of other authors.

The caterpillar (figured on Plate 41, Fig. 1, from a coloured drawing by Mr. A. Sich) is green, with three lines along the back, the central one dark green, the others whitish; a pinkish stripe low down along the sides, the points on the head and the first and last rings of the body are often pink also. It feeds on pettywhin (*Genista anglica*), also on broom (*Cytisus scoparius*) and gorse (*Ulex*) ; in captivity it seems to thrive on laburnum. Most frequently obtained in the springtime after hibernation.

The moth is to be found in June and July on moorlands and commons pretty well throughout the British Isles, but it seems not to have been noted north of Perthshire, in Scotland.

Odd specimens have been known to occur in late August or early September, but this is quite exceptional.

The Large Emerald (*Geometra papilionaria*).

This charming green species (Plate 40, Figs. 1 and 4) varies in tint and in the distinctness of the whitish wavy cross lines. In some examples, one or other of the lines is absent, and far more rarely there is but little trace of any of these markings. Occasionally, the discal mark is preceded by a whitish wedge-shaped spot on the fore wings (ab. *cuneata*, Burrows).

When newly laid the eggs are whitish, but soon change to greenish yellow, and finally to pinkish.

The caterpillar hatches in late summer, and feeds on birch, hazel, and beech, until the leaves begin to fall in the autumn ; it then constructs a carpet of silk on a twig, and near a bud, upon which it takes up its position for the winter. When thus seen, its reddish brown colour, variegated more or less with green, assimilates so closely with its surroundings that the creature is not easy to detect. In the spring, when it awakens, the green colour increases in extent as the buds open and the leaves unfold ; when they are fully expanded, the caterpillar sits among the foliage towards the tip of a twig, and is then almost entirely green, the reddish brown only showing on the head, slightly on the warts, and more distinctly on the hinder parts which are in touch with the twig. The chrysalis, enclosed in a flimsy silken web among the dead leaves, usually on the ground, is of a delicate green colour, dotted with buff on the

1, 4. **Large Emerald.** 2, 3. **Small Emerald.**

1. **Grass Emerald :** *caterpillar.*
2. **Blotched Emerald :** *caterpillar.*
3. **Common Emerald :** *caterpillar.*

1. Orange-tailed Clearwing.   2, 3, 5. ***Zygæna achilleæ.***
4, 6, 8. Brindled Beauty, variety ; 7. Caterpillar of do.

back, and shaded with buff on the wing cases. The early stages are figured on Plate 42.

The moth is out in June and July, and may occasionally be beaten out of a hedge or bush, but is most frequently obtained late at night, when it is active on the wing, and is attracted by a brilliant light.

The species occurs in woods, on heaths and moors, and in fens, throughout the British Isles, except the most northern parts of Scotland and the isles.

Abroad, the range extends to Amurland and Japan.

The Small Emerald (*Geometra vernaria*).

This species (Plate 40, Figs. 2 and 3) is smaller than the last mentioned, the green colour is of a softer tint, and the lines crossing the wings, two on the fore wings and one on the hind wings, are whitish, and not waved.

The caterpillar hatches from the egg in August, and after hibernation is to be found in May and June on Traveller's Joy or Old Man's Beard (*Clematis vitalba*). It is then green, with white dots arranged in lines along the back and sides ; the head is deep reddish brown, and this, and also the first and last rings of the body, have raised points. Transformation to the greenish chrysalis is effected among the leaves, drawn together with silk. (Plate 44, Figs. 3 and 3*a*.)

The moth flies in the evening in July and August, and in the daytime may be disturbed, by the application of the beating stick, from its retreats in hedges, etc., where the food plant flourishes. Found in most of the southern and eastern counties of England, most frequently on the chalk ; its range extends to Worcestershire. One specimen has been reported from Argyllshire, 1913 ; and one example of each sex from Co. Tyrone, Ireland, 1917. The distribution abroad extends to Amurland.

The Blotched Emerald (*Euchloris* (*Comibæna*) *pustulata*).

When quite fresh, this moth (Plate 43, Fig. 1) is exceedingly pretty ; the pale blotches vary a little in size, as also do the reddish marks upon them.

The caterpillar adorns itself with particles of its food as soon as it leaves the egg in July ; after hibernation it uses the scales or husks of the oak buds for the same purpose. When stripped of its trappings it is found to be reddish brown in colour, with three slightly darker lines along the back ; hooded bristles arising from raised brownish spots afford means for the attachment of the masquerading outfit, each moiety of which is covered with silk on one side before being placed in the required position. When beating oaks for larvæ in May and June, the contents of the umbrella or beating tray should not be too hastily thrown away, but allowed to remain therein for awhile, and closely watched for any movement among the litter. The spectacle of a cluster of oak bracts suddenly becoming active will certainly arouse curiosity, and on examination the cause of the commotion will frequently be found to be the caterpillar of this species. (Plate 41, Fig. 2 ; after Auld.)

The moth is out in June and July, and flies at dusk in and around oak woods. In the daytime it may be jarred from its perch in oak trees, and once I found a specimen on a fence in the Esher district. It has been known to visit light, and examples of a September emergence have been recorded.

As a British species it only inhabits England, and it has been noted from Staffordshire and Leicester, but seems to be rare in the midland counties generally. It is more frequently found in the southern and eastern counties.

Abroad, the range extends through Central Europe to Southern Sweden, S. Russia, N. Asia Minor, and Andalusia.

The Essex Emerald (*Euchloris smaragdaria*).

In some examples of this species (Plate 43, Figs. 2, 3) the green colour is brighter than in others, and very occasionally it is tinged with bluish; typically, there are white cross lines on the fore wings, but the inner one is not infrequently absent, and more rarely both are missing. The white central spot is very rarely absent, and the edges of the fore wings are yellowish.

The caterpillar feeds on the sea wormwood (*Artemisia maritima*), and adorns itself with fragments of its food plant in much the same manner as that of the species last referred to. Although obtained in the autumn in some numbers from its food plant, it seems to have been rarely met with in the spring after hibernation. It is, therefore, advisable to collect the caterpillars about September, and transfer them to plants of the garden *Artemisia abrotanum*, locally known as "Southern-wood," "Old man," or "Lad's love," or, where available, wormwood (*A. absinthium*) will suit it admirably. Upon either of these plants the larvæ will hibernate, feed up in the spring, and become full grown about May. The early stages are figured on Plate 42, larva and pupa from photos by Mr. H. Main.

The moth is out in June and early July, but it is rarely seen in the open, although over sixty years ago a few specimens were put up from among grass and netted at St. Osyth; in later years an example or two have been taken at Sheerness in Kent. Possibly, others may also have been captured in one or other of the insect's haunts, but records are silent on the matter. Barrett mentions a specimen emerging in September, and the Rev. C. R. N. Burrows notes that part of a brood of caterpillars reared from eggs, and fed on *A. absinthium*, attained the moth state during the autumn. So far as concerns the British Isles it seems to be almost exclusively an inhabitant of the salterns, or sea marshes of Essex.

Abroad, the species occurs inland, and is not confined to the coast ; its range extends eastwards to Siberia and Amurland.

The Small Grass Emerald (*Nemoria viridata*).

This species, represented on Plate 43, Figs. 5 and 6, is readily distinguished by its small size and the well-defined white cross line on each wing. In most examples there is a more or less distinct whitish inner line on the fore wings. Ab. *mathewi*, Bankes, has all the wings dusted with orange scales, more especially on the outer marginal areas. A few examples of this form were reared in 1905, with a number of normal specimens, from eggs laid by a female captured in South Devonshire.

The caterpillar (figured from a skin on Plate 44, Fig. 1) is green, roughened with whitish points ; a dusky line along the middle of the back, marked on the front and end rings, also between the rings, with purplish red. Head, and first ring of the body, notched, the points reddish ; last ring of the body pointed. When at rest on a twig it assumes a rigid posture, and the legs are tightly drawn together. It feeds on heather, sallow, and birch, but the general experience appears to be that in captivity it thrives best on a diet of hawthorn, and is especially partial to the young shoots. It may be obtained in July and August, and the moth comes out in the following May or June. In 1905, Mr. A. J. Scollick reared some caterpillars from eggs laid June 2nd, and hatched June 16th ; all duly pupated, and a moth came up on December 20th of that year. Four others appeared in January and February, 1906.

The Rev. F. E. Lowe states that in Guernsey the species occurs exclusively among furze on cliffs by the sea, and chiefly where the plant is cut down from time to time. In Britain it inhabits heaths and mosses, but is very local. It is found in

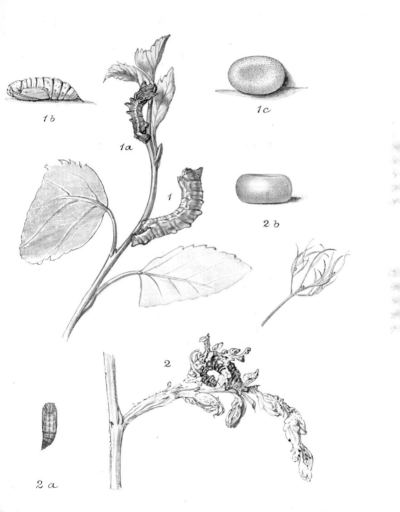

*Pl. 42

1, 1a, 1b, 1c. **Large Emerald:** *egg, caterpillars and chrysalis.*
2, 2a. **Essex Emerald:** *eggs, caterpillar and chrysalis.*

1. Blotched Emerald.   2, 3. Essex Emerald.
4, 7. Little Emerald.   5, 6. Small Grass Emerald.
8, 9. Common Emerald.

the English counties of Hants (New Forest, etc.), Dorset (Poole Heath, etc.), Devon (Woodbury, Exeter district, etc.), Norfolk (Horning), Worcester (Malvern district, rare) ; also at Methop, Witherslack, and other localities in Westmoreland and Cumberland. Only doubtfully recorded from Scotland and Ireland.

Abroad, the range extends to Amurland, Corea, and China.

The Little Emerald (*Iodis lactearia*).

The green tint in this species (Plate 43, Figs. 4 and 7) is even more unstable than in others of the group. When quite fresh the wings can often only be described as whitish with a delicate green tinge, but even when the greatest care is taken to preserve it, the colour is apt to fade.

The caterpillar (Plate 44, Fig. 2, from a coloured drawing by Mr. A. Sich) is long and thin, with two points on the edge of the first ring, and one on the last ring, of a bright green colour, paler between the rings ; the spots along the back are reddish, as also is the whitish-fronted deeply notched head. It feeds on the leaves of various trees and bushes, such as birch, oak, hawthorn, sallow, etc. It may be obtained by beating or searching from August to September.

The moth is out in May and June, in some seasons later, and may be beaten out of hedges, as well as from trees in woods. Generally distributed, and often common, throughout England, Wales, and Ireland. In Scotland it is locally common in Clydesdale, and occurs in other southern parts of that country.

Abroad, the range extends to Amurland, Corea, China, and Japan.

The Common Emerald (*Hemithea strigata*).

When freshly emerged from the chrysalis, this species (Plate 43, Figs. 8 and 9) is darkish green, but it soon fades to a greyish tint. Easily distinguished by its shape, and by the chequered fringes. It is the *æstivaria* of Hübner, and *thymiaria* of Guenée. The long, thin, green caterpillar is ornamented with reddish brown, the V-shaped marks on rings 5 to 8 are sometimes whitish; head, deeply notched, brown; the first ring of the body is also notched. It hatches from the egg in August, when it is said to feed on mugwort (*Artemisia vulgaris*), and other low plants; after hibernation it feeds on the foliage of oak, birch, hawthorn, rose, etc., and attains full growth in May or June. In late June and in July the moth may be put up from the undergrowth in woods, or from bushes in well-timbered hedgerows bordering lanes and fields. Specimens so obtained are poor in colour as a rule, and it is well, therefore, to rear the species from the caterpillar. (Plate 41, Fig. 3; after Hofmann.) This remark applies to all " Emeralds."

The species is often common in the south and east of England, and along the western side, including Wales, up to Cheshire and Lancashire, but it becomes local in Worcestershire and northwards. There are few records of it from Yorkshire, and its occurrence in Durham, Northumberland, and Scotland is doubtful. In Ireland it appears to be widely distributed, but scarce.

The range abroad extends to Amurland, Corea, and Japan.

[*Thalera fimbrialis*. A specimen of this Central European species (identified by the late Mr. C. G. Barrett) was taken on August 7, 1902, by Mr. C. Capper, from a blade of grass growing on a slope under Beachy Head, Sussex. The species is somewhat similar in appearance to *H. strigata*, but is larger; the hind wings are notched above the angle on the outer margin; the fringes of all the wings are chequered with red, and the antennæ of the male are bipectinated.]

ACIDALIINÆ.

Purple-bordered Gold (*Hyria muricata*).

Two forms of this pretty little species (known also as *auroraria*) are shown on Plate 45. Fig. 1 represents the more usual form, but between this and the almost entirely purple variety (Fig. 4), which occurs chiefly in the north, there are various modifications. Then again, especially in the south of England, there is a tendency to become entirely yellow, the purple, inclining to crimson in such specimens, being confined to the front margin and cross lines on the fore wings, and a narrow band on the outer margin of all the wings.

The caterpillar is pale brownish, inclining to ochreous at each end, marked with irregular blackish lines on the back, and dots and streaks on the sides. The Hon. N. C. Rothschild records *Comarum palustre* as its natural food plant, but when reared from the egg the caterpillar will eat knotgrass, and sometimes a few will feed up and attain the moth state the same year. August to May.

The moth occurs in late June and in July, and frequents fens, boggy heaths, and mosses. Although odd specimens may, occasionally, be flushed during the day, the collector will need to be up early in the morning if he would see this species on the wing, as it seems to fly most freely about sunrise. The New Forest in Hampshire is a noted district for it, as also are Ranworth, Horning, etc., in Norfolk, and Witherslack in Westmoreland. In Ireland, it is found in counties Galway, Kerry, and Mayo.

Abroad, the range extends to Amurland, China, Corea, and Japan.

Weaver's Wave (*Acidalia* (*Ptychopoda*) *contiguaria*).

The earliest known British specimen of this species (Plate 45, Figs. 2 and 5) was taken in North Wales by Weaver, in 1855, and was figured and described in *The Entomologist's Annual* for 1856 as *Dosithea eburnata*, Wocke. About seven years later Greening captured a female specimen, and he subsequently reared the insect, when it became known as " Greening's Pug." Still later, about 1875, the English name was changed to " Capper's Acidalia."

Fortunately, the species seems not difficult to rear from the egg, otherwise specimens in collections would be not only very limited in number, but frequently very indifferent in condition.

In colour the moth is whity brown, more or less dusted or clouded with dark grey ; except in the darker forms, three irregular black lines on the fore wings, and two on the hind wings, are clearly seen. It flies at dusk in June and July, and sits by day on lichen-covered rocks.

The caterpillar is pale ochreous brown, with irregular dark brown lines. It feeds on ling (*Calluna*) and crowberry (*Empetrum*) from September to May ; but when eggs are obtained, the caterpillar hatching from them may be kept on chickweed, knotgrass, etc., and the moth be reared the same year.

Mr. R. Tait records the finding of ten caterpillars on navel-wort (*Cotyledon*) growing among heather in a very sheltered corner among rocks in North Wales, at Easter, 1906. He also notes that moths reared in captivity pair readily.

The British localities, all in North Wales, are Aber, Bangor, Barmouth, Bettws-y-coed, Conway, Dolgelly, Lanfairfechan, and Penmaenmawr.

The Least Carpet (*Acidalia (Ptychopoda) rusticata*).

The whitish fore wings of this species (Plate 45, Figs. 3 and 6) are crossed by a blackish central band, and there is a blackish patch at the base of the wings, with an extension along the front margin, almost or quite to the central band ; the hind

Pl. 44

1. **Small Grass Emerald:** *caterpillar.*
2. **Little Emerald:** *caterpillar.*
3 3a. **Small Emerald:** *caterpillar, chrysalis and cocoon.*

1, 4. **Purple Bordered Gold.**   2, 5. **Weaver's Wave.**   3, 6. **Least Carpet.**
7, 10. **Rusty Wave.**   8, 11, 14. **Small Dusty Wave.**
9, 12. **Dotted Border Wave.**   13. **Silky Wave.**   15, 18. **Dwarf Cream Wave.**
16. **Isle of Wight Wave.**   17. **Satin Wave.**

wings have a central dot, and three or four dark grey wavy
lines, the space between the first and second darkened, and
appearing to be a continuation of the fore wing band. The
thick set, pale ochreous-brown, or grey-brown, caterpillar (Plate
48, Fig. 1, drawn from a skin) has three more or less distinct
pale lines along the back, and a series of darker diamonds
along the central area; head, brown. In the open, its food
probably consists of decaying or withered leaves, but when
treated in captivity it will eat and thrive upon growing knotgrass, groundsel, dandelion, etc. August to May. Mr. Mera
mentions that some caterpillars he reared on dandelion
produced moths that were larger in size than most captured
specimens.

The moth is out in July, and specimens have been bred in
September from eggs laid in July of the same year. To obtain
this species, a journey will have to be made to one or other
of its special haunts in Kent, lying between Greenhithe and
Sheerness. Other localities from which it has been recorded
are Kingsdown, Dover, Folkestone (Kent); Brighton, Lewes,
West Horsham (Sussex); Isle of Portland (Dorset); Rame
Head, Torquay (Devon); and single specimens have been
reported from Stowmarket and Felixstowe (Suffolk).

The Rusty Wave (*Acidalia* (*Ptychopoda*) *herbariata*).

In *The Entomologist's Annual* for 1856, two species of
Acidalia were brought forward as new to the British list. One
of these has been referred to under *A. contiguaria*, the other
was the present species, which at the time was wrongly referred
to *circuitaria*, Hübner. The specimens depicted on Plate 45,
Figs. 7 and 10, are of continental origin.

Although other specimens were then known to exist in at
least two British collections, the first recorded example was that
mentioned above. This was captured in Bloomsbury Street,

London. In June, 1868, three or four examples were found in a herbalist's shop in Holborn; one occurred on a shop window in Oxford Street in 1873 ; one example was taken from a doorpost in Cannon Street, July 21, 1879 ; and two others have been noted from the same street, but dates were not given. The later records are that of a specimen on July 21, 1898, in a shop in Southampton Row, Bloomsbury, and one at Stroud, Gloucestershire, July, 1910 ; it thus appears that almost all the British specimens known to us have been taken in London.

The eggs are laid on dry or withered plants, upon which the long brownish or greenish caterpillars feed throughout the autumn, winter, and following spring. They pupate towards mid-May, and the moths appear in June and July. According to Guenée, caterpillars seem to have been found only in herb or drug stores, and the moths occur in gardens and houses in July and August.

The Small Dusty Wave (*Acidalia* (*Ptychopoda*) *virgularia*).

In most parts of the southern half of England this species, of which three specimens are shown on Plate 45, Figs. 8, 11, 14, is more or less common, and is often to be seen on garden walls, pales, and other kinds of fences. Although apparently infrequent in the Midlands, it has been recorded as common at Rugely in Staffordshire ; in several parts of Cheshire it is not uncommon, and its distribution is known to extend to Northumberland. Possibly the species is more widely spread over England than the records show it to be. In Wales, it has been found in the North ; in Scotland, it occurs locally from Berwick to Aberdeen ; and it is doubtfully recorded from Ireland. The long, thin caterpillar is ochreous-brown, with a pale stripe on each side. It feeds on the leaves of various low plants, and seems, at times, to like its food best when withered. Some that l reared from eggs deposited in September, 1904, fed for a time on fresh dandelion, but on the approach of winter they apparently ceased feeding, and were allowed to remain in the box with the food last supplied. In March it was found that they had been, and were then, eating the old provender. Some fresh dandelion was added, but this was not touched until all the old had been consumed. The same thing was repeated until the caterpillars were nearly full grown, when the fresh food was eaten as well as the stale. The moths resulting from them emerged during the last week in April, 1905, and were all well above the average size, and considerably larger than the female parent. One example is represented by Fig. 14 on the plate.

There are certainly two generations of the moth during the year ; in some years possibly more.

Dotted Border Wave (*Acidalia (Ptychopoda) straminata*).

In its ordinary form this moth (Plate 45, Figs. 9, 12) is greyish white, sometimes with a tinge of brown, especially on the fore wings ; the darker cross lines are slightly wavy ; each wing has a central black dot, and there is a more or less distinct series of black dots on their outer margins. Ab. *circellata*, Guenée (Plate 61, Fig. 3), has the first and second lines of the fore wings strongly defined and deep brown, and the first is united with the central shade above the inner margin ; the corresponding lines on the hind wings are also deep brown. This form, which occurs on the Lancashire and Cheshire mosses, and is known as the Obscure Wave, has been considered a distinct species, but it is connected with typical *straminata* by intermediate aberrations which occur together with *circellata* and the ordinary form on the same ground. Similar intergrades also occur in the New Forest, Hampshire, the Dover district of Kent, and probably elsewhere.

Series II. I

The rough-looking, long and slender caterpillar is pale greyish, with a black-edged pale line along the middle of the back, the black edging interrupted on rings 4–9 ; on each side of the central line, and lower down along the sides, are other black streaks ; head, notched on the crown, and marked with brown.

Some eggs laid August 8th, hatched on September 1st ; the infant caterpillars were long and thread-like, the colour was black, and there was a whitish stripe low down along the sides. They would not feed on knotgrass and other plants offered to them, and I failed to rear them. Moths have, however, been bred, as a second generation, in the autumn from caterpillars reared from the egg, on bramble and knotgrass.

The moth occurs in July and August on bush-sprinkled heaths, or heathy ground, where it may be disturbed from the herbage in the daytime, or netted as it flies in the evening. South of England from Kent to Dorset ; also in Berkshire ; Cheshire (one specimen, Whitegate Heath, 1901, one ab. *circellata* in Delamere Forest, July, 1903) ; Yorkshire (Thorne Moor, and rather plentiful on Skipwith Common in 1900 and subsequent years ; ab. *circellata* also occurred).

The Dwarf Cream Wave (*Acidalia* (*Ptychopoda*) *interjectaria*).

This moth (Plate 45, Figs. 15, 18) is said to be referable to *fuscovenosa*, Goeze, and as this is an earlier name than *interjectaria*, Guenée, it may have to be adopted. For many years it was known in England as *osseata*, and was described by Haworth, Stephens, and others, under this name. It is also the *dilutaria* of some authors, but not of Hübner. Hübner's *dilutaria* is considered by some writers to be the *holosericata* of Duponchel, and therefore an earlier name for the species generally known by the latter name.

The present species, to which Haworth gave the English name here used, is whitish straw-coloured, and silky in appearance ; the wings have a central black dot and four or five dusky cross lines, some of which are more distinct than others ; the front edge of the fore wings is tinged with reddish brown, in which is often a dark dot at the ends of the first and central lines ; a series of linear blackish dots at the base of the fringes, most distinct on the fore wings.

The somewhat stumpy caterpillar is dull smoky brown, marbled and variegated with ochreous, the darker colour most in evidence in front, and the ochreous behind ; an ochreous line along the middle of the back, and one along the region of the spiracles ; white spots on rings 5–7. (Adapted from Porritt.) It feeds from August to April on dandelion and other low-growing plants, and especially on the withered leaves. The moth occurs among weeds growing on banks, and hedgerows, and the outskirts of woods, in greater or lesser plenty throughout the South of England ; but it becomes local, and more or less rare in the north of the country. In Scotland it is said to be uncommon in Clydesdale, but has not been noted from Ireland, or from Wales.

Isle of Wight Wave (*Acidalia* (*Ptychopoda*) *humiliata*).

This species (Plate 45, Fig. 16) is the *osseata* of Fabricius, but not of Haworth and other British authors. It is very similar in general appearance to the species last considered, but the wings are somewhat less ample, and rather yellower in tint. It is most readily recognised, however, by the distinctly reddish stripe on the front edge of the fore wings. Previous to 1891, when specimens were obtained by Mr. A. J. Hodges in the Isle of Wight, the species was not certainly known to be an inhabitant of the British Isles, although it seems to have been represented in many collections. The insect is still found by those who know where to look for it on the sea cliffs of its island home, but so far as appears to be known at present, it does not occur in any other part of Britain. For this reason, it does not seem desirable to indicate the exact locality more definitely; but it may be added that the moth flies in July.

Silky Wave (*Acidalia* (*Ptychopoda*) *holosericata*).

Somewhat similar to A. *interjectaria*, but tinged with pale brown, and even more glossy; the front edge of the fore wings is of the general coloration, and the only markings on the wings are darker cross lines, the third on the fore wings, and the second on the hind wings, being the most distinct. (Plate 45, Fig. 13.)

The rough and rather stumpy caterpillar tapers towards the small notched head; general colour dusky reddish-brown, a pale line along the middle of the back, finely edged with black. It feeds from August to May on rock rose (*Helianthemum*), eating the withered and even mouldy leaves. Will eat knot-grass, and, no doubt, dandelion also.

Here, again, we have an ancient name brought forward to supplant that which the species has borne for years, and by which it is well known to entomologists. As I am not quite certain that Hübner's (Fig. 100) *dilutaria* does represent this species, Duponchel's name is here retained.

As a British insect, it has only been known since 1851, when the capture of a specimen in the neighbourhood of Bristol was recorded in *The Zoologist*. Subsequently it transpired that the scene of capture was Durdham Down, Gloucestershire, and here it has been found annually, and in some plenty, among the bushes and low vegetation covering the ground in that rugged locality. Specimens have also been noted from Berkshire (Newbury), Bucks (Chalfont St. Peter), Dorset (Halstock), and Norfolk (Thetford). Possibly there are other localities in England, more especially in the west, where this species may be awaiting discovery.

The Satin Wave (*Acidalia* (*Ptychopoda*) *subsericeata*).

The wings of this species (Plate 45, Fig. 17) are glossy whitish, with a faint greyish, or sometimes yellow greyish, tinge; the cross lines are grey, oblique and straight on the fore wings, but the outer two on the hind wings are curved or bent.

Var. *mancuniata*, Knaggs, a local form found in Lancashire and Yorkshire, is rather more tinged with yellowish, the lines being distinct, and some more or less distinct dusky dots on the outer margin of the fore wings.

A blackish form, with white fringes, has been recorded from North Cornwall, where the species, in its usual form, has been noted as abundant.

The rough-looking caterpillar is pale greyish, inclining to reddish above; three black lines along the back, the central one slender, and the outer ones widening out towards each end. It feeds on knotgrass, dandelion, chickweed, and other kinds of weeds, and will eat plum. Hatching in August, it hibernates, as a rule, and attains full growth in the following spring; but sometimes caterpillars feed up quickly, and produce moths the same year.

The moth, which is out in June and July, is partial to heathy ground, but not confined to heaths, as it has been met with in lanes bordered by pasture fields. Widely distributed throughout England and Wales, rare in Scotland, where it has only been recorded from the Solway. In Ireland it has been found commonly at Howth, near Dublin; and in the counties Cork and Waterford.

Portland Ribbon Wave (*Acidalia (Ptychopoda) degeneraria*).

This reddish-banded species (Plate 46, Fig. 1) is only found, in Britain, at Torquay, Devon, and in the Isle of Portland, Dorset, where it was first noted on June 24th, 1831. It will be seen that apart from its different colour, the bands in this moth are placed nearer the base of the wings than in *A. aversata*; on the fore wings the band is limited by the first and central lines, but sometimes it encroaches on the basal area; on the hind wings, it occupies more or less of the basal area, from the first line inwards; the front edge of the fore wings is also reddish.

The caterpillar is ridged along the sides of the roughened body, and tapers towards the slightly notched, blackish marked head; the general colour is reddish-ochreous, darker on the back of the middle rings, along which are three interrupted pale greyish ochreous lines, and dark V-shaped marks. The natural food plant is not known, but it may be reared from the egg on bramble, traveller's joy (*Clematis*), and, of course, knot-grass and dandelion, both of these plants being generally acceptable to larvæ of the Acidaliinæ, as well as to those of many other species of Geometridæ.

The moth is out in June and July in the open, but has been bred as early as June 2. Some of the caterpillars from eggs laid in June will feed up quickly, and produce moths in September; from these, other eggs may be obtained, the caterpillars from which will feed for a time and then hibernate; as also do the slow-growing individuals of the earlier hatching.

Abroad, this seems to be a Mediterranean species, ranging eastward through Asia Minor to parts of Central Asia; and northwards to Austro-Hungary, Castile, France, and West Central Germany.

1 Portland Ribbon Wave.   2. Plain Wave.   3-6. Riband Wave.
7-10. Small Fan-footed Wave.   9. 12. Single-dotted Wave.
8, 11. Treble Brown-spot   13, 14. Lace Border

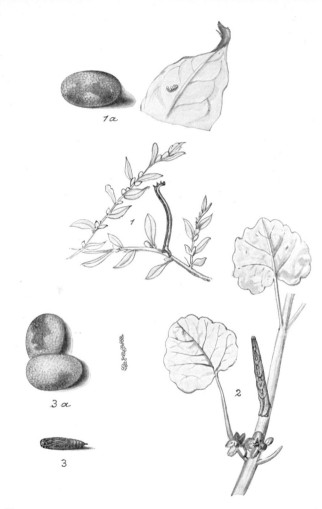

1, 1*a*. **Single-dotted Wave:** *eggs and caterpillar.*
2. **Riband Wave:** *caterpillar.*
3, 3*a*. **Plain Wave:** *eggs, caterpillar and chrysalis.*

The Plain Wave (*Acidalia* (*Ptychopoda*) *inornata*).

Somewhat similar to the last in appearance, but without reddish bands, and front edging to the fore wings ; the second or outer line of the fore wings is generally distinct, but the others, especially the central, are often obscure. This species, one example of which is shown on Plate 46, Fig. 2, may be distinguished from the plain form of *A. aversata* by its generally smaller size and more silky appearance ; the cross lines are less distinct, and the outer one of the fore wings is not indented below the front margin. The eggs (Plate 47, Fig. 3*a*) are laid in strings of from 6–20 ; at least this is so in captivity. Like the eggs of other species in this genus that I have seen, they are at first whitish bone colour, changing to reddish. They were laid in July, and most of the caterpillars that hatched from them attained the moth state in September; about one-third hibernated, but died off during the winter.

The much-wrinkled and rough-looking caterpillar is pale reddish brown, varying to greyish ; the back with V-shaped marks, and a light coloured spot on rings 5 and 6. It feeds, from August to June, on dandelion, dock, and other weeds, also on sallow, bramble, heather, etc.

The moth is out in July, earlier or later in some seasons; it affects woods in which there is plenty of heather or bilberry, and may often be seen resting on tree trunks, especially those of the pine. It is on the wing in the evening, and is said to visit the sugar patch, as well as flowers growing in its haunts. Widely distributed over England and Scotland to Moray, but does not appear to have been noted in Wales. Reported from Kingstown, Killarney, and Londonderry in Ireland.

The Riband Wave (*Acidalia* (*Ptychopoda*) *aversata*).

There are two distinct colour forms, one is greyish white (ab. *spoliata*, Staudinger), and the other decidedly ochreous ; the former is sometimes tinged with ochreous, and sometimes heavily sprinkled with dark grey.   In the type form of *aversata*, the general colour is greyish white, and the space between the central and outer lines of the fore wings, and that enclosed by the first and central of the hind wings, is more or less entirely filled up with dark grey inclining to blackish ; occasionally the dark colour spreads beyond the outer line, and covers a large portion of the outer area.   These bands also occur in the ochreous and intermediate colour forms.   A specimen, bred in June by Mr. W. G. Sheldon, from a caterpillar found on a fence at West Wickham in May, had the wings and abdomen black, but the head, thorax, anal tuft, and fringes of the wings were normal.   (Plate 46, Figs. 3–6.)

The caterpillar (Plate 47, Fig. 2 ; from coloured drawing by Mr. Sich) is much wrinkled, rather thickened behind, and tapers gradually towards the small, black-flecked head ; the general colour is brownish, merging into ochreous on the hinder rings ; a darker brown shade along the back, interrupted on the middle rings by V-shaped marks, encloses a slender whitish line, and there is a whitish spot on ring eight ; a wavy pale ochreous line low down along the sides.   (Adapted from Fenn.)   It feeds on dandelion, dock, primrose, bedstraw, knot-grass, and many other low-growing plants ; after hibernation, from April to May, it will thrive on the young growth of sallow, birch, hawthorn, etc.   It will sometimes feed up and reach the moth state in August or September.

The moth flies in June and July, and is generally distributed ; but in Scotland does not seem to have been observed north of Moray.

Small Fan-footed Wave (*Acidalia (Ptychopoda) bisetata*).

One form (Plate 46, Fig. 10) has whitish wings, with a deep, dark-grey border on the outer area of all the wings ; this border is traversed by a whitish, wavy line (ab. *fimbriolata*, Stephens). Another form (Plate 46, Fig. 7) is more or less typical, and in this it will be noted that the marginal borders are much paler, and are broken up into bandlets. Between these two forms there are modifications, and sometimes a greyish shade spreads over all the wings.

The caterpillar is long and slender, with a somewhat flattened appearance, and gradually tapered towards the notched head ; the general colour of the roughened body is greyish brown, the middle ring divisions, and V-shaped marks on the back, are blackish or dark brown ; there is also a double dark brown line along the back, not always distinct. It feeds, from August to May, on a variety of low-growing plants, and is partial to withered leaves, especially those of bramble and dandelion. The moth is out in June and July, and is often common, and pretty generally distributed throughout our islands, except that it seems not to have been noted north of Moray, in Scotland.

Abroad, the range extends to East Siberia and Amurland.

The Single Dotted Wave (*Acidalia (Ptychopoda) dimidiata*).

The most noticeable feature in this whity brown moth (Plate 47, Figs. 9 and 12), sometimes known as *scutulata*, are the larger dots at the costal end of the dotted cross lines, and the blackish or dark-brown chain-like mark on the lower part of the outer marginal area of the fore wings ; the latter is sometimes obscured in a cloud of its own colour.

Eggs (Plate 47, Fig. 1*a*), laid in a batch on a dried leaf of dandelion, were whitish at first, but turned reddish later.

The elongated and somewhat flattened caterpillar (figured on Plate 47, Fig. 1, from a coloured drawing by Mr. Sich) is ochreous, with brown lines on the back, the central one double, and interrupted on the middle rings, upon which are oblique pale-brown dashes. It feeds, from September to April, on beaked parsley (*Anthriscus sylvestris*), burnet saxifrage (*Pimpinella*), etc., and may be reared on withered leaves of dandelion and other weeds. The moth is out in June and July, and in northern localities in August. Generally distributed, and often common.

Treble Brown Spot (*Acidalia* (*Ptychopoda*) *trigeminata*).

This species (Plate 46, Figs. 8, 11) is similar to the last, but generally rather larger and somewhat paler ; the front edge of the fore wings is marked with blackish or dark purplish grey, and there is a band of the same colour on the outer marginal area ; the inner edge of this band is formed by the second line, and the outer edge is wavy, interrupted above the middle, and sometimes below also.

The rough and rather flattened caterpillar tapers towards the head ; in colour it is dusky brown. The markings comprise interrupted black lines and V-shaped blackish marks on the back. Buckler states that this caterpillar may be distinguished from those of its nearest allies by having a rather long, dingy ochreous bristle from each of the raised dots ; these bristles, which are of the same thickness throughout, curve forwards on all rings to the ninth, and on the other three backwards. It feeds, from September to April, on various low-growing plants, ivy, birch, etc. If kept warm, it is said that whole broods will attain the moth state in July or August ; this may happen some-times, but in my experience only a few individuals have obliged

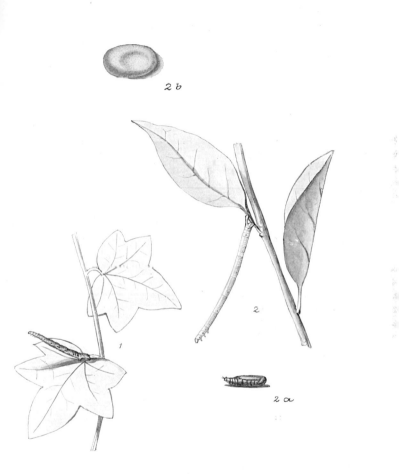

Pl. 48.

1. **Least Carpet**: *caterpillar.*
2, 2*a*, 2*b*. **Small Blood-vein**: *egg enlarged, caterpillar and chrysalis.*

1, 2. **Cream Wave.**   3, 4. **Lesser Cream Wave.**   5-7. **Mullein Wave.**
9. **Lewes Wave.**   8. **Sub-angled Wave.**   10. **Rosy Wave.**
11, 12. **Small Blood-vein.**

in this way. The moth is another inhabitant of the hedgerow and the bushy wood-border, where it may be disturbed in the daytime during late May and June. It flies in the evening, and will visit light, and occasionally the sugar patch. Always a local species, but not uncommon in its special haunts in Kent, Surrey, Wiltshire, Essex, and Suffolk; it is also found more or less frequently in Sussex, Hampshire, Dorsetshire, Gloucestershire, Herefordshire and Worcestershire. In Scotland, it is reported as scarce in Renfrew; and Kane notes that it does not occur in Ireland.

The Lace Border (*Acidalia* (*Craspedia*) *ornata*).

The conspicuously marked white moth depicted on Plate 46, Figs. 13 and 14, is unlikely to escape the notice of the collector who visits rough fields and hillsides in some of the chalk districts of Southern England, especially in the counties of Kent, Surrey, and Sussex. Usually there are two generations of the moth during the year; one is on the wing in May and June, and the other flies in August and September.

The caterpillar is of long and slender build, the head is notched, and the skin of the body is roughened. In colour it is ochreous brown above and greyish beneath; there are three lines along the back, the central one pale, except towards the head, edged with dusky, the others dark brown. On each ring, from four to eight, are two dark V-shaped marks; low down along the sides there is a dusky edged and mottled, pale ochreous stripe. It feeds, from October to May, and in July and August, on thyme, marjoram, and may be reared on garden mint. Abroad, the species ranges over Central and Southern Europe, and through Asia to Amurland.

NOTE.—According to Prout (*Entom.* xxxix. 267), this species is the type of the genus *Scopula*, Schrank.

The Cream Wave (*Acidalia* (*Leptomeris*) *remutaria*).

This species (Plate 49, Figs. 1, 2) has the wings white or ochreous white, becoming rather smoky grey on the front edge of the fore wings, and sometimes this tinge spreads all over the wings. In well-marked specimens there are two dark, wavy, cross-lines, a dusky central shade, and a dusky shade-like stripe along the outer area beyond the second line; the first line of the fore wings is often placed close to the central shade, and sometimes it is merged in it. Not infrequently the lines are barely traceable, but almost as often the wings appear to have a pair of lines only, and these distinctly darker than usual.

The caterpillar is rough, long and slender; grey-brown with irregular darker marks, a pale line along the middle of the back, and a dark cross on the back of ring ten. The notched head is pale brown with a black V-mark. It feeds, from July to September, on bedstraw (*Galium*), woodruff (*Asperula*), dock, sallow, etc.

The moth is out in May and June, and often is plentiful in woods throughout the greater part of England and Wales; in Yorkshire and northwards through Scotland up to Moray it is rather local. In Ireland it has been found in Wicklow and Louth, but more commonly in the south and west.

The range abroad extends to Amurland and Japan.

The Lesser Cream Wave (*Acidalia* (*Leptomeris*) *immutata*).

White, more or less tinged with ochreous or ochreous grey in the male, is the general colour of this moth; the wings are crossed by several ochreous lines, the third line of the fore wings and the second line of the hind wings rather wavy. All the wings with central black dots, most distinct on the hind pair, occasionally absent from fore wings. (Plate 49, Figs. 3 ♂, 4 ♀.)

The long caterpillar is pale greyish-brown, with three dusky lines on the back; the black spiracles are set in a pale stripe, and below this is a dusky line; head small and round (Barrett). August to May. The natural food appears to be *Valeriana officinalis*, and *Spiræa*, but it has been reared from the egg on groundsel, knotgrass, etc., also hawthorn, and moths obtained the same year, about September.

In the open the moth is to be found in fens, bogs, and marshy places in fields and woods, during June and July. It is not uncommon, in suitable spots, in most of the southern and eastern counties of England. In the west, including Wales, and through the Midlands, it is local to Yorkshire, but is widely distributed in the south of the latter county; it occurs, rarely, in Durham. In Scotland it has only been definitely noted from Arran. Widely distributed, and common, in many parts of Ireland.

Abroad, the range extends to Amurland.

The Mullein Wave (*Acidalia* (*Leptomeris*) *marginepunctata*).

This species exhibits more variation than is usual in this group. Typically, the moth is greyish white, but in some specimens the grey is most in evidence, and in others the white. A practically black form, with white fringes, has been noted from North Cornwall, and at Eastbourne and Portland many of the specimens have a clear, bone-coloured ground, with fine but very distinct cross-markings; these seem to be referable to ab. *pastoraria*, Joannis. The cross lines in both dark and light forms are sometimes very indistinct, but occasionally the first and second of the fore wings are united, and so form an irregular dusky band; the greyish clouding on the outer marginal area is also variable. Three specimens are shown on Plate 49; two from Eastbourne, Figs. 5 ♀, 6 ♂, and one from Essex, Fig. 7 ♀.

The long caterpillar is very pale slaty-olive, with three paler lines along the back, the central one edged on each side with olive, darkest on the last three rings; spiracles black, and under surface of the body pale slate blue (adapted from Porritt). It feeds on various low-growing plants, among which, yarrow, mugwort, chickweed, cinquefoil, and knotgrass have been mentioned; also, it is said, on sallow. There are certainly two broods in the south, one feeding up in the summer, and the other hatching in September, and after hibernation attaining full growth in May or June. Moths of the first generation are on the wing in June and July, and of the second in August and September. Although sometimes found inland, the species is more especially attached to the coast, and is found in nearly all the seaboard counties of England, Wales, and Ireland. In Scotland, it occurs in Wigtownshire, and very dark specimens have been obtained on rocks in dry pastures at Ardrossan; June to end of July.

The Lewes Wave (*Acidalia* (*Leptomeris*) *immorata*).

Although the late Mr. S. Stevens exhibited a British specimen of this species, as a curious variety of *Strenia clathrata*, at a meeting of the Entomological Society of London in 1868, it was not until the year 1887, when Mr. C. H. Morris captured two specimens in Sussex, that the insect became recognized as a native. It is probable that the earlier example, taken some years before it was shown at the meeting referred to, may have come from the same locality in the Lewes district where the later specimens were captured. Anyway, the species has, so far, not been recorded from any other part of our islands, but it continues to be found in its original haunts, described as "some heathy ground," up to the present day. (Plate 49, Fig. 9.)

The long, slender, and roughened caterpillar is pale greyish brown; the central line along the back is greyish-white, each side edged on the hinder half with brown, having at the beginning of each ring after the third a black dot on either side; side stripes dark brown, inclining to black above; a slender brown line below the black spiracles. (Adapted from Barrett.) It feeds from August to May on ling (*Calluna vulgaris*), marjoram, thyme, knotgrass, etc.

From eggs laid on July 1 and 2 caterpillars hatched on July 17 and 18. These were placed on leaves of ribwort plantain (*Plantago lanceolata*), and as soon as large enough transferred to a potted plant, and kept out of doors. Two of the caterpillars grew up quickly, and on August 24 were taken indoors, where they spun up for pupation, one on August 28, and the other on September 1. A female moth emerged September 14 from the first chrysalis (F. C. Woodbridge, 1906).

The range abroad extends to East Siberia and Amurland.

The Sub-angled Wave (*Acidalia (Leptomeris) strigilaria*).

This species is greyish white, sometimes brownish-tinged; dusky cross markings, of which the oblique shade following the central black dot of the fore wings, and that before the central black dot of the hind wings, are usually most distinct, forming a narrow band across both pairs of wings; the outer margin of the hind wings is angled.

The long, slender caterpillar has a roughened appearance; the colour is greenish grey, and the markings comprise a dull green line along the middle of the back, spotted with black on each side; the grey head is variegated with very pale brown. (Adapted from Porritt.)

This species (Plate 49, Fig. 8) was known to Haworth, who gave it the English name which it bears to-day. Stephens, writing of it in 1831, states that it was very rare, and that specimens in his collection were from a lane near Darenth, in Kent. With one exception (Hastings, Sussex, 1876), the only present known locality in the British Isles for the species is the Warren, near Folkestone, Kent, where it was discovered in 1859. Here it occurred more or less freely for several years, then it became scarce, and finally, about 1890, seemed to be practically extinct. In 1906, however, Mr. G. H. Conquest netted a female specimen in the Warren on July 24, and as she laid a few eggs, it may be presumed that others had been deposited before capture. From the eggs obtained by Mr. Conquest, nine moths were reared in July, 1907. The caterpillars thrived on traveller's joy (*Clematis vitalba*), which is probably the natural food ; but they will also eat dandelion, knotgrass, etc., and like the withered leaves. By keeping in a warm place, it is possible to get moths out the same year, but, as a rule, the caterpillars prefer to hibernate.

The range abroad extends to Amurland, China, Corea, and Japan.

The Rosy Wave (*Acidalia* (*Leptomeris*) *emutaria*).

Figure 10, Plate 49, shows an example of this species, which also has angled hind wings. In coloration it is whiter and more silky than the last, and when fresh is delicately tinged with pink ; the first and second lines are dotted or represented by dots, and the greyish central shade is obliquely inclined in the direction of the tips of the wings. In the marshes on the Essex and Kentish coasts the species is generally rather more rosy (ab. *subroseata*, Haworth), but this form occurs occasionally in the New Forest also. The long, slender caterpillar is whitish ochreous, inclining to pinkish ; on the back of each ring is a broad grey shade enclosing a white spot, and a faint grey line on each side. Spiracles, black, with black spots below them on rings four to eight ; undersurface bluish-grey with a central white stripe. (Adapted from Fenn.) When reared from the egg, the caterpillar will feed on knotgrass, chickweed, birdsfoot trefoil, etc. The moths sometimes appear in August or September, but the more usual habit of the larva is to hibernate when small and complete growth in the following spring.

The moth, which is out in July and early August, conceals itself by day among the vegetation growing in its somewhat restricted haunts. These are chiefly the marshes on the east coast, and similar spots in Kent and Sussex; also the bogs of Hampshire and Dorset, but especially those between Lyndhurst and Brockenhurst in the former county. It is not readily put up during the day, but towards evening it becomes active on the wing, and after its flight may be found sitting about upon the herbage.

Abroad, it seems to be pretty much confined to Southern Europe and North-west Africa.

The Small Blood-vein (*Acidalia* (*Leptomeris*) *imitaria*).

All the wings of this pale reddish-brown species are angulated (Plate 49, Figs. 11 and 12). A conspicuous character is the reddish or purplish-red stripe crossing both the wings, and to which its English name no doubt refers. It varies somewhat in the amount of reddish in the general coloration, also in the tint and the width of the prominent oblique cross stripe.

The early stages are shown on Plate 48, Figs. 2–2b. The eggs, when laid on June 18 and 19, were whitish-green, but soon turned pinkish, inclining to coral red. The caterpillars hatched July 3 to 6, and were reared on a diet of privet leaves—a food that I have always found they preferred to any other that has been offered to them, and upon which I have found them in the open. They are exceedingly easy to rear, and if, as sometimes happens, they refuse to feed up and get through to the moth state in

September of the same year, they do not die off during the winter or early spring, as do so many larvæ of other hibernating species. Enclosed in a suitable receptacle, such as a roomy glass cylinder, with some twigs of privet plugged in a bottle of water, the caterpillars may be left in any odd corner until spring, when fresh twigs should be introduced from time to time. Other food plants are dock, groundsel, dandelion, knotgrass, bedstraw, etc. In colour the caterpillar is pale ochreous brown, with three darker brown lines on the back, the central one broken on the front rings, and the others edged above with whitish; the spiracles are black, and the stripe along the side pale drab.

The moth affects hedgerows, banks, bushy places on rough sloping ground, and sandhills by the sea. It flies in the evening, and may be met with in July and August, sometimes in September, in most English and Welsh counties, and in the south of Ireland. It is local and somewhat rare in Northern England, and seems not to occur in Scotland.

Tawny Wave (*Acidalia* (*Leptomeris*) *rubiginata*).

This attractive little moth (Plate 50, Figs. 1, 2), known also as *rubricata* Fab., varies in colour from ochreous brown with a purplish or reddish tinge, to purplish brown or crimson; the first line of the fore wings is curved, and the second is parallel with the central shade. Sometimes the space between the last two lines and between the first and second lines of the hind wings is paler than the general colour. A dusky brown form has been recorded from boggy heaths in Norfolk.

The roughish caterpillar, which gradually tapers to the notched head, is greyish inclining to yellowish or greenish; three blackish lines on the back, the central one widened on the middle rings, and the others only distinct on the front rings; a black-edged pale line above the black spiracles, and a dusky stripe below them (Barrett). It feeds from August to May on clover, trefoil, knotgrass, etc. Sometimes as a second generation in June and July.

According to Stephens, who figured this species in 1831, a specimen was taken, near Dover, somewhere about 1825; he also refers to Yorkshire specimens, one of which he had in his collection. Since that time the species has been obtained in Lancashire (Ashton-on-Mersey), and it was noted, not uncommon from the first to third week in July, 1875, on low heathery ground at Winch Bridge, Upper Teesdale, Durham. Casual specimens have also been recorded from Folkestone, Kent; Hastings, Sussex, and South Devon; the last concerns a specimen taken in the Newton Abbot district in 1902. What may be termed the British home of the species is, however, the Breck sand district in the eastern counties, where, since 1860, it has been found in greater or lesser plenty, in June, each year up to the present time. The best known localities are Tuddenham, Brandon, Thetford, and Bury St. Edmunds. It sits among the vegetation in fields or the borders thereof, and also on heaths. Occasionally, it indulges in flight in the afternoon, but it is more often put up as the collector approaches its place of retreat. At night it is usually active, and light has a strong attraction for it.

Abroad, its range extends to Amurland and Corea.

The Smoky Wave (*Acidalia* (*Pylarge*) *fumata*).

The sexes of this greyish-white moth are figured on Plate 50, Figs. 4 ♂, 5 ♀. It will be seen that the female is smaller than the male. The caterpillar is very slender, and finely wrinkled; pale ochreous brown, with three pale lines along the back, each of which is shaded on both sides with brown. Beneath the ridge, low down along the sides, is a dark stripe, and the under surface is pale. It feeds on bilberry, sallow and heather, and will eat knotgrass, chickweed, and dandelion. Hatching in August, it hibernates when nearly mature, but it resumes feeding in the spring. The moth is out in June and July, and frequents moors and mosses. Plentiful in Scotland and in the north of England, its range extends through Wales and the west of England to Devonshire, where it occurs on Exmoor and is common in some parts of that extensive area. In Ireland, recorded by Birchall as widely distributed; Kane notes it from counties Kerry, Waterford, and Galway.

The range abroad extends to Amurland and Japan.

Bright Wave (*Acidalia* (*Sterrha*) *ochrata*).

At one time this ochreous brown species (Plate 50, Fig. 3) was an inhabitant of the Essex coast, and was found commonly at Southend among other places. Deal and other parts of the Kentish coast are more frequently mentioned in connection with later records of the species. In the present day it is far less plentiful at Deal than formerly, but it is still to be found there. Specimens have been taken in the Isle of Wight (Barrett), and one has been noted from Suffolk (Aldeburgh).

The pale ochreous brown or greyish ochreous caterpillar has three broken greyish lines on the back; it tapers towards the small head, and the skin of the body is closely wrinkled. It feeds from August to May, or a little later, on the flowers of hawk's-beard (*Crepis*), dandelion, coltsfoot, golden rod, etc., and in confinement it seems to accept most kinds of flowers that are offered, even when widely different. Thus, Mr. Conquest, in 1907, had some caterpillars which hatched during the first week in August from eggs laid on July 25 ; these were at first supplied with flowering sprays of yellow bedstraw (*Galium verum*), and later on with the flowers of golden rod (*Solidago*). Instead of hibernating, which is no doubt the normal habit in the species, some larvæ reared from the egg in confinement and subjected

1, 2. Tawny Wave.

3. Bright Wave.

4, 5. Smoky Wave.

6. *Acidalia perochraria.*

7, 8. Small Scallop.

9, 10. Blood-vein.

1, 1a, 1b. **Dingy Mocha:** *eggs, caterpillars and chrysalis.*
2. **Mocha:** *caterpillar.*

to fostering warmth will grow very quickly and produce moths the same year.

This species has been referred to the genus *Sterrha*, Hübner, but authorities are not agreed as to the validity of this.

Acidalia perochraria.

The species last referred to as *A. ochrata* was formerly known in Britain as *pallidoria*, and was figured by Curtis in 1831 under that name. Afterwards the name was changed to *perochraria*, and later still the correct name was found for it.

How far there may have been confusion of the two species in the records of the present one, I have no means of ascertaining, but probably all but two should properly refer to *ochrata*. The only two known British specimens of *perochraria* therefore appear to have been captured in the Redhill district of Surrey, one in 1865 and one in 1869. As will be seen on reference to Plate 50, where a portrait of a Continental specimen will be found (Fig. 6), the general colour is much brighter than that of *ochrata*. It will be noted, also, that there are four darker cross lines on the fore wings, and three on the hind wings. The antennæ, too, of the male are toothed, and therefore differ from these organs in *ochrata*.

The Small Scallop (*Ania emarginata*).

As will be noted on turning to Plate 50, Figs. 7, 8, the male of this pale ochreous brown species is generally rather larger than the female, and the more ample wings are less acutely angled in outline; the latter sex is also more clouded with reddish brown.

The caterpillar is variable in colour; one form is of a dusky ochreous colour with a pale line along the middle of the back, edged on each side with a darker tint, and most conspicuously so on the hinder rings ; the back is also dotted with black, and has some dark V- or X-shaped marks upon it; the body tapers to the notched dark-brown head. It feeds on bedstraw (*Galium*), convolvulus, etc., and, like others of its tribe, has a taste for withered leaves. August to May or June, according to the season. In confinement it has been induced by warmth to feed up quickly, and appear as a moth the same year. Only a short time is passed in the chrysalis stage. July is perhaps the best month for the moth, but it may be seen at any time from late June to early August. Its haunts are fens, marshes, and moist woodlands, etc., and although it is more frequent in the south, it is widely spread throughout England, but in the north it is rare, and its occurrence more or less casual.

In Wales it has been recorded from Glamorganshire and Flintshire; but it is apparently unknown in Scotland and Ireland.

The Blood-vein (*Timandra amata*).

The stripe across the wings of this pretty species (Plate 50, Figs. 9 and 10), extending from the apex of the fore wings to near the middle of the inner margin of the hind wings, is normally pinkish red, but it may be of a more crimson or purplish hue ; it also varies in width. The fringes are usually pinkish red, and occasionally the margins of the wings are tinged with the same colour. The whitish-ochreous ground colour is normally finely powdered with grey, but sometimes so thickly that a greyish tinge is imparted to the wings. Barrett mentions a specimen with pale smoky brown wings, and, excepting that the tips of the fringes are tinged with pink, the usual markings are absent. In another example, "the space between the central and second lines is filled up with purple brown."

The caterpillar is brownish grey, with three whitish lines on the back, the central one intersecting a series of four dark lozenges. It feeds on various low-growing plants, such as persicaria, orach, sorrel, etc., but dock seems to be the most frequently selected pabulum. July to May, sometimes feeding up and appearing as a second generation of the moth in August.

Weedy ditches, hedge banks, or moist waste places, are the favourite resorts of the moth ; and when one example is flushed from its lurking place, others are almost certain to be hiding in the immediate vicinity.

Widely distributed throughout England, but most common in the south ; found also in North and South Wales ; and sparingly in Scotland to Aberdeenshire, also recorded from Arran. Apparently rare in Ireland, as it is only noted from Kerry and Galway.

False Mocha (*Ephyra porata*).

The wings are pale ochreous brown, finely flecked with purplish grey, and more or less tinged with reddish ; the cross lines are indicated by blackish dots, the central shade is greyish inclining to reddish, and the rings enclosing white dots are blackish or dark brown, but sometimes indistinct on the fore wings ; occasionally there are some purplish grey clouds on the outer marginal area, and this is more frequent in examples of a second generation. Sometimes the wings are entirely suffused with dull reddish brown, and all the markings, except the white dot on the hind wings, are obscured. (Plate 53, Figs. 7 and 8.)

The caterpillar is pale pinkish ochreous, with inconspicuous wavy white lines, and brownish dots, on the back ; dark oblique marks on the sides ; the head is pencilled with darker brown. It feeds on oak and birch in June and July, and individuals of a second brood sometimes occur in September or October.

The moth is out in May and June, and rests in the daytime

among the foliage of trees and bushes in or around woods. Like others of the genus, it is attracted by light, and is said to visit the sugar patch. Specimens of a second generation sometimes appear in August and September, but, I believe, more frequently in the breeding cage than in the open. Although it has been recorded from several of the northern counties from Staffordshire to Cumberland, this is more especially an inhabitant of the south and west of England, and of Wales. In Scotland, it is known to occur singly and rarely in Clydesdale and Arran, and has been found in Perthshire.

NOTE.—This species, and the other five here included in *Ephyra*, have been referred to *Zonosoma*, Lederer, and more recently to *Cyclophora*, Stephens.

Maiden's Blush (*Ephyra punctaria*).

In a general way, this moth (Plate 53, Figs. 10–12) is not unlike the last mentioned. Apart, however, from the absence of ringed dots on all the wings, the central line is more prominent. Certain vagaries occur in connection with this line, which is generally reddish, or purplish brown. Occasionally, it may be visible on the fore wings, but absent on the hind wings ; or it may change its course about mid-way, and turn inwards to the base of the fore wing. I have a specimen from Surrey in which this line is double the normal width, and dark purplish in colour. Examples of the second generation have brownish clouds on the outer margin (Fig. 12).

The caterpillar is pale reddish-ochreous or bright green; a black line along the middle of the back, and a brownish one along the sides ; a black horse-shoe mark, edged below with yellow, on the back of rings four to nine.

It feeds, in June and July, on oak, but may be reared on birch ; also found in September as a second brood.

The moth is out in May and June, and specimens of a second generation are often not uncommon in August. It occurs in woodlands throughout England, but is most plentiful in the south. In Scotland, it appears to be local in Clydesdale, but is found thence up to Moray. In Ireland, only recorded from Galway (two specimens).

Clay Triple-Lines (*Ephyra linearia*).

This species (Plate 53, Fig. 13) varies in the general colour from yellowish to pale reddish ochreous; the cross lines are also variable, often the first is missing (Plate 53, Fig. 14), and not infrequently the dark central line is the only visible marking, but very exceptionally the central line is very little, if at all, more distinct than the normal first and second. A very rare form ab. *fasciata*, Prout, has a smoky band on all the wings. The ringed white dots are rarely very conspicuous, and may be absent.

The caterpillar is pale brownish, with a brown-edged yellowish line along the middle of the back, and some yellow-edged dark-brown streaks on the sides. In another form, the head is brown and the body green.

It feeds in June, July, and again in September, on beech. The moth is out in May and June, and again in August and September. Beech woods are its favourite haunts, and it seldom strays far from them. It is generally common in the south, and its range apparently extends to Northumberland; but it is local and infrequent in the north. Three specimens have been recorded from Co. Galway, and one from Co. Cork, in Ireland.

NOTE.—Nearly fifty years ago, at Brighton, a single specimen was reared from one of eight larvæ that hatched from the same number of eggs deposited by a female *E. linearia* that had paired with a male *E. orbicularia*. This hybrid has been named *brightoni*, Tutt.

The Mocha (*Ephyra annulata*).

Normally, the wings of this species (Plate 53, Figs. 6, 9) are yellowish white, inclining to ochreous yellow with the blackish central shade near to and sometimes united with the blackish irregular and outwardly toothed second cross line on both fore and hind wings; the rings are deep brown or blackish. There is variation in the width and intensity of the central shade, and the rings sometimes are absent on the fore wings (ab. *obsoleta*, Riding), and occasionally all the wings are devoid of the annular mark (ab. *biobsoleta*, Riding). Examples of a second generation reared in captivity are rather deeper coloured, and have a sprinkling of black scales, chiefly on the fore wings.

The caterpillar (Plate 51, Fig. 2, after Hofmann) is dark green, yellow between the rings; there are three yellow lines along the back, the outer ones waved; head reddish brown, paler marked. (Adapted from Porritt.) There is also a pale ochreous brown form.

It feeds on maple in June, and as a second generation in August and September. It may be reared on sycamore. The moth frequents lanes, woods, and thickets, especially those in which maple is plentiful ; it flies at dusk, and in the daytime may be beaten from hedgerows in which the food plant grows. It has also been found among hornbeam. The species is most frequent from Kent to Hampshire, but widely distributed over England up to Worcester and Herefordshire, and eastward to Norfolk, occurring also in Northampton and Yorkshire.

The colour and ornamentation of this charming little insect seem to have struck Haworth, who named the species in the vernacular, as bearing some resemblance to the Mocha stone from Arabia, a kind of transparent agate in which are seen brownish moss-like markings.

Dingy Mocha (*Ephyra orbicularia*).

The wings are greyish, thickly striped with darker grey; the markings similar to those of the next species, but the rings are nearly always reddish or purplish, and the central line is wavy. (Plate 53, Figs. 4 and 5.)

The egg (which, together with the caterpillar and chrysalis, is figured on Plate 51) is at first bone-coloured; later, pink dots and patches appear.

The caterpillar is bright green with three lines along the back, the central one edged on each side with dark green and the others wavy; the sides are blotched with pink or pale purple, or sometimes whitish and unmarked; head slightly notched on the crown, pale brown, marked with darker; fore legs tipped with pink. (Porritt, abridged.) In another form of the green coloration, the sides are pinkish with dark-brown oblique stripes; in a third the general colour is pale brown. The first brood of caterpillars feeds in June on sallow and alder, and a second in August and September.

The moth appears in May and June, and again in July and August; sometimes a third brood has been reared in captivity. It is less frequently met with than the other species of *Ephyra*, even in its most favourite haunts, such as the New Forest, in Hampshire. Other localities for it are Abbots Wood, St. Leonards and Tilgate Forests, and elsewhere in Sussex; Red-stone, Haslemere, and the Croydon districts, in Surrey; and in some Kentish woods. It has also been taken rarely in Dorset, Devon (Tiverton), S. Wales, and Suffolk (Lowestoft).

Birch Mocha (*Ephyra pendularia*).

The general colour of this species (Plate 53, Figs. 1, 2) is whitish, more or less powdered or suffused with grey; all the

wings have two blackish dotted cross lines and a greyish, sometimes reddish, central shade ; not infrequently there is an
interrupted grey or dark greyish band on the outer marginal
area, and this margin itself is always dotted with black; the
rings enclosing white dots on all the wings are usually black,
but sometimes reddish. In some specimens having a reddish
central shade, the general colour, especially of the fore wings,
is delicately tinged with reddish. Var. *subroseata*, Woodforde
(Fig. 3), a form of this species occurring in N. Staffs. is slaty
grey, with the space between the inner and outer cross lines of
fore wings rosy pink or reddish. A somewhat darker form
(*nigro-roseata*, Wood), occurring in Kent and Surrey, is,
according to Mr. Prout (Entom, 1920, 52), identical with *E.
decoraria*, Newman (1861).

The caterpillar is of a green colour with slender yellowish
lines along the back and sides ; between the rings the colour
inclines to yellowish, and the head, legs, and prolegs are
reddish brown. In another form the general colour is greyish,
inclining to reddish, and the lines paler grey. It feeds on birch
in June and July, and again in August and September. It is
said to eat alder and oak.

The moth, which appears in May and June, and in some
seasons in August, frequents woodlands and heaths where birch
flourishes. Although fairly plentiful in most of the southern
English counties, it appears to be rare in Dorset and Devon,
and more or less so in the eastern counties. It is very local in
Nottinghamshire and Yorkshire, but not uncommon at Stren-
sall in the latter county; and although it has been recorded
from Cumberland, it seems to be absent from Lancashire and
Cheshire. Doubtfully reported from North Northumberland,
but found in Wells Wood, Roxburghshire, and appears to be
widely distributed in Scotland, although generally scarce in
that country. In Ireland it is local, but not uncommon sometimes.

Pl. 52.

1. **Mallow**: *caterpillar.*
2. **Shaded Broad bar**: *caterpillar.*
3. **Chalk Carpet**: *caterpillar.*

1, 2, 3. **Birch Mocha.**   4, 5. **Dingy Mocha.**   6, 9. **The Mocha.**
7, 8. **False Mocha.**   10-12. **Maiden's Blush.**   13, 14. **Clay Triple-lines.**

HYDRIOMENINÆ.

The Vestal (*Sterrha sacraria*).

The fore wings are pale yellow inclining to ochreous, and the front edge is more or less tinged with the same colour as that of the oblique stripe from the tips of the wings to the middle of the inner margin. In the type, this stripe is purplish-brown, but in ab. *labda*, Cramer, it is crimson, and in ab. *atrifasciaria*, Stefan, it is blackish. In ab. *sanguinaria*, Esper, the ground colour is pinkish. The hind wings are always white. (Plate 54, Figs. 1 and 2.)

From 1857, in which year the first specimen recorded as British was captured in September at Plymouth, to 1874, one or more examples of this interesting migrant seem to have occurred during the autumns of most years, in some part of the British Isles, but chiefly in the South of England. The years in which it was apparently unrecorded were 1860, 1861, 1870, 1872, and 1873. Since 1874 there have been very few records. In 1879 a male specimen was taken at Chingford, Essex, August 17th, and a female (ova obtained) on September 1st; a specimen occurred at Christchurch, Hants, October, 1893; a male was obtained in the Isle of Purbeck, Dorset, September, 1895, and one was secured at Timoleague, Co. Cork, in August, 1898; one was accounted for at Malvern, Worcestershire, in August, 1901; a female in fine condition was captured, as it flew in the sunshine over a Cambridgeshire meadow, in the autumn of 1906. Mr. Edelsten obtained a male specimen in South Devon, on September 12, 1908. Mr. B. H. Smith secured a specimen in Cornwall, September 8, 1911. In 1867, nearly thirty were secured, and of these four were taken in May in the Isle of Wight, where also two females were captured on

August 14th and 16th, and one specimen on September 3rd. Six or seven occurred during August in Lancashire, and three in Perthshire, also in August.

The long caterpillar is variable, but is usually some shade of green above, inclining to whitish beneath, and yellowish between the rings ; the lines along the back are paler green, reddish, and olive green. It feeds on low-growing plants, such as knot-grass and dock, and has been reared from the egg in August and September. If eggs were obtained in May it would be possible to raise two generations of moths, or, perhaps, even three, during the year.

The species is an inhabitant of Southern Europe and North Africa, and its range extends to India, Madeira, and the Canaries. In Central Europe, including the British Isles, its occurrence is always a more or less casual event.

NOTE.—It is possibly incorrect to assign this species to *Sterrha*, Hübner, which is adopted by some authors for the Acidaliid *ochraria*.   There is, however, considerable doubt among authorities about accepting the Hübnerian genus, but Herrich-Schäffer's genus *Sterrha* appears to be valid and is here employed. If it has to give way, *Pseudosterrha*, Warren, or *Rhodometra*, Meyrick, may have to be used.

Lythria purpuraria has long been reported as a British species, but there does not appear to be any very convincing record of its capture in the British Isles. It is widely distributed in Europe, and generally common. As it is a sun-loving insect, it could hardly escape detection if it occurred in any part of our isles. A note by Mr. V. R. Perkins, in *The Zoologist* for 1861, p. 7449, should, however, not be overlooked. This refers to the capture, on June 18th, of two male specimens that were disturbed from broom, "not far from the city of Perth, by Mr. D. P. Morrison."

Lead Belle (*Ortholitha plumbaria*).

Two ordinary examples of this species are shown on Plate 54, Figs. 4, 5. The ground colour is greyish, ranging in one direction to whitish, and in the other to brownish ; on the fore wings there are three cross lines, usually reddish-brown in colour, but sometimes dark brown inclining to blackish ; the first of these lines is always slender and sometimes very indistinct ; the second is often shaded on its outer edge, and the third on its inner edge, with brownish ; occasionally the space between the second and third is more or less dusky, especially on the lower half ; sometimes these two lines approach each other very closely on the inner margin ; the short oblique streak from the tip of the wing to the wavy submarginal line, and also the blackish central dot, are far more distinct in some specimens than in others.

The long stick-like caterpillar is pale ochreous brown, often striped with darker brown or blackish. It feeds on furze (*Ulex*) and broom (*Cytisus*), from August to April. The moth is out in May and June, earlier or later according to the season, and is to be found almost everywhere that its food plants flourish.

The Mallow (*Ortholitha cervinata*).

The fore wings of this species are normally ochreous brown, inclining to reddish, but sometimes the general colour is of a light chocolate tint, and in such specimens the slender white lines edging the dark markings, and the white wavy submarginal line, are more distinct ; the central band-like marking occasionally tapers towards the inner margin. (Plate 54, Figs. 6, 7.)

The long caterpillar (figured from a coloured drawing by Mr. A. Sich, Plate 52, Fig. 1) is of a greenish colour, inclining to yellowish between the rings ; there are indications of darker lines on the middle of the back and along the sides ; the usual dots are whitish and the spiracles black ; in some specimens the central line on the back is pinkish. It hatches from the egg in March or April, and feeds until June on mallow (*Malva sylvestris*) ; will also eat hollyhock.

The moth appears in September and October, and is sometimes seen in November. It hides under the mallow, and other plants around, and is not much inclined to move during the day, but it becomes active in the evening, and then flies pretty briskly. The occurrence of this species in any locality will, of course, largely depend upon the presence of the food plant, but it seems to be widely distributed throughout the greater part of the British Isles. It is, however, most frequent in the southern half of England.

Shaded Broad-bar (*Ortholitha limitata*).

To the earliest British entomologists this species (Plate 54, Figs. 8 and 9) was known by the English name given to it by Moses Harris, which is here revived. Haworth's popular name for the insect is the "Small Mallow," but this seems less suitable.

The fore wings are usually ochreous brown in colour, with a darker brown band, the inner area of which is often paler. The ground colour, however, varies considerably, in some examples tending to whity brown, and in others to a smoky hue. The whitish hind wings are generally more or less dusky clouded, chiefly from the base of the wing to the dark brown or blackish cross shade ; but sometimes these wings are entirely blackish, with just a trace of a pale cross stripe.

The caterpillar is greyish, with a pinkish tinge and black dots ; there are three lines along the back, the central one slaty blue, and the others ochreous, shaded on each side with

Pl. 54.

K 144.

1, 2. The Vestal.   3, 10. Oblique-striped.   4, 5. Lead Belle.
6, 7. Mallow.   8, 9. Shaded Broad-bar.   11, 12. Chalk Carpet.

1, 2. **Drab Looper.**   3. **Grey Carpet.**   4, 5. **Chimney Sweeper.**
6-8. **Treble-bar.**   9, 10. **Manchester Treble-bar.**

pale brown ; a pinkish irregular ridge runs low down along the sides. It feeds on clover, vetch, grass, etc., from September to June. (Plate 52, Fig. 2, after Hofmann.)

The moth is out in July and August, and is often common in fields and grassy places, generally throughout the greater part of the British Isles. In ancient times it was dubbed the " Aurelian's Plague." The range abroad extends to Amurland.

Ortholitha moeniata.—Except that one specimen was said to have been taken near Baron Wood, Carlisle, some years prior to 1855 ; and another, in 1866, near York ; there is no evidence that this species is an inhabitant of the British Isles.

Chalk Carpet (*Ortholitha bipunctaria*).

In this species (Plate 54, Figs. 11 and 12) the ground colour of the fore wings is white (inclining to bluish-white in some specimens), more or less stippled and scored with greyish brown ; the cross band is darker grey brown, and there are two black dots placed :-wise (sometimes united) in the paler central space of the band. Hind wings, smoky grey, with a darker shade across the middle, and a pale one parallel with the outer margin. In some rare instances, the ground colour of the fore wings is entirely white, and the band exceedingly dark ; but specimens with the general colour, slaty-black and the band and basal patch grey, are extremely rare ; Barrett mentions one such example, from Box Hill, Surrey, in Mr. R. Adkin's collection.

The caterpillar is whity brown, more or less tinged with pink, dotted with black, and lined with grey along the back, the sides, and the under surface. It feeds, at night, on clover and trefoils, from September to June. (Plate 52, Fig. 3, after Hofmann.) The moth is out in July and August, and in suitable localities, such as chalk downs, lime-stone hills, etc., is generally plentiful throughout England and South Wales. It does not appear to have been noted in Ireland, or in Scotland, except that it has been recorded from the Isle of Arran.

Oblique Striped (*Mesotype virgata*).

The sexes of this species are shown on Plate 54, Figs. 3 ♂, 10 ♀. The fore wings are greyish, inclining to whitish or to brownish, with two white-edged oblique bands, which in the lighter coloured specimens are broad and show up conspicuously, but in the darker are narrower and much less distinct.

The caterpillar is brownish, but varies in tint, in some cases inclining to pink; there are three lines along the back, the central one dark green or brown, and the others more or less yellowish; a blackish or dark grey line low down along the sides. It feeds on yellow bedstraw (*Galium verum*), and may be reared on other kinds of *Galium*. There are two broods, one in May and June, and the other in August and September.

The moth, which frequents sand-hills and shelving banks by the seaside, is found resting upon its food plant or other vegetation around, in May and June, and again in July and August.

The species has a wide distribution, and occurs in suitable localities around the coasts of England (except the north-east), and on the west coast of Wales. It also inhabits the Breck sand district of Norfolk and Suffolk, and has been found on chalk downs and hills in the south of England, and in Cambridgeshire and Berkshire. In Ireland, it has been recorded from the counties of Down and Kerry.

Abroad, its distribution spreads to Eastern Siberia and Amurland.

Drab Looper (*Minoa murinata*).

The grey brown or ochreous brown wings of this delicate, but unattractive little moth (Plate 55, Figs. 1 and 2), are silky in texture. After it has flown for a time, the wings become paler, and lose most of their sheen.

The thick-set, roughish caterpillar is reddish brown, dotted with pale ochreous; there is a slender white line along the middle of the back, and black oblique streaks on the sides; a blackish wavy line along the area of the spiracles is bordered below with yellowish. It feeds on wood spurge (*Euphorbia amygdaloides*) and also, I have reason to believe, on petty spurge (*F. peplus*), a rather common weed in some gardens, from July to September. In forward seasons the moth, which flies in the sunshine, has been noted in late April, but May and June are the best months for it. In the New Forest, and else-where, it has occurred in August. On one occasion I remember that, in a garden at Brockenhurst, several specimens were taken in the autumn, and it was supposed that they resulted from eggs laid by a damaged female that had been captured in the woods and turned out into said garden. It has been taken at gas lamps, at Dorking among other places.

The species has been recorded from Pembrokeshire, Glamorganshire, and Monmouth, in South Wales; and it appears to be found in most of the counties of England southwards from Worcester, Hereford, Gloucester, Oxford, and Bucks. Except that it has been doubtfully recorded from Stowmarket, Suffolk, it does not seem to be found in the eastern counties; and I cannot find that it has been noted from Devon or Cornwall.

The range abroad extends to Amurland.

Chimney-sweeper (*Odezia atrata*).

This white-tipped but otherwise plain black moth (Plate 55, Figs. 4 ♂, 5 ♀) is very constant, and except that specimens after having been on the wing for a day or two become sooty brown, there is nothing much to note. It is the fringe at the tip of the

fore wings rather than the tip itself that is white, and this
sometimes extends for a short distance along the fringe of the
outer margin. Haworth's English name for this insect (his
chærophyllata) was "The Looping Chimney Sweeper" in
reference to its caterpillar, and to distinguish it from his
"Chimney Sweeper," "Chimney Sweeper's Boy," and other
oddities in the vernacular among the Psychids.

The caterpillar, which feeds in the spring on flowers of the
earth-nut (*Conopodium denudatum*, or *Bunium flexuosum*), is
green, and paler on the sides than on the back; there are three
darker green lines along the back, the central one merging into
reddish on the last ring, and the others narrowly edged on each
side with white; a whitish stripe runs below the red spiracles.

The moth is a sun lover, and flits about flowers growing
among or near its food plant, in June and July.

The species is widely distributed over England, Wales,
Ireland, and Scotland, but it does not appear to have been
noted north of Moray in the last-named country. It is always
very local, frequents moist fields, borders of woods, and even
waysides.

The range abroad extends to Amurland.

The Grey Carpet (*Lithostege griseata*).

The more or less greyish moth, shown on Plate 55, Fig. 3,
varies in tint, some specimens being decidedly more grey than
others. At the apex of the fore wings is a short blackish dash,
and from this a curved dusky line may be traced to the inner
margin. The female has the wings rather shorter than those of
the male.

The slender, dark-lined, greenish caterpillar feeds on the
seed pods of flixweed (*Sisymbrium*), and treacle mustard
(*Erysimum*), in July and August. When reared in captivity
it will thrive on other kinds of Cruciferæ.

The moth is out in June, sometimes late May; it is exceedingly local in Britain, and only occurs in the Breck district, where it was first met with about fifty years ago. Tuddenham, in Suffolk, is a noted locality, as also is Thetford, in Norfolk.

The Treble-bar (*Anaitis plagiata*).

This is a greyish white species, of which specimens of both generations are shown on Plate 55, Figs. 6 ♂, 7 ♀ (1st generation), Fig. 8 ♂ (2nd generation). The chief variation is in the cross central bars of the fore wings, which are sometimes much widened, and occasionally joined from the middle to the inner margin; or the space between these two bars is more or less filled up with dark grey. On the other hand, the bars are sometimes very faint, but such aberrations are perhaps most frequent in the second generation, which consists of smaller specimens.

The long caterpillar is brown, inclining to reddish or to greenish, with several darker and paler lines on the back and a yellowish line low down along the sides. It feeds on St. John's wort (*Hypericum*) in June and July; the caterpillars, hatching in the autumn, are not mature until the following April.

Usually there are two generations of the moth, the first appearing in May and June, and the second in August and September. The species is pretty generally distributed over the British Isles, extending to the Hebrides and the Orkneys; and will probably be found in all localities where its food plant occurs freely. It affects cliffs and sandhills by the sea, rough places on chalk slopes, and sometimes the moths fly up in numbers as we walk over the herbage in such spots.

The range abroad extends to Western India and Japan.

Manchester Treble-bar (*Carsia paludata*).

In general character this species somewhat resembles that last considered. It is, however, much smaller, and there are reddish clouds on the outer marginal area.

This reddish shading is more or less absent in the type, which is otherwise less variegated than var. *imbutata*, the form to which our British specimens are almost entirely referable. (Plate 55, Figs. 9 and 10.)

The caterpillar is of somewhat stoutish build, and reddish brown in colour ; three darker lines along the back, and yellow stripe low down along the sides, the latter edged above with black on the front three rings, and blotched with pinkish on the middle rings ; the head is rather paler than the body, and the dots on the latter are yellow. It feeds on cowberry (*Vaccinium vitis-idæa*) and cranberry (*V. oxycoccos*), and seems to have a preference for the flowers of these plants : April to June.

The moth is out in July and August among the *Vaccinium* in its swampy haunts on the heaths and moors of the north of England, and Scotland, even to the Shetlands. McArthur took a specimen in the Isle of Lewis in 1901. It also occurs in Ireland. In England it does not seem to have been noted south of Staffordshire.

The range abroad extends to Eastern Siberia and Amurland.

The Streak (*Chesias spartiata*).

The most striking features of this shining brownish coloured species are the oval-shaped marks on the disk of the fore wings, and the long whitish streak running to the tips of the wings. (Plate 57, Figs. 3 ♂, 4 ♀.)

The long caterpillar (Plate 56, Fig. 2) is deep green, with a darker line along the middle of the back, and whitish lines

2 *a*

1 *a*

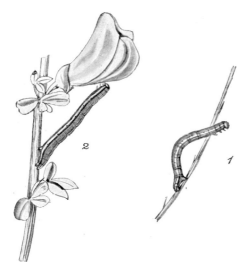

2

1

Pl. 56

1, 1*a*. **Broom-tip**: *caterpillar and chrysalis*.
2, 2*a*. **Streak**: *egg (enlarged) and caterpillar*.

1, 2. The Broom-tip.   3, 4. The Streak.   5, 6. Barred Tooth-striped.
7, 8. Early Tooth-striped.   9, 10. The Seraphim.

along the sides and the under surface ; the spiracles are reddish, encircled with black, and the head is flecked with brown. It feeds in the spring on broom (*Cytisus scoparius*).

The moth is out in September and October, and secretes itself during the day, but may be found at night flying about the broom bushes for a short time, and later on it sits upon the twigs. It occurs in almost every part of the British Isles where the food plant of the caterpillar is well established.

Broom-tip (*Chesias rufata*).

A noticeable character in this glossy, greyish moth (Plate 57, Figs. 1 ♂, 2 ♀) is the black mark on the upper part of the second cross line of the fore wings (which probably suggested the English name " Chevron " given to the species by Donovan) ; following the mark is a reddish or ochreous flush, extending to the tips of the wings.

The long, green caterpillar inclines to bluish above, and to paler green beneath ; a darker line along the middle of the back, then a slender whitish line edged with darker green, and between this and the white spiracular line there is another slender whitish line. It feeds, in August and September, on broom ; when full grown it enters the earth, and there turns to a reddish brown chrysalis, the wing cases of which are greenish. I am indebted to Mr. A. J. Scollick for the caterpillar and chrysalis figured on Plate 56, Figs. 1, 1a.

The moth emerges the following year, from May to July, but its time of appearance is uncertain, and it may come up in early spring or not until early autumn. Sometimes it will remain in the chrysalis for two winters.

In England the species occurs in the counties of Kent, Surrey, Sussex, Berks, Hants, Devon, Somerset, Hereford, Worcester, Stafford, Leicester, Cheshire (rare in the last five), Cumberland and Yorkshire (recorded once from each county),

Norfolk, Suffolk; also Glamorgan, and other parts of South Wales. In Scotland it is found in the south, but is more frequent from Perthshire to Moray. Probably occurs in other British localities where there is plenty of broom.

The Barred Tooth-striped (*Lobophora* (*Trichopteryx*) *polycommata*).

The general colour of the species represented on Plate 57, Figs. 5 ♂, 6 ♀, is greyish, inclining to ochreous or to whitish; but occasionally it is clouded with dark greyish on the basal area, and there is a broad band of the same colour on the outer marginal area; in such specimens the central band becomes less conspicuous.

The caterpillar (Plate 59, Fig. 2) feeds in May and June, on privet, at first on the leaf buds, and afterwards on the expanded leaves. It will also eat ash and honeysuckle. In colour it is rather deep green, with three fine lines along the back, the central one darker than the ground colour, and the others whitish and irregular; a whitish stripe low down along the sides; two points on the last ring of the body. The chrysalis (Plate 59, Fig. 2a), which is enclosed in an oval earthen cocoon, is dark yellowish brown, inclining to blackish on the wing cases.

The moth may be found at night, in March and April, sitting on the privet hedge, and may then be easily boxed, as it seems very disinclined to fly at that time, but earlier in the evening it flits along the hedgerows, and is equally easy to net. When resting, however, one is able to select just the finest specimens.

The species appears to be very local in Britain, but it occurs in the Brighton, Lewes, and Emsworth districts of Sussex; Hants, Wilts (Salisbury), Somerset, Devon (Sidmouth), Gloucestershire, Herefordshire, Worcestershire (Malvern),

North Lancashire, Cumberland, Northampton, Berks, Essex, and Kent. In Scotland it has been reported from Clydesdale and Arran, but has not been noted from Ireland.

The Early Tooth-striped (*Lobophora* (*Trichopteryx*) *carpinata*).

The whitish fore wings of this species are tinged with grey or greenish grey, the cross lines and bands vary in intensity, and, as a rule, are more distinct and complete in the female than in the male. A form of not infrequent occurrence in Scotland (ab. *fasciata*, Prout) has blackish bands, which show up in strong contrast with the general whitish colour of the wings. The ordinary form is represented on Plate 57, Fig. 7 ♂, and Fig. 8 on the same plate shows the named variety referred to.

The caterpillar is green, with rather darker lines along the back, and a yellow stripe low down along the sides; the two points on the last ring are also yellow. It feeds, in June and July, on honeysuckle, sallow, birch, and alder. The moth is out in April and May, and seems to be more or less common in woodlands throughout the greater part of the British Isles. In Scotland it appears to be most plentiful from Perthshire northwards to Sutherlandshire, but it has not been reported from the Orkneys, Shetlands, or Hebrides. (Early stages are shown on Plate 59, Figs. 3–3*b*.)

The boles of trees are favourite resting places, and upon them, and also upon gate-posts, etc., the moth is often met with in the daytime.

Abroad, the range extends to Eastern Siberia.

Yellow-barred Brindle (*Lobophora* (*Trichopteryx*) *viretata*).

The general colour of the fore wings is olive green, varying from pale to dark, the wavy cross lines are blackish, dotted with black, and sometimes there are whitish lines between them ; those on the central area are often united by a blackish cloud, and so form a band, and not infrequently the basal area is also blackish marked. (Plate 58, Figs. 3 and 4.) The ground colour is very apt to fade if the insect is exposed to moisture of any kind, as, for instance, when pinned in a damp collecting box, but I have one bred specimen of a reddish ochreous colour, and I am assured that it was of this tint when it emerged from the chrysalis. An old English name was "The Brindle-barred Yellow."

The thick-set caterpillar is green, more or less tinged with pinkish ; three interrupted pink lines on the back, the central one sometimes inclining to purple, and broken up into spots ; the head is brown, sometimes marked with purplish, and there are two tiny points on the last ring of the body. It varies in the green tint and also in marking. It feeds on flowers and leaves of holly, ivy, dogwood, privet, etc., in June and July, and in some sheltered southern localities again in September and October.

The moth is out in May and early June, and where a second generation is developed, in August and early September. It sits in the daytime on tree-trunks, but more especially those with smooth bark ; the stems of holly are a favourite resting place, but at Box Hill I have occasionally seen a specimen on the trunk of a beech tree. Barrett states that it also rests on the trunks of fir trees, and that it is then very easily seen. Night is its time of activity, and it is then attracted by light.

The species seems to be widely distributed, but locally and not generally common, throughout England, Wales, and Ireland ; it has only been recorded from Rosemount, Ayr, and one or two other localities in the south of Scotland.

The range abroad extends to Western India, Amurland, and Japan.

1, 2. **Small Seraphim.**
5-7. **Northern Winter Moth.**

3, 4. **Yellow-barred Brindle.**
8-10. **The Winter Moth.**

1. **Northern Winter-moth:** *eggs.*
2, 2*a.* **Barred Tooth-striped:** *caterpillar and chrysalis.*
3, 3*a*; 3*b.* **Early Tooth-striped:** *eggs and caterpillar.*

The Seraphim (*Lobophora halterata*).

Fore wings whitish, with two greyish bands on the basal area; first and second lines greyish, variable in width, and sometimes only represented by marks on the front or inner margins; there is a black central dot, and the outer area beyond the submarginal line is clouded with dark grey, especially on the upper half. Sometimes the wings are so thickly stippled with the darker colour that they appear to be greyish, with interrupted and indistinct whitish cross lines. A rather frequent form has the fore wings tinged with ochreous, and of this tint is ab. *zonata*, Thnbg., which has the basal bands and outer marginal border blackish, the central area being without cross lines. (Plate 57, Figs. 9 ♂, and 10 ♀.)

The caterpillar is green, darker below and between the rings; the most distinct markings are two yellow lines along the back; head, notched; body wrinkled, and with two points on the last ring. It feeds on aspen, and other kinds of poplar, in June and July.

The moth appears in May, and continues out well into June, especially in its northern localities. It rests on the trunks of poplar trees, or on the stems of bushes around, and is sometimes easily alarmed, and flies off on the collector's approach, whilst at other times it sits quietly, and may be easily boxed. At dusk it may be seen flying around the poplars.

Widely distributed in the southern half of England, and only found where poplars, chiefly aspens, are well established. From Worcester its range extends northwards to Staffordshire, Leicestershire, Derbyshire, and Cheshire; and it has been recorded from Yorkshire and Cumberland; also from Glamorganshire, South Wales. In Scotland it seems not to have been noted in the south, but is found more or less frequently from Perthshire to Sutherlandshire. Rare in Ireland.

Abroad, its range extends to Amurland and Japan.

The Small Seraphim (*Lobophora* (*Mysticoptera*) *sexalisata*).

This is a much smaller species than the last. The fore wings are whitish, with brownish-grey, or blackish-grey, cross lines and bands ; the central most distinct towards the front margin, where it encloses a black dot ; hind wings greyish, with black central dot. (Plate 58, Figs. 1 and 2.)

The green, much wrinkled caterpillar has three whitish lines or stripes along the back, and in some examples there is a white line low down along the sides ; the head, which inclines to yellowish, is notched, and there are two pinkish points on the last ring of the body. It feeds on sallow in August and September.

The moth is to be found in May and June, and, in some years, again in July and August. It inhabits woods and hedgerows where sallow is plentiful, but, perhaps, is obtained more freely in fens. Occasionally it may be beaten from the hedges, but it is active on the wing just before the close of day, and then disports itself over and about the sallow bushes. It occurs in suitable localities in most of the eastern and southern counties of England, and has been reported from some of the northern ones, also from Glamorganshire, in South Wales, and from Perthshire in Scotland. Kane states that it has been found throughout Ireland, but is always local and scarce.

NOTE.—Prout considers this species to be the *sexalata* of Retzius (1783).

Winter Moth (*Cheimatobia brumata*).

In orchards and gardens wherein are fruit trees one may have noticed that the trunks of the trees have broad bands around them. If these bands are examined, they will be seen to be covered with a sticky compound, which has been put there for the purpose of trapping the almost wingless females of the Winter Moth, as they crawl up the tree after emergence from the chrysalis. In spite of such devices, and other precautionary measures taken to safeguard the trees from attack, the foliage of apple, pear, etc., will not be quite free from the caterpillars of this species in their season.

The male has greyish brown fore wings, which are crossed by rather darker lines, and a dark, more or less distinct, central band (ab. *hyemata*, Hufn). The ground colour is very much darker in some specimens than in others, and examples of a sooty brown colour are not infrequent; Barrett mentions an almost buff-coloured specimen. In the female, the tiny affairs representing wings are brownish, with indications of a darker band towards the outer margin of the front pair.

A small, purplish brown form, reared in January, 1882, from caterpillars found in Cumberland, feeding on sweet gale (*Myrica gale*), was described as a new species under the name *myricaria*, Cooke (*Entom.*, xv. 57). This has been referred by Staudinger to *C. boreata*, as a form of that species, but it is probably an aberration of *C. brumata*.

The caterpillar is green, with a stripe of darker green along the back; on each side of this are two white lines, and along the black spiracles is a pale yellowish line; head, green, sometimes marked with blackish. It feeds on the foliage of trees and bushes, and sometimes abounds in April and May.

The moth appears during the winter months, and has been noted as early as October and as late as February. (Plate 58, Figs. 8–10.)

Generally distributed throughout the British Isles.

Northern Winter Moth (*Cheimatobia boreata*).

This species is generally larger than the last-mentioned. The fore wings are marked somewhat as in that species, but they are paler in colour and more glossy; hind wings whitish and glossy. In the female, the wings are useless for flying, but still they are larger than those of *brumata*. The front pair have a blackish band. (Plate 58, Figs. 6 and 7 ♂, 5 ♀; ova. Plate 59, Fig. 1.)

The caterpillar is greenish, with a greyish stripe along the back, another edged above with yellow along the black spiracles, and a greyish line between the stripes; the head is black. It feeds, in May and June, on birch, and the moth does not appear until October or November.

At one time considered to be a purely northern species: the earliest known British specimens, four in number, having been captured at Petty Pool, Delamere, Cheshire, on October 31, 1848. It is now known, however, to have a wide distribution in the south of England. Northwards, its range extends throughout England and Scotland up to Moray. It is found in South Wales; also in Galway, Monaghan, and Connemara, in Ireland.

The Tissue (*Triphosa dubitata*).

The fore wings of this glossy species (Plate 60, Figs. 1, 2) are pale brown, tinged more or less strongly with rosy or purplish; there are numerous darker and paler cross lines, the most distinct and constant being the blackish basal, and the two forming the edges of the central band; the latter are marked with black; the submarginal line is whitish, wavy, and sometimes broken up into dots. The species varies considerably in tint, some specimens inclining to pale greyish brown, others to smoky brown. Hind wings, whitish grey, with several darker grey cross lines; in dark specimens these wings are smoky grey. Ab. *cinereata*, Stephens, is a small pale greyish form, almost without rosy tinge and with fewer cross lines.

The caterpillar (Plate 62, Fig. 1) is yellowish green with

darker green stripes and lines. In another form there are four pale yellowish lines along the back and a yellow stripe low down along the sides. It feeds on buckthorn (*Rhamnus*), the leaves of which it fastens together with silk, and so forms a retreat. It will also eat sloe and bird-cherry (*Prunus padus*).

The moth is out in August and through the autumn, when it sometimes visits the flowers of ivy, ragwort, etc. ; after hibernation it is again seen, perhaps even more frequently, in April and May, and is then occasionally found at sallow catkins. The species seems to have been noted from nearly all the English counties, but becomes rare from Yorkshire northwards. In Wales, and in Ireland, it is apparently widely distributed, but in Scotland it seems confined to southern localities, and is only rarely met with.

Abroad, the distribution spreads to Amurland, China, and Japan.

The Scarce Tissue (*Eucosmia* (*Calocalpe*) *certata*).

This species is very similar to the last, but the wings are not glossy, only reddish on the outer margin, and the black marked lines edging the central band of the fore wings are less irregular, the inner ones usually being much straighter. On the under side of the hind wings of the male is a fold enclosing hairs ; this is on the inner margin, just above the anal angle. (Plate 60, Fig. 3 ♀.)

The thickset caterpillar (Plate 62, Fig. 3, after Hofmann) is greyish inclining to greenish ; four white lines along the back, the central pair enclosing a dark line, the others are bordered below with dark greyish ; the black spiracles are set in yellowish blotches, and the plates on first and last rings are brown ; head, reddish-brown, glossy (adapted from Fenn). It feeds on the barberry (*Berberis vulgaris*) and the holly-leaved barberry (*B. aquifolium*) grown in gardens, in June and July. The moth is out in May and June, but in favourable seasons has appeared in late April. When on the wing at night it is freely attracted by light, but otherwise not often noticed. The species has occurred in many of the English counties from Devon to Durham, but it seems to be only common in the eastern counties, and most frequent perhaps in Suffolk. It has been recorded from South Wales, but is seemingly absent from Ireland.

The range abroad extends to Amurland.

The Scallop Shell (*Eucosmia undulata*).

Wings pale greyish, sometimes ochreous tinted, and crossed by numerous dark-grey wavy lines inclining to blackish on the front margin of the fore wings ; the waves of the central pair of lines on the fore wings often meet and so form a series of rings ; sometimes the space between the eighth and twelfth lines is of a dusky hue, and occasionally it is distinctly darker and band-like ; the outer margin of all the wings is brownish and traversed by a wavy white line. The male has tufts of blackish hair in a fold on the inner margin of the hind wing, this is noticeable on the upper side, but is best seen from the under side. (Plate 60, Figs. 4 ♂, 5 ♀.)

The somewhat dumpy caterpillar is reddish-brown with four yellowish lines along the back ; a greyish stripe along the sides, and a creamy stripe along the black spiracles ; head, pale brown and glossy. It feeds on sallow, aspen, and bilberry, and may be found from August throughout the autumn in spun-together leaves at the tips of the shoots. (Plate 62, Fig. 2.)

The moth is out in June and July, and occurs in woods where there is a good growth of bilberry, or in marshy spots where sallow bushes abound.

In England the species is widely distributed over the southern and eastern counties ; its range extends through the Midlands to Cheshire, Lancs., Cumberland and Westmorland, rarely in

1, 2. The Tissue.   3. Scarce Tissue.   4, 5. The Scallop Shell.
6. The Brown Scallop.   7, 8. The Dark Umber.

1. Netted Carpet.
2. Speckled Yellow, var.
3. Dotted Border Wave (ab. *circellata*).   4. Garden Carpet (ab. *costovata*).
5, 6. Yellow Shell, aberrant forms. 7 Tawny-barred Angle (ab. *nigrofulvata*).
8, 9. Broken-barred Carpet, Scottish form.

Lincoln and Yorks., and once recorded in Durham ; it occurs in Wales and in Scotland, but only in the more southern part of each country. It is not plentiful in Ireland, but widely distributed. The range abroad includes Amurland.

The Brown Scallop (*Scotosia vetulata*).

The male is always smaller than the female, and is noticeable for its long body with tuft of hairs at the extremity. The wings in both sexes are dingy brown, or greyish brown, and the usual lines on fore wings are blackish, the space between first and second often dusky. (Plate 60, Fig. 6.)

The caterpillar is short and stout, and in form very like that of the winter moth ; the back and a central dorsal stripe are black, the latter bordered with white, the sides are yellow ; the spiracular line is black, broken, and unconnected ; the spiracles are black ; the head is black, and the edge of the first ring of the body is yellow. (Crewe.) It feeds, in May and June, on purging buckthorn (*Rhamnus catharticus*), and is to be found between two or more leaves, which it spins together as a hiding place.

In June and July the moth may sometimes be obtained by beating bushes of buckthorn, or the herbage below and around ; this plan works best when operated just before dusk. As a British insect it is only found in England, and is most frequent in the southern and eastern counties, but widely distributed in the west to Worcester, and has been found in Lancashire, Westmorland, and Yorks. In the last-named county, caterpillars were obtained freely at Askham Bogs in 1900.

When Stephens wrote of this insect in 1831 he noted its occurrence "in a lane near Fulham." Even so recently as 1906 I obtained specimens on the Putney side of Wimbledon Common.

The range abroad extends to Eastern Siberia.

Series II.   **M**

The Dark Umber (*Scotosia rhamnata*).

The blackish oblique band on the fore wings of this ochreous brown species (Plate 60, Fig. 7 ♂, 8 ♀) is sometimes indicated only by the blackish lines, the space between them being hardly darker than the general colour. Sometimes all the wings are suffused with blackish brown, and in such specimens the only distinct marking is the whitish submarginal line.

The caterpillar is green, with three lines along the back, the central one dark green, and the others yellow ; the hind wings are marked with purple, and a stripe of the same colour runs along under the spiracles. In another form the general colour is greyish with a reddish-brown stripe along the back, and series of spots of the same colour along the sides. It may be found in May and June, concealed between leaves that it has fastened together to form a retreat.

The moth flies in late June and in July, and may be disturbed in the daytime from buckthorn bushes. It is widely distributed, and often common in the South of England, but is rare in the north ; and has also been recorded from South Wales.

NOTE.—This species has been referred to *transversata*, Hufnagel, and as this is an earlier name it may have to be adopted. According to Prout, both this and the preceding species should be placed in the genus *Philereme*, Hübner.

Small Phœnix (*Eustroma silaceata*).

In its typical form (Plate 63, Fig. 3) the blackish band of the fore wings is entire, but in ab. *insulata*, Haworth (Fig. 4), this band is interrupted by two whitish lines along the median veins, and so divided into three or four portions, the smaller section placed between the lines ; occasionally, the dividing lines assume stripe-like proportions, and the main portions are

1. **The Tissue :** *caterpillar.*
2. **Scallop Shell :** *caterpillar.*
3. **Scarce Tissue :** *caterpillar.*

1, 2. **The Phœnix.** 3, 4. **Small Phœnix.** 5-7. **The Chevron.**
8-10. **Northern Spinach.**

consequently smaller in size and further from each other, but one "island" still remains. In another form, the lower outer corner is distinctly separate from the costal portion; thus the band is broken into four parts.

The long caterpillar is green, with a reddish-brown stripe along the back; this is broken up into spots, except on the first three rings; there are some reddish-brown spots on the sides. It feeds on various kinds of willow herb (*Epilobium*), and enchanter's nightshade (*Circæa lutetiana*) in July, and sometimes in August and September.

The moth should be looked for in beech and other woods amongst the food plants, from which, and the surrounding herbage, it is readily evicted. It flies at twilight, and later on, when it has been known to visit the sugar patch; it is also attracted by light. It is out in May and June, and specimens of a second generation sometimes occur in the South. The species occurs locally throughout England, probably Wales, and in Scotland up to Ross. In Ireland, it is widely distributed and locally common in the North, but apparently not noted in the South.

Netted Carpet (*Eustroma* (*Lygris*) *reticulata*).

The white veins and white lines passing through the blackish blotches at the base and on the front margin of the fore wings, give these wings a curious netted appearance; the hind wings are smoky grey, with two white lines which appear to be continuations of the white second line and sub-marginal of the fore wings. (Plate 61, Fig. 1.)

The caterpillar is green, inclining to yellowish, and more or less tinged with pinkish, especially on the sides; three lines on the back, the central one reddish, the others whitish; a central line along the pinkish spiracles. It feeds at night on yellow balsam (*Impatiens noli-me-tangere*), preferring the flowers,

seeds, and young foliage, and rests by day on the undersides
of the leaves : September and October.   (Plate 64, Fig. 2, after
Hofmann.)

The moth is out in July and August, and, of course, will only
be found in localities where the balsam flourishes ; these are
very limited, and in Britain are confined to Westmorland and
the northern border of Lancashire, and North Wales. The
species was first introduced as British in 1861, when the late
Henry Doubleday recorded the capture of three specimens in
August, 1856, on the border of one of the lakes in Westmorland, by his friend the late Thomas H. Allis. It seems that
other specimens had been taken at the same time, but these
passed into collections as the "second brood of *silacearia*."
The caterpillar is said to have been found in North Wales, but
has been more frequently obtained in the English Lake District.

The range abroad extends to Eastern Siberia, Amurland,
Corea, and Japan ; but in the three last-named countries it is
chiefly represented by var. *ærosa*, Butt., a large form.

The Phœnix (*Lygris prunata*).

The English name here retained was given to this species
(Plate 63, Figs. 1 ♂, 2 ♀) by Harris, in 1775, but in 1782 he
changed it to " Clouded Carpet."

In ground colour the fore wings are pale brown, more or less
clouded with darker brown, or with reddish-brown ; the basal
patch, central band, and blotch on outer margin below the tip
of the wing, are all chocolate brown clouded with blackish and
edged with white. Hind wings, whitish, suffused with smoky
grey, except on front area ; three dusky whitish-edged wavy
lines, inclining to blackish on the inner margin. The egg
(Plate 67, Fig. 3) is yellowish when laid, and then changes to
purplish with a whitish bloom.

The caterpillar is green, varying to brownish ; along the

middle of the back is a series of purplish-edged, brown-centred, whitish, triangular markings ; the third ring is swollen, and has a black collar. It feeds at night on the foliage of red and black currant, also on gooseberry, and may be found in April and May, earlier or later according to season, sitting by day upon the bushes.

The moth flies in July and August, and occurs in gardens, but is said to be partial to sloe bushes and hedges. It is always more or less local, although it is distributed over the greater part of the British Isles.

This species occurs in the Northern United States of America.

The Chevron (*Lygris testata*).

The fore wings of this rather variable species (Plate 63, Figs. 5-7) are yellowish or reddish grey, with a darker basal patch and central band ; a reddish blotch below the tip of the wing is edged with white, and the central band is also outwardly edged with white. Hind wings, whitish, with two lines, and dusky hind marginal border, the latter sometimes inclining to reddish. Occasionally, the fore wings are entirely pale ochreous, and the basal patch and the central band only very slightly darker, but the limiting lines are reddish, and the patch under the tip of the wing is bright orange red. Var. *insulicola*, Staud., from the isles of Scotland, has the fore wings rather narrower, and suffused with purplish brown or deep violet grey ; the hind wings are smoky grey. The female is usually smaller than the male, and often more yellow in colour.

Eggs, whitish brown, mottled with darker. The early stages are shown on Plate 67, Figs. 2-2*b*.

The long caterpillar is pale yellowish brown, with three lines along the back, the central one dark brown, and most distinct at each end ; the others are white, irregularly shaded above with reddish ; another white line along the region of the spiracles. It feeds, in May or June (earlier or later in some seasons), on sallow and birch. The moth is out in July and August, and frequents heaths and bogs more especially, but is also found in or around woods, and I have captured male specimens as they flew along hedgerows bordering fields, at dusk, in Middlesex. The female is rarely seen on the wing.

The species, which ranges through Central and Northern Europe to the Ural and Altai, is generally distributed throughout the British Isles ; it is found also in the Atlantic States of America.

Northern Spinach (*Lygris populata*).

The fore wings are yellow, with a reddish or purplish-brown basal patch, central band, and small patch on outer margin below tip of the wing, the central band more or less clouded or mottled with yellow. Hind wings, whitish, tinged with yellow. The female is usually smaller, the colour generally paler, and the markings frequently only represented by cross lines. Specimens from the Isle of Arran have the ground colour of fore wings more or less dappled with brown of the same tint as that of the central band and other markings ; the hind wings are tinged with a smoky hue. In other parts of Scotland the brown colour becomes more and more general, until the fore wings are uniformly brown, and the hind wings dusky. On the mountains in the north nearly black specimens occur, and these seem to be referable to ab. *musauaria*, Freyer. (Plate 63, Figs. 8–10.)

The long caterpillar is variable in general colour, brown, mottled with greyish, pale grey, reddish brown, or yellowish green ; all have darker or whitish lines along the back, and whitish or pinkish triangles or X-marks. It feeds, in May and June (earlier in some localities, and later in others), on bilberry, crowberry, and sallow ; it may also be reared on willow.

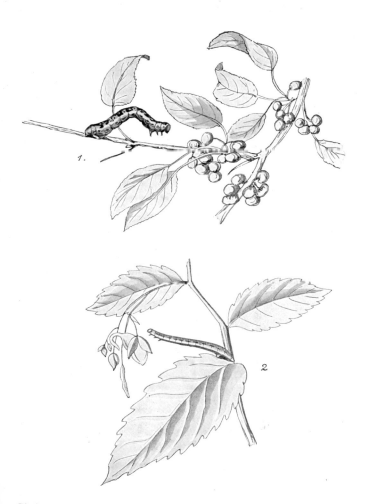

1. **Dark Umber**: *caterpillar.*
2. **Netted Carpet**: *caterpillar.*

1, 2. **The Spinach.**   3-5. **Barred Straw.**   6, 7. **Barred Yellow.**
8-10. **Broken-barred Carpet.**

The moth is out in July and August, and may be found on the leaves and among the sprays of *Vaccinium myrtillus* growing in woodlands (especially the more ancient), bogs, and moorlands.

The species is widely spread, and generally abundant in suitable districts, over the greater part of the British Isles ; but it seems to be more or less casual in England south of the Midlands, although its range runs through Gloucestershire and Somerset into Devon. In the last-named county it sometimes swarms at Martinhoe, on the edge of Exmoor.

The distribution abroad includes Eastern Siberia, Amurland, Labrador, and North America.

The Spinach (*Lygris associata*).

The fore wings are pale ochreous, more or less clouded with darker ; three brownish cross lines. Hind wings, paler, with indication of cross lines on the inner margin. Fringes of all the wings chequered with brown, most distinct on the fore wings. (Plate 65, Figs. 1, 2.)

The long caterpillar is green, inclining to yellowish ; three lines along the back, the central one dark green and the others whitish ; there is also a whitish line low down along the sides. It feeds at night, in May and June, on currant (*Ribes rubrum* and *R. nigrum*), and may be found on the underside of a leaf in the daytime. (Figured on Plate 67, Fig. 1, from a coloured drawing by Mr. A. Sich.)

During July and August the moth flies in the evening, and after dark it often comes to any bright illumination. It is essentially a garden insect, and where currant bushes are there also spinach is often grown ; hence it was probably connected with the vegetable rather than the fruit when Haworth named it *spinachiata*. The species seems to be found more or less frequently in suitable spots through England. In Wales it has

been recorded from Glamorganshire, and from Rhyl, Flintshire; in Scotland, Renton states that it is common in Roxburgh
gardens; and it is also noted from Paisley. It has been
doubtfully recorded from Ireland.

The range abroad extends to Amurland.

Barred Straw (*Cidaria pyraliata*).

In certain respects this species (Plate 65, Figs. 3–5) is not
unlike that last referred to. The fore wings are yellowish straw-
colour, the cross lines are brownish, but the central two are
closer together, especially on the inner margin, than they are
in *associata*, and are straightly oblique from the angle, or elbow,
below the front margin; there is often a line of brownish dots
between the second line and the outer margin, and the fringes are
brown, not chequered. Occasionally there are darker clouds
on the second line, at the angle, and such clouds sometimes
appear in the central space. Not infrequently the markings
are very faint. Staudinger and others refer this species to
dotata, L., but there seems to be some doubt in the matter.

The caterpillar feeds, in April and May, on the common
cleavers or goose-grass (*Galium aparine*) of our hedgerows,
etc., but it also eats *G. mollugo* and other kinds of bedstraw.
It is to be found low down on the stems.

The moth may be disturbed from the herbage along hedges
and ditches in lanes, and the borders of woods, but it seems
most partial to the former.

The species is generally distributed, and often plentiful, in
the southern half of England; but although widely spread
in the northern half, it is only common locally. It occurs in
Wales, both North and South; is common in Roxburghshire
and Clydesdale, and is said to be found on the Aberdeenshire
coast and in West Ross. In Ireland it is widely distributed,

and sometimes abundant; but more frequent on the coast than inland.

The distribution abroad includes Eastern Siberia and Amurland.

Barred Yellow (*Cidaria fulvata*).

This very pretty, and most distinct, little species (Plate 65, Figs. 6, 7) does not vary very greatly; there is certainly some modification in the general colour, and in that of the markings, but in both it is only a matter of tint.

The caterpillar is somewhat wrinkled, and in colour is green, with three greyish lines along the back, the central one double; the ring divisions are yellow, and there is a yellow line low down along the sides. It feeds at night, in May and June, on the leaves of wild rose, and does not object to the garden kinds. (Plate 69, Fig. 3, after Hofmann.)

The moth is out in June and July. It hides by day under leaves in hedges, and although not often induced to get on the wing at that time, the male commences its evening flight at an early hour. It is generally a common species in England and Wales; it occurs here and there through Scotland, up to the Orkneys; and although somewhat local, it is common enough, where found, in Ireland.

Broken-barred Carpet (*Cidaria corylata*).

The fore wings have an olive-brown basal patch and central band, both are edged with white, wavy lines, and the band is contracted below the middle (Plate 65, Fig. 9), and often broken at this point (Fig. 10); the inner marginal portion sometimes very small; the space between the basal patch and central band is pale brown, and so also is the outer marginal area; but there are dark clouds and white marks beyond the white wavy submarginal line.   Variable in tint and in marking, the variety generally known as *albocrenata*, Curtis (Plate 65, Fig. 8), is perhaps most frequent in Perthshire and Sutherland. Two other examples of the Scottish form, which Staudinger has named *effusaria*, are depicted on Plate 61, Figs. 8, 9.

The caterpillar is green, inclining to yellowish ; three stripes on the back, the central one reddish brown and broad, but only distinct at each end, the other paler green ; spiracles, white, placed in a reddish-brown stripe, which is sometimes broken up.   It feeds on sloe, birch, oak, and the foliage of other trees, and may be found from July to September, and even later.

The moth is out in May and June, and is to be beaten from hedges, or may be found at rest on tree-trunks, palings, etc.

Generally distributed, but not extending to the Scottish Isles.

Abroad, the range spreads to Amurland and Japan.

Common Marbled Carpet (*Cidaria truncata*).

Six examples of this very variable species are shown on Plate 66, and these have been selected to illustrate the more important forms.   There are a number of modifications of each of the forms, and several of these have been named. Fig. 1 of our plate represents the typical form, and this is Haworth's *centumnotata* (Common Marbled Carpet) ; Fig. 2 is ab. *commanotata* of Haworth (Yellow Marbled Carpet) ; Fig. 3 is ab. *perfuscata*, Haworth (The Brown Marbled Carpet), and Fig. 4 is a modification of the same form.   A specimen from Arran is shown in Fig. 5 ; this example agrees fairly well with that figured in Wood's *Index* as *concinnata* from Arran. In his description of the form, Stephens does not mention fulvous bands in his type.   Fig. 6 shows a specimen from Stornoway, Isle of Lewis, which appears to be a modification of

1-6. **Common Marbled Carpet.** 7-12. **Dark Marbled Carpet.**

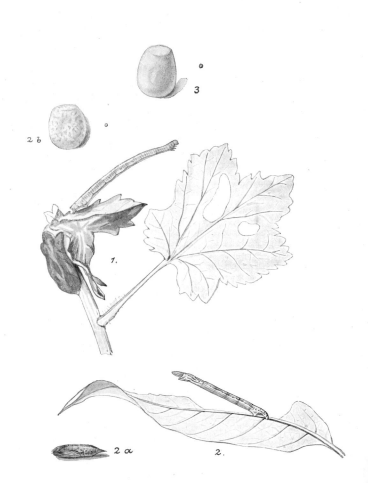

2 Pl. 57.

M 171.

1. Spinach : *caterpillar.*
2, 2a, 2b. Chevron : *eggs, caterpillar and chrysalis.*
3. Phœnix : *eggs.*

the typical form of *truncata*, but it has some of the character of *concinnata*. The latter, it may be mentioned, is considered by Mr. L. B. Prout to be a distinct species, and as the genitalia have been found, on examination by Mr. Pierce, to differ from these organs in *truncata* and *immanata*, there seems to be reason to accept it as such.

The caterpillar is long, slender, and wrinkled, especially on the sides ; the ground colour is green, inclining to yellowish ; three lines along the back, the central one dark green, and the others yellowish ; sometimes a rosy stripe, or a series of dashes along the sides ; the points on the last ring are green, or rosy. It feeds, in the autumn and again in the spring after hibernation, on sallow, birch, hawthorn, bilberry, wild strawberry, etc. It will also eat rose, but as the specimens resulting from caterpillars reared on rose are frequently small, such food is probably unsuitable ; garden strawberry, on the other hand, is an excellent pabulum. A photograph of the caterpillar by Mr. H. Main is shown on Plate 69, Fig. 1. There is a second brood in late June and in July. The first generation of the moth is out in May and June, and the second emerges in the autumn ; specimens, possibly of a third generation, have been seen in December in favourable localities.

The species, which frequents woods and hedgerows, and is pretty generally common, is to be found almost everywhere throughout the British Isles. It has not, however, been noted from Shetland.

The distribution abroad extends to Amurland, China, and Japan.

Dark Marbled Carpet (*Cidaria immanata*).

This is another exceedingly variable species (Plate 66), and here again six examples have been chosen to illustrate something of the range of aberration. Figs. 7 and 8 are of the typical form, and Figs. 9 and 10 show the form *marmorata*, Haworth (Marbled Carpet); while Figs. 11 and 12 represent specimens from Shetland, and are referable to the island race known as *pythonissata*, Millière; neither of the specimens figured, however, quite agrees with the type of this form, but Fig. 12 does so fairly well. In some specimens the general colour of the fore wings is tawny or rust-colour, or they are strongly suffused with that tint (ab. *ferruginea*, Prout). I have such examples in my series of specimens from Lewes and the Shetlands. Ab. *thingvallata*, Staud., from Iceland, has the fore wings white, with black basal patch and central band, and I have seen at least one example from Yorkshire that closely approached this variety.

The caterpillar is not very unlike that of the last species, but it is rounder in appearance, the general green colour is paler, and the points on the last ring are blunt. It feeds from April to June on sallow, birch, bilberry, and wild strawberry. (Plate 69, Fig. 2, after Hofmann.) The moths are out in July and August, and may be found resting on tree-trunks, rocks, or stone walls; at night, when it is active on the wing, it is said to be often seen in numbers on the flowers of the rush, and this habit has been noted more particularly in Scotland.

The species affects woods and moors, and appears to be found more or less commonly throughout the British Isles.

Marsh Carpet (*Cidaria sagittata*).

The fore wings of this very distinct species are brown, with white-edged black bands at base and across the central area, the latter with a strong projection on its outer edge, almost reaching a white spot on the outer margin; sub-marginal line whitish, often only traceable on the front edge. The central band is always narrowed below the middle, sometimes divided, and occasionally this part of the band is finely cut off from both upper and lower portions. (Plate 68, Figs. 7, 8.)

The caterpillar is yellowish green, merging into pinkish on the sides ; the pink is edged below with black, and this is followed by a dark olive stripe ; rings 1–3 and 10–12 are wrinkled, whilst all the others are ridged across the back and along the sides. It feeds, in August and September, on the unripe seeds of meadow-rue (*Thalictrum flavum*), also on *T. minus,* and, according to Barrett, on old withered leaves of columbine.

The moth is out in July, occasionally at the end of June, and occurs locally in " Fenland."

Doubleday introduced it as British in the *Zoologist* for 1848. He there states, "A single example of this pretty species was obtained last season near Peterborough, but I believe it was not in very good condition. A splendid female was sent to me from the same neighbourhood this week (July 15, 1848)."

In 1853 and 1854 the species was discovered in the fens of Huntingdonshire and Cambridgeshire. Later it was found to inhabit the fens of Norfolk and Suffolk. It is still obtained in the Cambridge fens from Bottisham to Chatteris. Outside " Fenland " it has been recorded from Worcestershire (Bewdley Forest) and Warwickshire (Rugby).

The range abroad extends to Amurland.

Red-green Carpet (*Cidaria siterata*).

The general colour of the fore wings of this species (Plate 68, Figs. 1–4) is greyish green, with more or less of rosy suffusion ; the basal patch and central band are darker green, and the latter is outwardly edged with whitish below the front margin, and towards the inner margin. The female has rather more ample wings, and is generally of a darker hue, but in both sexes the basal patch and central band are blackish ; the hind wings are dark greyish brown, inclining to blackish in some females, and there is a blackish central dot and two or three curved lines.

The long caterpillar is yellowish green, with an interrupted red line along the middle of the back; two green points on last ring are usually pink-tipped. It feeds on oak, birch, ash, sloe, apple, etc., in July and August.

The moth occurs in woodlands, but is not easily disturbed in the daytime from its lurking-place in bush or tree. In the autumn it may be found at ivy-bloom, and in the spring, after hibernation, has been taken at sallow.

The species appears to be widely distributed over England and Wales, Scotland up to Moray, and Ireland.

Autumn Green Carpet (*Cidaria miata*).

Somewhat similar to the last, but the general colour of the fore wings is paler, inclining to whitish, and the basal patch and central band are pale green tinged with greyish; there is no rosy suffusion, but the wavy sub-marginal line is distinctly white. The hind wings are greyish white, with black discal dot, and dark-grey curved lines. (Plate 68, Figs. 5, 6.)

The caterpillar is pale green, inclining to yellowish, especially between the rings, and with a more or less distinct dark-green line along the middle of the back; the points on the last ring are pinkish brown, and there is a line of the same colour along the centre of the under surface of the body.

It feeds on alder, birch, oak, sallow etc., and may be beaten out from June to August.

The moth is out in September and October, when it may be obtained at ivy-bloom, and in the following spring, after hibernation, it visits sallow catkins.

The range in the British Isles agrees pretty closely with that of the last species, but in Scotland it extends to the Hebrides and to the Orkneys and Shetlands.

1-4. **Red-green Carpet.**   5, 6. **Autumn Green Carpet.**   7, 8. **Marsh Carpet.**

1. **Common Marbled Carpet:** *caterpillar.*
2. **Dark Marbled Carpet:** *caterpillar.*
3. **Barred Yellow:** *caterpillar.*

NOTE.—According to Prout, *sagittata* is not a *Cidaria*, as its larva is of a very different form; and *siterata* and *miata* are referred to *Chloroclysta*, Hübner.

Grey Pine Carpet (*Thera obeliscata*).

In its typical form, the fore wings of this species are greyish, and from this the colour ranges through various tints of greyish brown to smoky brown or blackish; sometimes these wings are shades of ochreous brown. The usual markings are a basal patch, more or less clearly defined, and a central band, and these may be either brown or blackish; the band varies in width, is not infrequently narrowed or contracted below the middle, occasionally broken at this point, and more rarely only represented by a small angular spot near the front margin.

Four examples are shown on Plate 70, and of these 1 and 2 represent our ordinary form *obeliscata*, Hübner (Shaded Broad Bar, of Newman). Fig. 6 is a blackish banded specimen of the *obeliscata* form, and Fig. 3 is the almost entirely blackish form *obliterata*, White (*scotica*, Staud.), which is not uncommon in the Paisley district, and other parts of Scotland, and also occurs in a modified form in some pine-woods in the South of England.

The long caterpillar (Plate 71, Fig. 1), which feeds on the needles of Scots pine in April and May, also in July, and sometimes in September, is bright green, with three whitish lines along the back, the central one broad, and a yellowish line low down along the sides; the green roundish head is lined with white.

The moth is generally common in pine-woods throughout the greater part of the British Isles. The May–June flight is the most abundant, but there is occasionally a good sprinkling of moths in the autumn.

Thera variata. This is now ascertained to be a distinct species. See Appendix.

Chestnut-coloured Carpet (*Thera cognata*).

This is a generally smaller species than that last referred to and it is more glossy in appearance. The fore wings are brown sometimes grey-brown, more or less tinged with reddish, and the basal patch and central band are darker; these markings are usually white-edged, and there is a wavy whitish sub-marginal line. Hind wings whitish, tinged with smoky grey. Specimens from the Hebrides are strongly purplish; and Kane states that some he reared from Sligo caterpillars are more richly coloured than any that he has seen from Scotland. (Plate 70, Figs. 9 ♂, 12 ♀.)

The bright green caterpillar is stouter than that of the last species. It is of a bluish hue along the back, and marked with three lines, the central one greenish and the others whitish and broad; there are sometimes reddish markings low down on the sides, just edging the broad white spiracular line. It feeds in May and June, earlier or later in some seasons, on juniper; it turns to a dark-green chrysalis in a frail cocoon spun up among the litter under the juniper bushes.

The moth is to be found in July and August among juniper growing in the hilly and maritime haunts of the species in North England, Wales, Scotland, and Ireland.

This species, long known as *simulata*, Hübner, has been referred to *cognata*, Thunberg, and as this is an earlier name it will have to be used.

Pine Carpet (*Thera firmata*).

The pale reddish-grey fore wings have a rather darker central band and round-edged basal patch, but the latter is often indistinct, and the band, which is always deeply indented about the middle of its inner edge, is sometimes not well defined.

1, 2, 3, 6. **Grey Pine Carpet.**   4, 5, 7, 8. **Juniper Carpet.**
9, 12. **Chestnut-coloured Carpet.**   10, 11. **Pine Carpet.**

1. **Grey Pine Carpet** : *caterpillar.*
2. **Pine Carpet** : *caterpilla*
3. **Welch Wave** : *caterpillar.*

The hind wings are whitish, tinged more or less with greyish or pale brownish, but always paler than in any form of *T. variata*, with which it is often confused. (Plate 70, Figs. 10, 11.)

The caterpillar is bluish-green above, and green beneath ; three lines along the back, the central one a darker tone of the ground colour, the others whitish ; head reddish, marked with brown on each cheek. It feeds in April and May (June in Scotland) on Scots pine ; Barrett states that there is a second brood in August. (Plate 71, Fig. 2.)

The moth is out in September and October, and may be disturbed from the pine boughs, or occasionally seen resting on the trunks, but it is more frequently met with at night when it flies naturally, and has been known to visit the sugar patch. Barrett, who considered this species to be double brooded, gives June and July for the first flight of moths. Certain it is that moths have been reared even as late as October from Spring caterpillars. As adverted to, the pale reddish forms of *T. variata* are sometimes confused with *T. firmata*, but in addition to other differences indicated above, it may be noted that in the male of the latter the antennæ are bipectinated except towards the tips. Most of the pine woods throughout England seem to produce this delicate insect more or less frequently ; the same remark applies to Wales. In Scotland it is found up to Aberdeen, and also in the Hebrides. The only localities mentioned by Kane for Ireland are in counties Westmeath, Dublin, and Fermanagh.

Juniper Carpet (*Thera juniperata*).

On Plate 70, Figs. 4 and 5 represent the sexes of the typical form of this species ; the small and rather more strongly marked Scottish form is shown by Figs. 7 and 8. In these small forms a noticeable character is the brownish band on the fore wings, between the central band and the outer margin ; this band is only indicated by a dusky greyish shade in the larger form. Most of the examples of the small form from the Isle of Hoy have also a dark central line on the hind wings. The central band of the fore wings is often broken below the middle, in both forms.

The caterpillar is yellowish green, inclining to a black tinge on the back, along which are three lines, the central one dark green, and the others yellow and rather broad ; a whitish stripe low down along the sides is sometimes marked with yellow and red, and there is a red thread above it ; head, pink tinged ; two points on last ring of the body. It feeds in July and August, on juniper. The moth is out in October and November, and may be found plentifully flying at night about the juniper bushes.

Berkshire, Kent, Surrey, and Sussex appear to be the only English counties in which it is established, and it is probably most plentiful in the last named. It has, however, been recorded from Suffolk, Lancashire, York, and Durham ; also from Carnarvonshire in North Wales. It is more widely spread throughout Scotland, including the Orkneys and Shetlands, where the moths fly in July. Only doubtfully reported from Ireland.

Water Carpet (*Lampropteryx suffumata*).

The fore wings are whitish, more or less clouded with brownish, with dark brown, inclining to blackish, basal patch and central band. The variation tends in two opposite directions ; in the one the general colour is so clouded and suffused with blackish-brown, that the entire fore wings become almost entirely of that colour (ab. *piceata*, Stephens), N. England and Scotland ; the other extreme is ab. *porrittii*, Robson, in which the central band and basal patch are black, and the white ground colour is almost free of brown clouding ; the last named occurs at

Huddersfield, Yorks., and a modification of it at Dover. On Plate 72, Fig. 1 shows the typical form, Fig. 3 ab. *piceata*, and 2 the Dover form. The caterpillar varies from greyish, with pinkish or greenish tinge, to ochreous brown ; the upper surface is rather darker than the under, and there is a series of dark V-shaped marks and arrow-heads on the back of rings 4-8 ; there is a whitish central stripe on 1-3, and a dark one on 9-12 ; head, brownish, marked with black. It feeds on goose-grass (*Galium aparine*), and other kinds of hedstraw, in May and early June. It seems to thrive best, however, on the goose-grass. (Plate 74, Fig. 1, after Hofmann.)

The moth may be found in weedy lanes and along hedge-rows, pretty well throughout England, Wales, Scotland to Moray, and Ireland. It cannot, however, be said to occur in all suitable places, as although it may be found in some plenty in one lane or hedgerow in a district, it may be quite absent in similar spots just around. Wherever it is noted one year it may be almost certainly obtained there in subsequent years. April and May are the months in which it is usually seen, but it has been taken in June in late seasons, and occasionally in July.

Large Twin-spot Carpet (*Coremia* (*Ochyria*) *quadrifasciaria*).

The ground colour of the fore wings of this species is most often of a pale reddish brown, but sometimes it inclines to grey brown ; the outwardly angled central band is often black, but more frequently perhaps the middle area is pretty much of the ground colour or greyish, with a black dot in the upper portion, and limited by two black lines which approach, or join, in the lower half. A dusky basal blotch is not always present, but it is sometimes well in evidence, as also is a dusky shade before the whitish submarginal line ; frequently there are two blackish or brownish dots on the upper part of this line, and a third dot above them, but nearer the outer margin. (Plate 72, Figs. 4, 5.)

The caterpillar is pale yellowish brown, finely freckled with grey, and with greyish V-shaped marks on the back; three greyish lines along the back, the central one broken, and the others most distinct at each end. It feeds on bedstraw (*Galium*) and other plants, such as primrose, groundsel, etc., from August to April. The moth is out in June and July, and should be looked for on tree-trunks growing around the borders of woods or in lanes near by. It may also be beaten out of hedgerows in the vicinity of woods.

A very local species and only found with us in the southern half of England. Its chief haunts appear to be in the counties of Kent, Surrey, Hants, Essex, Suffolk, Cambridge, and Norfolk (the Breck sand district); thence its range extends through Hertford, Buckingham, and Berkshire to Gloucester, where, however, it is scarce, as it is also in Lincoln. Abroad, the range extends to Eastern Siberia, Amurland, Corea and Japan.

Red Carpet (*Coremia* (*Ochyria*) *munitata*).

The typical form (Plate 72, Fig. 6) has pale greyish fore wings, and these are crossed by a black-edged purplish central band. In var. *hethlandica*, Prout (Fig. 7), the ground colour is ochreous and the band is reddish; this form is frequent in the Shetlands.

The caterpillar is yellowish green, with greyish clouds around white dots, tinged with pink between the rings; three lines along the back, the central one grey inclining to blackish, broken on three of the hinder rings, and edged with whitish; the others are double, wavy, brownish, a whitish stripe bordered above with grey along the area of the spiracles; head, ochreous, dotted with dark brown (adapted from Fenn). It

Pl. 72.

1-3. Water Carpet.   4, 5. Large Twin-spot Carpet.   6, 7. Red Carpet.
8-12. Red Twin-spot Carpet.

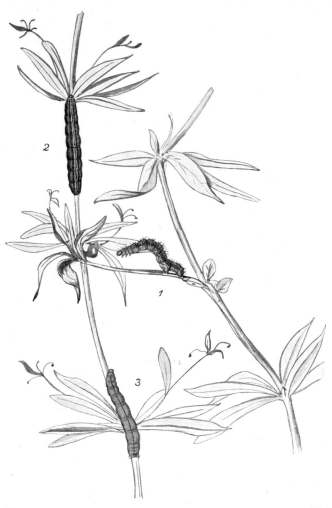

1. **Beech-green Carpet :** *caterpillar.*
2. **Striped Twin-spot Carpet :** *caterpillar*
3. **Mottled Grey :** *caterpillar.*

feeds on lady's mantle (*Alchemilla*), chickweed, groundsel, etc., from September to May.

The moth is out in July and August, and in England is only found in the mountain districts of Yorkshire and the more northern counties. It has been reported from the high-lying district on the border of Cheshire, between Macclesfield and Buxton (Day), and from Llantrissant, Glamorganshire, S. Wales (Evan John). Generally distributed through Scotland and the Isles. Widely spread, but local, and not always common, in Ireland.

Abroad, the range extends to Eastern Siberia, Amurland and North America.

Dark-barred Twin-spot Carpet (*Coremia* (*Ochyria*) *unidentaria*).

Portraits of three examples of this species will be found on Plate 75, Figs. 1–3. The ground colour of the fore wings is whitish tinged with pale ochreous or greyish; the central band is blackish with darker wavy lines running through it near the edges, and not infrequently the middle area is greyish, either on the upper half, or throughout from front to inner margins; a narrow patch at the base of the wings is of the same colour as the central band, and is followed by a reddish-brown streak; as a rule, there is an irregular reddish-brown line, commencing in a cloud on the front margin, and sometimes stripe-like, beyond the pale edging of the central band; in ab. *coarctata*, Prout, the central band is much narrowed; the two black dots on upper part of the outer margin, generally well in evidence, are occasionally united, but sometimes they are very tiny. The hind wings are whitish, more or less sprinkled with dusky scales, chiefly on the basal two thirds, and crossed by dark-grey wavy lines.

Sometimes the central band and the basal patch of the fore

wings are dull reddish-brown, inclining to purplish. This form which has been referred to *corculata*, Hufnagel, is pretty generally distributed abroad, but is apparently only of local occurrence in the British Isles.

The caterpillar is very similar to that of the next species, it feeds on the same kinds of plants, and during the same months of the year. (Plate 74, Fig. 2.) The first generation of moths is on the wing in May and June, and the second in August.

The species is widely distributed in England and Wales, often plentiful in some districts in the southern half of the former country, scarce and more local northwards from Yorkshire. Widely spread in Roxburghshire and Clydesdale in Scotland, but less frequent than *ferrugata;* this also seems to be the case in Ireland. The range abroad extends to North America.

NOTE.—It is to be regretted that the names by which this and the following species have been known for many years may have to be changed. It has been claimed that the reddish-banded form of *unidentaria*, Haworth, is indentical with *ferrugata* as figured by Clerck, *Icones*, Plate XI. Fig. 14, and is also referable to *corculata*, Hufnagel, both earlier names. If the red form referred to is adopted as the *ferrugata* of Clerck, then that name will supersede *unidentaria*, Haworth, and the species now known as *ferrugata*, Clerck, will become *spadicearia*. Authorities, however, are not agreed upon this point, so the question still remains open.

Red Twin-spot Carpet (*Coremia (Ochyria) ferrugata*).

Five examples of this variable species are shown on Plate 72, Figs. 8–12. The ground colour of the fore wings is usually greyish, more or less ochreous tinted, but sometimes inclining to whitish ; the basal patch and the central band are reddish brown, the latter usually entire in southern specimens, but frequently broken up (ab. *spadicearia*, Borkhausen), especially in northern examples. A bright, ochreous form, with the central band much streaked, occurring in Scotland, has been referred to ab. *salicaria*, Haworth. Occasionally the central band is dark purplish. The hind wings are whitish, more or less suffused with smoky grey, and lined with the same ; the outer margin is bordered with smoky grey.

The caterpillar is ochreous brown, mottled with greyish, and marked with pale diamonds and black spots on the back of the middle rings ; there are wavy lines along the sides. It feeds in June and July, and also in September and October, on various low plants : knotgrass, dandelion, bedstraw, garden marigold, and ground ivy (*Nepeta*) being especially useful in captivity. The moth is usually double-brooded, at least in the southern half of England, the first flight occurring in May and June, and the second in July and August.

The species is generally distributed, and often common, over the greater part of England and Wales, but somewhat local north of the Midlands and through Scotland to Aberdeen ; widely spread in Ireland.

Flame Carpet (*Coremia (Ochyria) designata*).

The ground colour of this rather common woodland species (Plate 75, Figs. 4–6) is pale grey, varying to whitish, or sometimes faintly brownish tinged. The purple band on the fore wings is always broadly edged in front with black, but the black outer edging is irregular, and sometimes only distinct towards the front margin of the wings ; it varies in width, and in tint, being, in some specimens, faint purplish grey.

The caterpillar is ochreous, inclining to greyish on the back, which is marked with whitish lines on the front rings, and with ochreous diamonds and black dots on the other rings ; there is also a row of black spots low down along the sides ; head, brownish, freckled with black. It feeds, in June and July, probably, in a wild state, on some kind of "cress," growing in the moister parts of woods ; in confinement, it will eat cabbage, horseradish, and wallflower, among other kinds of Cruciferæ. There is a second brood in August and September. (Plate 74, Fig. 3, after Hofmann.)

The moth is out in May and June, and again in August. It is fond of resting on tree-trunks in woods, especially where the ground is moist, but it may also be beaten out of hedges and bushes. It is most plentiful in the southern half of England, but is spread over the greater part of the British Isles, including the Orkneys.

Abroad, its range extends to Eastern Siberia, Amurland, Japan, and North America.

The Beech-Green Carpet (*Amoebe olivata*).

The species, depicted on Plate 75, Figs. 9, 10, when quite fresh has the fore wings greenish, and the central band more or less tinged with brown, in some specimens with blackish ; the inner edge of the band is not so clearly defined as the outer, the latter being followed by a narrow whitish wavy band ; a series of black dots edged with white represent the submarginal line. Hind wings, smoky grey, with a pale band beyond the middle, and a pale line nearer the outer margin.

The roughened caterpillar (Plate 73, Fig. 1) is ochreous brown, mottled with darker brown, and lined with grey ; the raised dots are black, each with a short bristle. It feeds at night on bedstraw (*Galium*), in the spring to May, after hibernation.

The moth is out, as a rule, in July and August, but sometimes much earlier. I reared specimens during the last week in May, 1907, from caterpillars sent from Torquay by Mr. Walker. It lurks among the vegetation growing on banks, and the hedge-rows of lanes, etc.

In the south of England the species chiefly affects the coasts of Dorset, Devon, and Cornwall; but it occurs locally in and around beech woods of Kent, and is more frequent in those of Berks, Oxford, and Bucks. From Somerset it spreads through the western counties, including part of Wales, to Lancashire. It is, however, most common among the hills and rills from Yorkshire northwards. In Scotland it is local in Roxburgh, widely distributed, and sometimes abundant in Clydesdale and throughout the Highlands to Sutherland. It has also been noted from Arran. Local in Ireland, but apparently abundant in some parts.

Green Carpet (*Amoebe viridaria*).

This species (Plate 75, Figs. 7, 8), also, has green fore wings, with a rather deeper green central band and basal patch. The former is limited by white lines marked with black, con-spicuously so on the front and inner margins; there are also black marks on the front edge of the basal patch, and at the tips of the wings. The green colour quickly fades to a yellowish or sandy tint.

The wrinkled caterpillar is olive brown, with bristle-bearing black dots; the back has a dark central line, and is adorned with reddish V-shaped marks except on the end rings. It feeds in the spring, after hibernation, on bedstraw (*Galium*), but it is said to eat sorrel, dead-nettle (*Lamium*), etc.

The moth is out in June, earlier in the south, and later in the north. It hides among herbage during the day, and may occasionally be seen resting on tree-trunks, etc., then flying just before dark about hedges, and on commons and heaths. Specimens have been noted in some years in September.

Except that it has not been detected in the Shetlands, the species seems to be found in all parts of the British Isles.

Striped Twin-spot Carpet (*Malenydris salicata*).

Portraits of a male and a female of this species will be found on Plate 75, Figs. 11 ♂ and 12 ♀. The fore wings are greyish white, crossed by several darker grey wavy lines; the central band is rather darker, and in some specimens there is also a darker basal patch. In an almost unicolorous form the fore wings are wholly suffused with darker; Kane, who states that such specimens occur with the paler form in Ireland, refers the aberration to *unicolorata*, Gregson.

The caterpillar is brownish, with three whitish lines along the back, and a pinkish line low down along the sides. It feeds, at night, on bedstraw (*Galium*), in September and October, but may be found on the plants in the daytime. (Plate 73, Fig. 2, after Hofmann.)

The moth is out in May and June, and in some localities again in August and September. It is fond of sitting on rocks, and also on tree-trunks.

Except that it has been found, not infrequently, on Dartmoor and Exmoor, in Devon, and has also been once noted from Dorset, the species in England is chiefly an inhabitant of the northern counties. It occurs in Wales, but almost exclusively in the north. In Scotland it appears to be widely distributed throughout; and in Ireland it occurs locally in all four provinces.

Mottled Grey (*Malenydris multistrigaria*).

The fore wings in the typical form of this species are grey, with a slight brownish tinge; basal patch, central band, and shade before the whitish submarginal line, sometimes darker. (Plate 77, Figs. 1 ♂, 2 ♀.) In some specimens the central band is very much darker (ab. *virgata*, Tutt); and in some parts of south-west Yorkshire a blackish form (ab. *nubilata*, Tutt) is not uncommon. (Plate 77, Fig. 3.)

The caterpillar is ochreous grey, with three brownish lines along the back, and two other lines on each side, the upper one yellowish, wavy, and edged above with dusky. It feeds on bedstraw (*Galium*) in May and June. (Plate 73, Fig. 3.)

The moth is out in March and April, and keeps pretty much to the shelter afforded by its food plant or other herbage around in its favourite haunts, which are damp woodlands, heaths, and mosses. Occasionally, however, it may be seen on the lower parts of fences, tree-trunks, rocks, etc. About dusk it may be found sitting on grass and other vegetation, and at such times is not much disposed to fly away from the collector.

Pretty generally distributed throughout the British Isles, including the Orkneys.

Twin-spot Carpet (*Malenydris didymata*).

The fore wings in the male are pale greyish, more or less tinged with ochreous brown, and crossed by a dark grey, inclining to blackish, central band ; the base of the wings is often banded with dark grey, as also is the outer marginal area ; on the latter, above the middle, are twin black spots, and there is a black spot or streak above nearer the tip of the wing. The female is smaller, paler, often whitish, and sometimes pale ochreous ; the latter form is prevalent in the Shetlands ; the central band is the only distinct cross marking in this sex. On the moorlands in the north of England a blackish form of the male occurs (ab. *nigra*, Prout), and this is very similar to ab. *nubilata* of the previous species ; ab. *ochroleucata*, Aurivillius, is uniformly greyish brown, with a white sub-marginal line, and I have a specimen near this from Durham.

The caterpillar is green, inclining to yellowish on the back, and to pinkish on the sides; three lines along the side, the central one dark green, and the others whitish. It feeds on primrose, red campion (*Lychnis diurna*), bilberry, etc., as well as on the flowers of coarse grasses; in North Devon I found it in profusion at night, on the blossoms of a wood-rush (*Luzula*), growing in a sheltered wood near the sea. April and May, later perhaps in the north. (Plate 77, Figs. 4-6 ☼, 7-9 ♀.)

The moth is out in July and August, and is common in almost every part of the British Isles.

November Moth (*Oporabia* (*Epirrita*) *dilutata*).

The more usual forms of this common autumnal species are those represented by Figs. 1 and 2, Plate 78. Fig. 3 is a small example of the pale form, ab. *christyi*, Prout, which, in many respects, is very similar to *autumnata*, Guenée, a form of the next species. Fig. 4 is a female approaching ab. *obscurata*, Staud., and Fig. 5 shows the uniformly blackish ab. *melana*, Prout. In some pale-coloured specimens the only conspicuous marking is a broad central band which is almost black in colour (ab. *latifasciata*, Prout).

The eggs (Plate 76, Fig. 1a) were yellowish when laid, but soon changed to crimson red.

The caterpillar is green, inclining to whitish below, often marked, more or less distinctly, with purplish red, as a central line, or series of spots, along the back, and sometimes as bands on the ring division. It feeds on the foliage of trees, such as elm, oak, birch, etc., also on sallow, hawthorn, sloe, apple, plum, and other fruit trees. April to June. (Plate 76, Fig. 1.)

The moth is out in October and November in the South, but earlier in the North. It is an inhabitant of woodlands, and may be disturbed from bushes, trees, and sometimes may be seen on the trunks of the latter, and on fences. At night it

1 **Water Carpet:** *caterpillar.*
2. **Dark-barred Twin-spot Carpet:** *caterpillar*
3. **Flame Carpet:** *caterpillar.*

1-3. **Dark-barred Twin-spot Carpet.** 4-6. **Flame Carpet.** 7, 8. **Green Carpet**
9, 10. **Beech-green Carpet.** 11, 12. **Striped Twin-spot Carpet.**

flies lazily and will occasionally visit ivy then, and even sugar, but is more frequently attracted by light.

The species is pretty generally common throughout England and Wales, Scotland up to Moray, and Ireland.

The Autumnal Moth (*Oporabia* (*Epirrita*) *autumnata*).

Three examples of this species are shown on Plate 78. Figs 6 ♂ and 7 ♀ represent the typical form except that the male should be rather more silvery white in the ground colour of the fore wings, and the cross bands more distinctly separated. Fig. 8, also a female, is very close to ab. *sandbergi*, Lampa, in the character of the central cross bands of the fore wings. Ab. *gueneata*, Prout (*autumnata*, Guenée, not Borkhausen), is a form with the typical coloration, but with fainter cross bands.

The caterpillar is somewhat similar to that of the last species, but there is a yellowish tint in the general green coloration, and it is rarely marked with reddish. It is found chiefly on birch, alder, fir, and larch, but will eat hawthorn, and probably the foliage of other shrubs and trees. May and June.

The moth is out in September and October, sometimes later. It may be dislodged from trees in the daytime, but it seems to be rarely noticed at rest on the trunks.

The species is so often confused with that previously mentioned that its distribution in our islands has not, so far, been clearly ascertained. However, it certainly occurs in the following northern counties of England—Lancashire (Liverpool district); Cheshire (Delamere Forest); Yorkshire (Cleveland district); North Durham (Birch woods); Cumberland (Carlisle). In Scotland it is found in Clydesdale, Perthshire, where it was first noted by Weaver in 1851, Kincardineshire, Aberdeen, and probably further north; in Ireland at Belfast and Enniskillen. Prout notes that he has seen a specimen from Swansea in South Wales.

Small Autumnal Carpet (*Oporabia* (*Epirrita*) *filigrammaria*).

This is most probably a small moorland form of *O. autumnata*, but it rarely assumes the silvery white typical coloration of that species. A male specimen and two examples of the female are depicted on Plate 77, Figs. 10 ♂, 11, and 12 ♀.

The caterpillar, which feeds in the spring on bilberry and heather, is green, with yellow lines, a line of darker green between the two central yellow lines along the back ; head, green, inclining to brown above.

The moth appears in August and early September, and may be found on the moors, resting on rocks, stones, and even on the ground, as well as on the stems of its food plants.

As a British species it was first recorded by Weaver, who obtained it in the Isle of Arran in 1841 ; but Edleston, writing in 1842, states that he had taken specimens off stone walls near Staley Bridge, in the Manchester district, "every year for the last three years." It appears to be peculiar to the British Isles and is found in suitable localities from North Staffs., through Cheshire, Lancs., Yorks., and northwards over England and Scotland to the Hebrides and the Orkneys. In Ireland it is known to occur in Antrim, Derry, Mayo, Galway, and Limerick.

The Welsh Wave (*Venusia cambrica*).

This moth, of which two portraits are given on Plate 78, Figs. 9 ♂, 10 ♀, is known also by the English name of "Cambric Wave." It was not ascertained to be an inhabitant of Britain until 1839, when it was figured and described by Curtis from specimens obtained in Cardiganshire in Wales.

In its typical form the fore wings are white, inclining to greyish, with a number of brownish or dark-grey cross lines ; two pairs on the central area are marked with black. Sometimes the wings are greatly suffused with smoky grey, and this tint in examples from the Sheffield and Rotherham districts of Yorkshire assumes a much darker hue, so that all the markings are obscured, but the veins are blacker.

The caterpillar is green, marked with some irregular reddish blotches , a yellowish line along the back. It foods in August, earlier or later in some seasons, on mountain ash (*Pyrus aucuparia*), and the moth, which rests by day on tree-trunks, is out in July and early August. The haunts of the species are chiefly in hilly localities of the northern counties of England, but it has also been reported from Gloucestershire (Cotswolds), Somersetshire (Weston-super-Mare), and Devon (Dulverton). In Wales it occurs in Merionethshire, as well as in Cardiganshire ; and in Scotland it spreads from Roxburghshire, where it is locally common among mountain ash, through Clydesdale to Inverness. It is widely distributed in Ireland. The range abroad extends to Japan and North America.

Grey Mountain Carpet (*Entephria cæsiata*)

The typical greyish form, with blackish wavy cross lines and dark central band, is shown on Plate 80, Fig. 1 ♂ and 2 ♀. Figure 3 represents a specimen from Shetland in which the band is sooty black (ab. *annosata*, Zetterstedt = *nigristriaria*, Gregson). The interesting blackish suffused form from the Isle of Arran (Fig. 4) leads up to a still blacker variety, occurring in the same isle, and also in the Shetlands, in which the whole of the fore wings is nearly as dark as the central band of Fig. 3, and the hind wings are also much darkened ; such specimens are referable to ab. *glaciata*, Germar. Ab. *prospicuata*, Prout = *gelata*, Staud., is a form with the fore wings whitish, and the base and the central band thereof blackish ; some Shetland specimens closely approach this pretty variety.

The caterpillar is green, with a brownish line along the middle of the back, and a series of pinkish or purplish-red oblique streaks which nearly meet at the central line and so form V-shaped marks ; a whitish or yellowish stripe low down along the sides, sometimes edged above with reddish. In some examples the general colour is reddish brown. It feeds in April and May, after hibernation, on bilberry, ling, and heath in a wild state, but may be reared on knot-grass or sallow.

The moth is out from June until early August, and may be found resting, often in numbers, on rocks and stone walls in mountain and moorland districts, from Herefordshire, northwards through England, North Wales, and over the whole of Scotland, including the isles, and Ireland. Kane states that in the latter country melanic forms, such as those from Yorks., etc., are nowhere met with.

Yellow-ringed Carpet (*Entephria flavicinctata*).

The general colour of the fore wings of British specimens of this species (var. *obscurata*, Staud.) is slaty grey ; the basal, central, and outer marginal cross bands are thickly sprinkled with yellowish-brown, and it is this feature that at once separates this species (Plate 80, Figs. 5, 6) from that last referred to.

The bristly caterpillar is green, chocolate, or red brown, but always of a dull shade ; on the back is a series of black V-shaped marks, and a central dark, slender line ; the front part of each V-mark filled up with pink or lilac, forming a triangle, the apex of which is yellow ; a yellowish stripe low down along the side (adapted from Fenn). It feeds in the spring till April, after hibernation, on saxifrage (*Saxifraga aizoides*, *S. hypnoides*, etc.), and also on stonecrop (*Sedum*), and is most partial to the flowers of these plants.

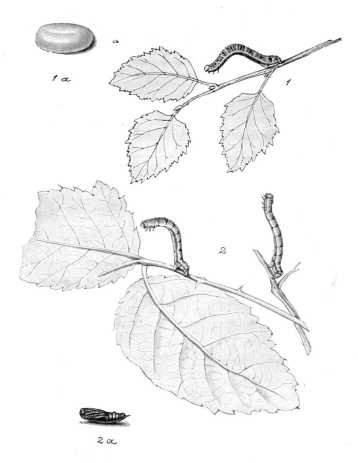

1, 1*a*. **November Moth:** *eggs and caterpillar.*
2, 2*a*. **Beautiful Carpet:** *caterpillars and chrysalis.*

1-4. **Mottled Grey.**   5-8. **Twin-spot Carpet.**   9-12. **Small Autumnal Carpet**

The moth flies throughout the summer, possibly in two generations, as, when reared in confinement, moths appear in May, and from eggs obtained from these, caterpillars feed in June and July, and attain the perfect state in August. Like the last species, its chief resting-places are the rocks, in its favourite haunts, in gorges among the hills and moorlands. It has been recorded from few parts of northern England, but one specimen is said to have been taken in Dovedale, Derbyshire. In Lancashire it has been noted as scarce about Clougha; and in Yorkshire one example was taken on Malham Moor in August, 1876, near Scarborough, July 16, 1891; and also Grassington, Aug., 1916. It is more plentiful in Scotland; in Clydesdale it is local, but not uncommon, the localities mentioned being Lochgoilhead, and watercourses above Ardentinny; more frequent in Perthshire, thence to Sutherland, and it occurs also in the Hebrides and the Orkneys. In Ireland, it is found in Co. Antrim; and Mr. Thomas Greer informs me that it is common at Murlough Bay, Fair Head.

Silver-ground Carpet (*Xanthorhoë montanata*).

Figs. 7 and 8 on Plate 80 represent the most usual form of this species, which is variable in the amount of clouding on the fore wings and in the intensity of the cross marking. In some specimens, chiefly from southern localities, the fore wings are almost clear white, and the central band is broadly blackish (Fig. 9). Shetland specimens, on the other hand, are much clouded or suffused with ochreous brown, and the central band is greyish brown (ab. *shetlandica*, Weir (Fig. 10)). Then there is variation in the central band, which is often entire, but more frequently broken up by bandlets; or it may be considerably narrowed, especially from the middle to the inner margin, and not altogether rarely it is completely severed below the middle, and the lower part almost or quite absent. A specimen with all

Series II.   O

the wings smoky leaden-grey, and the central bar of the fore wings pale grey-brown, was taken near Longfleet in Wiltshire, in the summer of 1881.

The caterpillar is wrinkled, with a ridge along the sides; in colour it is pale brown, inclining to purplish with blackish dots; three lines along the back, the central one dark greyish, the others paler and broader; below the latter the sides are greyish tinted with a lower edging of pale yellowish brown. It feeds at night on bedstraw, and various low-growing herbage, including grass. August to April.

The moth is out in June and July, sometimes earlier in the south. It is generally distributed, and, as a rule, common, in woodlands, lanes, etc., throughout the British Isles.

Garden Carpet (*Xanthorhoë fluctuata*).

Of this common frequenter of our gardens four examples are depicted on Plate 80. Figs. 11 and 13 are the more frequent forms, but specimens with the central band complete, as in Fig. 12, are not uncommon. Chiefly, but by no means exclusively, in Southern localities, some examples have the ground colour almost pure white; often the wings are more or less suffused with dark grey (ab. *neapolisata*, Millière), and this is especially the case in Scotland, where, in Aberdeenshire and in Shetland, a blackish form, ab. *thules*, Prout, occurs. Fig. 14 represents a specimen of this form from Aberdeen. Somewhat rarely, the central band is only indicated by a small spot on the front area of the wing (ab. *costovata*, Haworth), and more often the band is much narrowed or otherwise modified in the direction of that aberration. Fig. 4, Plate 61, shows an extreme example of this form. Specimens vary in size from rather under one inch to one inch and a half in expanse.

The caterpillar varies in colour from dark grey through yellowish green to obscure green, but the underside is always

1-5. **November Moth.** 6-8. **Autumnal Moth.** 9. 10. **Welsh Wave.**

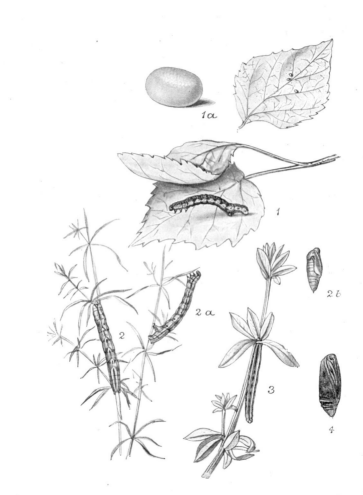

1, 1*a.* **Argent and Sable:** *eggs, natural size and enlarged, and caterpillar.*
2, 2*a*, 2*b.* **Wood Carpet:** *caterpillar and chrysalis.*
3. **Galium Carpet:** *caterpillar.*
4. **Common Carpet:** *chrysalis.*

paler ; on the back there is a series of pale blotches, and some
black spots on the middle rings ;
the head is rather paler than
the general colour, and marked
with black. It feeds, at night,
on cabbage, horseradish, wallflower, white arabis, and many
other kinds of Cruciferæ ; and
it is said to eat the foliage of
gooseberry and currant. June
—October.

There are certainly two
broods, and possibly more, as
the moths occur in greater or
lesser numbers throughout the
year, from late April to October,
but it seems to be most plentiful in May and June, and in
August and September.

FIG. 4.
Garden Carpet at rest.
(Photo by H. Main.)

Generally distributed over the British Isles. It is also an
inhabitant of North America.

The Galium Carpet (*Xanthorhoë galiata*).

The more usual forms of this species are represented on
Plate 81, Figs. 1, 2. Fig. 3 is the portrait of a form occurring
in Yorkshire, Sussex, Devon, and probably elsewhere, in which
the central band is blackish and solid-looking ; this seems to
be referable to *unilobata*, Haworth. Besides varying in tint of
ground colour, and in the amount of freckling or mottling, there
is modification in the width of the central band.

The caterpillar is brown, dotted with black, and striped with
blackish brown on the back, and with pale brown on the sides ;
the head is light brown, sprinkled with black, and marked with

a dark V. It feeds on bedstraw in late June and July, and there is a second brood in August and September. The figure of the caterpillar on Plate 79, Fig. 3, is from a coloured drawing by Mr. A. Sich.

The moth is out in June, sometimes later in the north and earlier in the south, where it occurs as a second generation in August. It is chiefly found in chalk and limestone districts, and may be easily put up from the herbage among which it secretes itself during the day. In the seaboard counties of England, from Kent to Cornwall, it is especially common on the coast, but is also to be met with in suitable inland localities in these counties, and also in Surrey, Middlesex, Herts, Bucks., and Oxford. It is always rare on the eastern side, but on the west, including Wales, it is more or less frequent from Somerset and Wilts. to Westmorland. Not uncommon in Yorkshire, principally in the West Riding, and an odd specimen has been recorded from Durham. Somewhat rare in Scotland, but it has been noted in Berwick, Wigtown, Arran, Clydesdale, and Perthshire. In Ireland it is local, although often plentiful on the coast.

Abroad, the range extends to Eastern Siberia.

Wood Carpet (*Xanthorhoë* (*Epirrhoë*) *rivata*).

The broad, clear white borders of both edges of the dark central band of the fore wings, coupled with the clearer white of the hind wings, and the generally larger size of the moth, should distinguish this species from its very close ally, *X. sociata;* but it must be added that some forms of the latter species approach the present one exceedingly close. (Plate 81, Figs. 4, 5.)

The caterpillar is brown or olive-brown, dotted and freckled with white ; three lines on the back, the central one black, the others whitish, not seen on rings 5–8, which have dark V-shaped

1-4. **Grey Mountain Carpet.**   5, 6. **Yellow-ringed Carpet.**
7-10. **Silver-ground Carpet.**   11-14. **Garden Carpet.**

1-3. **Galium Carpet.**   4, 5. **Wood Carpet.**
6-9. **Common Carpet.**   10-12. **Small Argent and Sable.**

marks enclosing white ones ; sometimes there is a V-mark instead of lines on ring 4; head, large, pale brown sprinkled with blackish, and marked with a blackish V, the apex of which appears to meet the central line of the body. It feeds, at night, in July and August, on bedstraw (*Galium mollugo*, and *G. verum*), but will thrive very well on cleavers or goose-grass (*G. aparine*). The chrysalis, which is enclosed in a cocoon of silk coated with earth, is reddish brown, thorax and wing-cases paler, shining. A coloured drawing of the caterpillar, kindly lent, with others, for this volume, by Mr. A. Sich, has been used for the figures on Plate 79, Figs. 2, 2*a* ; but the description of the caterpillar, and also of the chrysalis (Fig. 2*b*), are from material that Mr. Pope, of Exeter, was good enough to furnish. In captivity a second brood may be reared in August.

The moth is out in July and early August, and although local, is not uncommon in bushy places on downs, etc., also in lanes, in chalk districts, in most of the southern and eastern counties. In the north of England it is far more local and uncommon, but is known to occur in Cheshire, Yorkshire, and Cumberland, and has been recorded from Durham. It is found in Wales, and in Scotland has been noted as very local in Roxburghshire and rare in Clydesdale and Arran. Kane states that in Ireland it is " very rare and local."

Common Carpet (*Xanthorhoë* (*Epirrhoë*) *sociata*).

The white ground colour of this species is nearly always obscured, to a greater or lesser extent, by greyish markings and suffusions on the basal area ; the outer margin is broadly bordered with dark grey, and the white band between this and the dark-grey central band is intersected throughout its length by a grey line. As shown on Plate 81, Figs. 6, 7, the central band varies in width ; it is often contracted below the middle, sometimes completely severed at this point, and in ab. *degenerata*,

Haworth, both portions are much reduced in width. Figs. 8 and 9 represent two specimens from the Isle of Lewis; these brownish-grey examples are var. *obscurata*, South. There are intermediate modifications leading up to a form in which the whole of the central third of the fore wings is whitish, with the usual cross lines dingy grey, and some tiny clouds of the same colour around the black discal spot.

The caterpillar is very like that of the last species referred to, but it is rather smaller in size and rougher in appearance. There is variation in the general colour, from pale fawn through greenish-brown, to dull or bright green, and sometimes the markings are tinged with reddish (Hellins).

It feeds on bedstraw, in June and July, and a second brood occurs in September. The figure of the brownish, inclining to reddish, chrysalis (Plate 79, Fig. 4), is from a photo by Mr. H. Main, and is twice the natural size.

The moth is out in May and June, and, in the South especially, again in August and September. It is generally distributed over the British Islands, but so far has not been noted from the Shetlands.

The range abroad extends to Eastern Siberia and Amurland. According to Prout, the earliest name for this species is *alternata* (Müller).

Small Argent and Sable (*Xanthorhoë* (*Epirrhoë*) *tristata*).

On Plate 81 are shown three examples of this variable species. Fig. 10 represents the typical form from N. Devon. Fig. 11 is a black-marked specimen from Yorkshire, and Fig. 12 depicts a smoky-brown marked specimen from Clydesdale, in which the ground colour has a brownish tinge. All these have the central band more or less entire, but this character may be broader or narrower, and is sometimes divided into two parts, and these reduced to very small proportions; the white projections into the outer marginal border of all the wings is not infrequently enlarged, in some cases so much so that the borders are separated into two parts, and also reduced in width.

The caterpillar is grey brown, ochreous brown between the rings and on the underside ; a dark line along the back, and a dark-edged, pale line on each side ; a black dot on each ring at the junction of the dark upper and pale lower areas ; head, grey-brown, with blackish freckles. It feeds, in July and August, on bedstraw, preferring the heath kind (*Galium saxatile*), but will eat the large hedge kind (*G. mollugo*).

The moth is out in June, or from late May, and in some parts specimens are seen in August. Its haunts are moors and upland heaths, and its British distribution extends from Dartmoor and Exmoor, in Devon, through Western England and Wales to Westmorland. It appears to be very local in Somerset, Gloucester, Hereford, Shropshire, and Cheshire ; from Staffordshire and Derbyshire northwards, and through Scotland, it becomes more plentiful ; and has been recorded from the Shetlands. In Ireland it is local, but common where it occurs.

Sharp-angled Carpet (*Xanthorhoë (Euphyia) unangulata*).

This species (Plate 82, Figs. 1, 2) may be recognized by the distinctly angled outer edge of the blackish central band, which is thrown into strong relief by the usually broad white stripe following it. Wilkes, who figured the moth in 1742, called it the "White Stripe." By some authors the species is referred to *amniculata*, Hübner.

The caterpillar is pale whity brown, with a slightly darker but indistinct line along the centre of the back, and a black spot on the middle rings ; a pale line on the sides is edged with dark grey ; head, brown, marked with black. It feeds, in July and early August, on chickweed (*Stellaria media*).

The moth, which is partial to hedges and easily disturbed

therefrom, is out in June and July, and even later in some
seasons. The earliest hatched caterpillars reared in confinement sometimes attain the moth state in August of the same
year. Although certainly local, the species has a wide distribution in the southern half of England, and is not uncommon
in some localities. Its range extends into Wales, and also
northwards to Cumberland and Westmorland, but it is generally very much scarcer in the north than in the south. In
Ireland it is known to occur locally in counties Antrim, Tyrone,
Fermanagh, Waterford, Kerry, and Galway, but, as a rule,
only sparingly.

Abroad, the distribution includes North Amurland and North
America.

Cloaked Carpet (*Euphyia picata*).

An older English name for this species (Plate 82, Figs. 4, 5)
is " The Short Cloak Carpet," Harris (1782), but that given to
it by Haworth is here adopted. It is also the *biangulata* of
Haworth, Stephens, and others.

As will be observed on referring to the figures, the outer edge
of the blackish central band of the fore wings is twice angled
just above the middle; the basal area and the outer marginal
border are dark greyish brown, more or less tinged with olive;
the whitish ground colour only shows distinctly as a strip immediately beyond the central band, and from this an irregular
streak runs to the tips of the wings; some white wavy cross-
lines through the outer border are often obscure.

The stoutish caterpillar is yellowish brown, or sometimes
reddish brown; there is a series of blackish or dark-brown
spots along the back, and a stripe of dusky freckles along each
side; lower down are two slender wavy lines enclosing a dusky
stripe; head, yellowish-brown mottled with darker brown. It
feeds, at night, on chickweed and other kinds of *Stellaria*, in

August and September.   One of the mouse-ear chickweeds (*Cerastium glomeratum*) has also been mentioned as a food plant, and for rearing the caterpillars this would perhaps be useful, as common chickweed, unless in a growing state, is difficult to keep in a suitable condition for larval requirements.

The moth, which is partial to a hedgerow as a hiding-place, is out in June and July, and may be sometimes reared as a second generation in September.

The species is somewhat local, but it is not scarce in many parts of England ; its range does not appear to extend north-wards beyond Worcestershire on the western side, although it has been recorded from North Wales; on the eastern side it is found up to Norfolk.

The Argent and Sable (*Eulype hastata*).

About one hundred and sixty years ago Wilkes figured this species as " The Mottled Beauty," but Harris in 1778 gave it its present English name.   On Plate 82 are shown two examples of the typical form (Figs. 7, 8), also two specimens of the small form (Figs. 10, 11), var. *subhastata*, Nolcken (= *hastulata*, Hübner) ; the latter form in Britain occurs chiefly in Suther-landshire and the Isle of Lewis.   As regards variation there is, in the small form, a tendency to an increase of black ; whilst in the typical form there is a considerable reduction of the black marking—so much so occasionally that of the central black band only a few dots remain around the discal spot, and perhaps a speck or two below it, and a dot or two on the inner margin (ab. *demolita*, Prout).

The rather stumpy caterpillar is dark olive-green, inclining to blackish, and somewhat shiny ; the skin along the sides puckered and marked with ochreous ; a black line along the middle of the back ; head, black and glossy.   It feeds, in July and August, later in the north, on birch, *Vaccinium*, chiefly *uliginosum*, and sweet gale (*Myrica*). It spins together the leaves at the tips of the twigs, and so forms a cocoon-like habitation. The moth is out in May and June, and even July in the north. It flies in the afternoon sunshine around and over birch trees, and occasionally alights on the leaves. It has been taken in Kent, and more frequently in Essex and Suffolk, but it is more plentiful in Oxfordshire and Berkshire, and from Surrey to Dorsetshire and Wiltshire ; also in Herefordshire and Worcestershire, and on high ground in North Wales, Staffordshire, and Derbyshire ; its range extending through Cheshire and Lancashire to Cumberland and Northumberland, but only odd specimens have been reported from the last-named county and from Durham. The egg and the caterpillar are shown on Plate 79, Figs. 1 and 1*a*.

It is widely distributed, and often common in places, throughout Scotland. In Ireland it is local, but has occurred plentifully in some of its haunts in that country ; Kane states that var. *subhastata* has not been noted.

The range abroad spreads to Amurland, China, Iceland, Labrador, and North America.

Beautiful Carpet (*Mesoleuca albicillata*).

The English name of this species (Plate 82, Fig. 13) is exceedingly appropriate ; few of our native moths exhibit such a pleasing combination of colour and marking. It varies but very little in a general way, but a specimen taken in York some years ago has the fore wings dark leaden grey instead of creamy white (ab. *suffusa*, Carrington), and very rarely the ground colour inclines to yellow.

The stoutish caterpillar (Plate 76, Fig. 2) is green with reddish marks along the back ; a white line low down along the sides is edged below with purplish red on the first three rings ; the last ring, and the claspers, tinged with purplish red. It feeds at night on bramble and raspberry, in August and September, occasionally earlier or later. In the daytime it rests on the underside of a leaf. When full grown it forms a cocoon just under the surface of the soil, or among rubbish (in the cage), and therein changes to a dark reddish-brown chrysalis (Plate 76, Fig. 2a).

The moth is out in June, sometimes in late May, and occasionally there seems to be a few individuals about in August. The species is a denizen of the woodlands, and is generally to be found in the more open parts of woods where its food plants are well established. It is widely distributed over England and Wales, but most frequent in the south of the former country. In Scotland, it is local in Roxburghshire and Wigtownshire; and it occurs in many parts of Ireland. The range abroad extends to Amurland and Japan.

The Purple Bar (*Mesoleuca ocellata*).

The whitish fore wings of this species (Plate 82, Fig. 12) are often tinged with pale ochreous brown on the lower two-thirds of the outer marginal area, and this tint sometimes invades the central portion of the bluish-black central band. Rarely the ground colour is almost entirely white, and the central band is very slender (ab. *coarctata*, Prout), and perhaps rather more frequently the band is completely severed below the middle.

The caterpillar, which feeds at night on bedstraw (*Galium mollugo* and *G. verum*), is pale ochreous brown, or pale pinkish brown, netted with darker brown; on the back are a reddish ochreous central line, and some reddish edged pale V-marks : June and July, and sometimes again in the autumn.

The moth is out in June and early July, occasionally in late May in some southern localities. Individuals of a second emergence sometimes appear in August and September. It rests by day on tree-trunks or in hedges, and flies at night. Widely distributed over the British Isles, but, except perhaps in the highlands of Scotland, not very common.

Blue-bordered Carpet (*Mesoleuca bicolorata*).

The more usual form of this pretty little species is shown on Plate 82, Figs. 3 and 6. In the type the central band is only represented by a spot on the front margin of the fore wings ; in ab. *parvula*, Retz = *rubiginata*, Hübner, there is also a portion of the band showing on the inner margin. Ab. *plumbata*, Curtis, from Scotland has the central band entire and the ground colour inclining to creamy white. In ab. *fumosa*, Prout, the usual white parts of the wing are smoky or dark lead colour (Fig. 9). Barrett mentions a form with all the wings smoothly smoky black ; markings of the fore wings olive brown, margined with slender stripes of smoky white.

The long, thin, caterpillar is green, with a darker stripe along the back, and a yellowish green stripe on each side ; two points on the last ring. It feeds on alder, birch, sloe, and crab ; also in orchards and gardens on plum and apple : April to June.

The moth is out in July and August. It appears to occur most freely in districts where alder is plentiful, but it is not uncommon in country lanes, especially where these are rather moist. It is one of the earliest Geometrid moths to get on the wing, as it is generally active well before dark. Decidedly more common in some districts than in others, but it may be said to be generally distributed.

The range abroad extends to Eastern Siberia, Amurland, and Japan, but the ab. *fumosa* is only known from Britain.

Pretty Chalk Carpet (*Melanthia procellata*).

From almost any well-grown hedgerow, in which traveller's joy, or old-man's beard (*Clematis vitalba*) is plentiful, throughout

1, 2. **Sharp-angled Carpet.**   3 6, 9. **Blue-bordered Carpet.**
4, 5. **Cloaked Carpet.**   7, 8, 10, 11. **Argent and Sable.**
12. **Purple Bar.**   13. **Beautiful Carpet.**
14. **Pretty Chalk Carpet.**

1, 2. **Rivulet.**   3, 6. **Small Rivulet.**   4, 5. **Barred Rivulet.**
9, 12. **Heath Rivulet.**   10, 11, 13, 14. **Grass Rivulet.**   7, 8. **Pretty Pinion.**

the southern counties of England, this species (Plate 82, Fig. 14) may be disturbed by the beating stick. It is generally to be met with in July and early August, but may be obtained in forward seasons, or in sheltered localities, at the end of June.

On the fore wings the dark, slender and wavy cross lines are more distinct in some specimens than in others, and occasionally the blackish blotch on the front margin is traversed by a white line, sometimes by two lines.

The caterpillar is pale ochreous brown, with three darker brown lines along the back, the central one slender, spotted with black on the middle rings ; usual dots, black, encircled with white ; head, marked with a reddish brown triangle. It feeds on *Clematis* in August and September.

Distribution of the species abroad extends to Amurland, and in Japan, Corea, and China it is represented by the darker *inquinata*, Butler.

The Rivulet (*Perizoma affinitata*).

The whitish band crossing the brownish fore wings is generally fairly wide, sometimes broad, but occasionally it is very narrow ; the reduction in width is mainly the result of brownish suffusion of the outer half of the band, leaving the inner half white. Kane mentions a smoky form from Co. Derry, in which the band is absent, and refers this to ab. *unicolorata*, Gregson. In a specimen from Sligo in my series, the band is tinged with brownish throughout. The hind wings are usually smoky brown, with a paler central band, but in some specimens, referable to ab. *turbaria*, Stephens, the basal two-thirds are whitish. The moths also vary in size (Plate 83, Figs. 1 and 2).

The caterpillar is pinkish-ochreous inclining to brown ; three pinkish lines along the back, and a similar line along the blackish spiracles ; a dark plate on the first and last rings. It feeds in the capsules, on the seeds, of red campion (*Lychnis dioica*), and will eat those of the white *L. vespertina :* July to September. When eggs can be obtained early, it is possible to rear moths from them in August of the same year.

The moth is out in June and July, in some southern districts in late May.

As it conceals itself during the day among its food plant, or other vegetation around, it may be put up therefrom by gently stirring the herbage ; but it flies freely about sundown, and is then easily netted.

The species is widely distributed over England, Wales, and Scotland, up to Moray. In Ireland it is local and not plentiful, and the same is the case in the North of England.

Small Rivulet (*Perizoma alchemillata*).

This species (Plate 83, Figs. 3 and 6) is exceedingly close to the last mentioned, but in a general way it is to be distinguished by its greyish-brown coloration. A stippled whitish stripe before the central band, usually only faintly indicated in *affinitata*, is fairly distinct as a rule. Although the outer edge of the central band is rather more irregular, the middle tooth is not so prominent as in *affinitata*.

The rather plump caterpillar is purplish above and yellowish green below ; three yellow lines on the back, the central one broad ; the spiracles are black, and a little above them is another yellow line ; head, black and glossy, and there are black shining plates on the first and last rings of the body, that on the first ring divided by the yellow central line (adapted from Porritt). It feeds, in August and September, in the seed capsules of hemp nettle (*Galeopsis tetrahit*), sometimes on the rarer *G. ladanum*, and is said to eat woundwort (*Stachys*) occasionally.

The moth is out in June and July, and, as in the case of the last species, may be stirred up from among its food plant or the

3α

1. **Grass Rivulet:** *caterpillar.*
2. **Waved Carpet:** *caterpillar.*
3, 3*a*. **Yellow Shell:** *eggs and caterpillar.*

1, 2. **Sandy Carpet.**   3. **Barred Carpet.**   4-9. **Yellow Shell.**

surrounding vegetation, in lanes, and around wood borders. The species is widely distributed over the British Isles, except that it seems not to have been noticed in Scotland, north of Moray, although it occurs in the Hebrides.

Sandy Carpet (*Perizoma flavofasciata*).

The pale ochreous-brown, or sandy, markings on the white fore wings of this species readily distinguish it from either of its allies. Variable in size, and also in the brownish tint of the markings; the central band is usually contracted below the middle, and not infrequently it is completely severed at this point. It is the *decolorata* of Hübner, and although more generally known by that name, the earlier *flavofasciata*, Thunberg, will have to be adopted for this species. (Plate 85, Figs. 1 ♂, 2 ♀.)

The stoutish caterpillar is pale reddish ochreous with browner lines ; head, brown and shining, plate on first and last rings of the body brown. It feeds on the flower buds, and on the immature seeds, of the red campion (*Lychnis dioica*), and the white campion (*L. vespertina*), but is more partial to the first named ; in Ireland it is said to feed on bladder campion (*Silene inflata*).

In July and August, or even later, the moth may be beaten out of hedgerows, sandy banks, and borders of woods, and sometimes disturbed from patches of the campion growing in thickets ; in such places it is on the wing about sundown.

Although local to some extent, it appears to be common enough in most of the counties of England and Wales. In Scotland, it is more or less generally common in Roxburghshire and Clydesdale, and is said to have been an inhabitant of Perthshire (Moncrieffe Hill). It appears to be very local in Ireland, but is recorded from Antrim, Derry, and Kerry, and noted as common at Larne in the first-named county.

Grass Rivulet (*Perizoma albulata*).

Although some English specimens approach the larger and whiter typical form, the species as it occurs in the British Isles is generally greyer, var. *griseata*, Staudinger; two examples of this form are shown on Plate 83, Figs. 10 and 11. In the Shetland Isles, the species assumes a darker coloration, and is either well marked on the fore wings, as in Fig. 14, or almost plain, as in Fig. 13 (ab. *thules*, Weir), which is an extreme aberration of the form *subfasciaria*, Boheman. In other examples of a deep leaden grey, or brown tint, the central area is no darker than the rest of the wing. In the Isle of Lewis a white form with faint markings is prevalent, and this leads up to a clear white aberration devoid of markings, ab. *niveata*, Stephens, = *hebudium*, Weir.

The wrinkled caterpillar, which feeds, in July and August, on the seeds of the yellow rattle (*Rhinanthus crista-galli*), and lives in the capsule, is whitish, inclining to greenish, dotted with black, and striped with dark green on the back and sides; head, black and glossy; plates and first and last rings of the body dusky. (Plate 84, Fig. 1.)

The moth is out in May and June, sometimes later. It occurs chiefly in dry meadows where the yellow rattle flourishes, and is to be seen on the wing, often in large numbers, in the late afternoon about sundown. Generally abundant in suitable places, throughout the British Isles.

The Barred Rivulet (*Perizoma bifasciata*).

Haworth described two forms of this species, and a specimen of each is shown on our Plate 83. Fig. 4 represents *bifasciata* (*bifaciata*, the Double-barred Rivulet), and Fig. 5 depicts *unifasciata* (the Single-barred Rivulet). The chief difference appears to be that in the type (*bifasciata*) the "rivulets" are white and distinct, thus bringing out a dark band between the central one and the base of the wing.

The stoutish caterpillar is pale brown, inclining to ochreous on the back, along which are three lines, the central one greyish, and the others whitish shaded with greyish; a whitish stripe low down along the sides; the usual dots are black, and the spiracles are black, margined with ochreous (adapted from Fenn). In September and October it feeds in the seed capsules of *Bartsia odontites*, and is often plentiful; Mr. G. F. Mathew records obtaining nearly five hundred from three small bundles of the food plant gathered in the Harwich district.

The moth is out in July and August, but is not often seen in the daytime, and is not taken very frequently, even when flying at night, but it comes to light, and visits flowers.

From chrysalids obtained from caterpillars reared in 1900, Mr. Robert Adkin bred ten moths in 1901, eleven in 1902, two in 1903, five in 1904, and two in 1905.

The species is widely distributed over England, Wales, and the south of Scotland, but it is most frequent in the south of England. Not much is known of it in Ireland, but it has been noted from counties Dublin, Louth, and Derry.

Heath Rivulet (*Perizoma minorata*).

The British form of this species (Plate 83, Figs. 9, 12) is rather smaller and darker than typical *minorata*, Treitschke, and as Stephens has figured and described it as *ericetata*, this name should be adopted for our native race.

The white fore wings have a greyish basal patch and three bands of the same colour; the outer one is traversed by a more or less distinct wavy whitish line; the band nearest the basal patch is sometimes very faint; more rarely the markings are absent from the central area of the wings (ab. *monticola*, Staud.), and a specimen approaching this form has been taken in Perthshire.

The caterpillar is pale green with a dark-green edged ochreous brown stripe along the middle of the back, and green stripes on each side; the usual dots are black, and the plates on first and last rings are brown, as also is the head. It feeds, in September, on the seeds of eyebright (*Euphrasia officinalis*).

The moth is out in July and August, and is found very locally, flying in the late afternoon among its food plant, on the moorlands and pasture-grounds of Northumberland, Cumberland, Durham, and Westmorland; and has been reported from Hawkshead, in Lancashire. In Scotland, it is common in suitable parts of Roxburghshire and several localities in Clydesdale; thence widely spread to the Orkneys. Only noted from the Mourne Mountains in the north-east of Ireland, but probably to be found in other parts of that country.

Pretty Pinion (*Perizoma blandiata*).

This species (Plate 83, Figs. 7, 8) is also known as *adæquata*, Borkhausen, the name under which it is catalogued by Staudinger. As a rule the central band on the whitish fore wings is only represented by a round, or sometimes triangular, blackish spot on the front margin, a smaller blackish mark on the inner margin, and some dusky clouding between these two portions. In specimens from the Hebrides the band is more or less complete, and in some of them it is very much narrowed, especially towards the inner margin (ab. *coarctata*, Prout).

The caterpillar is green, with three crimson lines, the outer ones bent inwards to the central one on the middle of each ring; two lines above and one below the yellowish spiracular line are pink; head green, tinged and freckled with pink. It feeds in September on the flowers and seeds of the eyebright (*Euphrasia officinalis*).

The moth is out from late May to July, and its habits are similar to those of the last species. In Scotland it appears to be commoner than in other parts of the British Isles, its range extending from Clydesdale to the Hebrides, Orkneys, and Shetland ; but it has been recorded from Cumberland, and once from Durham. In Wales it has been taken at Dolgelly, in Merionethshire. Prout states that in 1902 he secured two specimens near Cwm Bychan, and that the species has since been captured regularly in the locality. It is widely distributed throughout Kerry and Galway, and also recorded from Cork and Derry, in Ireland.

The Barred Carpet (*Perizoma tæniata*).

This species is shown on Plate 85, Fig. 3. There are two forms of the central band of the fore wings, which in the type as figured by Stephens is broad, but is narrow in ab. *arctaria*, Herrich-Schaeffer = *angustifasciata*, Staud. The colour of the bands may be greyer or browner than in the specimen figured, and the ochreous general colour of the fore wings is more tinged with brown in some specimens than in others.

The rather bristly caterpillar is light brown with a pinkish tinge ; the back is marked with browner diamonds and some black dots, and there is a yellow stripe along the sides. It feeds on moss (Hodgkinson, *Entom.* xxviii. 241) growing in damp places, hibernates when quite small, and reappears about April, when it seems to prefer the fruit of the moss, but will also thrive on chickweed. The moths appear from the end of June, and may be found, but in wasted condition, up to early September.

The species is extremely local, and in its secluded haunts may be found on the trunks of holly and yew trees, or it may be disturbed from the branches of such trees, or from hedge-rows, etc.

In Britain the species seems to have been first noted in Castle Eden Dene, Durham (1825), and subsequently in Cumberland (Flimby, near Maryport), Westmorland, Lancashire (Arnside and Silverdale), Yorkshire (Scarborough), Derbyshire (Dove-dale), Arthog in North Wales, and Tintern in Monmouthshire. The only English localities for it south of Monmouth are Waters-meet, near Lynton, in North Devon, and Torbay, in South Devon. It has been noted from Rannoch and Pitlochrie, in Perthshire, and from Dalmallin, in Argyllshire. It has a wide distribution in Ireland, and is common in some parts of that country, as at Killarney, Co. Kerry, and Rockwood, in Sligo.

Abroad, the range extends to Amurland ; it is represented in Japan by *fulvida*, Butler, and in North America by *basaliata*, Walker.

Yellow Shell (*Camptogramma bilineata*).

This very common and generally distributed species is subject to a good deal of variation in the tint of ground colour, and also in the greater or lesser amount of black marking. On Plate 85 six specimens are shown ; Figs. 4, 5 represent the more fre-quent form in most localities, but in many districts ab. *infus-cata*, Gumppenberg (Fig. 6), is hardly less common ; in some specimens the central band is entirely blackish, and occasion-ally the middle area of the band is partly or wholly whitish. Sometimes the wings are uniformly yellow without markings, but such aberrations are scarce, or have not been noted often. A small form occurring in the Hebrides and the Shetlands, var. *atlantica*, Staud., has the wings generally darkened ; Figs. 7–9 depict three specimens from the Isle of Lewis. Portraits of two very local Irish forms will be found on Plate 61 ; one

1-6. **July Highflyer.**   7-10. **May Highflyer.**   11, 12. **Ruddy Highflyer.**

1. July Highflyer: *eggs and caterpillars.*
2. May Highflyer: *caterpillar.*

is ab. *hibernica*, Prout (Fig. 5), and the other approaches the dark ab. *isolata*, Kane (Fig. 6).

The eggs, which are laid loosely, are yellowish or pale straw colour (Plate 84, Fig. 3*a*). Caterpillar, stoutish, green inclining to yellowish ; three lines on the back, the central one dark green, and the others yellowish, as also are the ring divisions; a pale wavy line low down along the sides. In some examples the general colour is pale greyish-brown, inclining to reddish brown. It feeds on grass, dock, chickweed, and various low-growing plants, from August to May, and is often abundant in hay meadows (Fig. 3, Plate 84, is from a coloured drawing by Mr. A. Sich). The moth occurs throughout the summer, and is very plentiful (often a pest) in almost every hedgerow and most bushy places.

July Highflyer (*Hydriomena furcata*).

Some idea of the variable character of this species (*sordidata*, Fab., and *elutata*, Hübner) may be formed from the selection of half a dozen examples shown on Plate 86. The typical form has the fore wings greyish, with dark bands as in Fig. 1, and a modification without the dark bands seems to be ab. *cinereata*, Prout. In the form *sordidata*, Fabricius, the general colour of the fore wings is greenish, and the bands are dark; ab. *obliterata*, Prout, is of the same colour, but the bands are absent. Ab. *fusco-undata*, Donovan, has the general colour reddish, with dark bands ; without dark bands it becomes *testaceata*, Prout. Blackish or sooty forms are referable to *infuscata*, Staud. (Fig. 4). Frequently in the green forms, and less often in the reddish, there is a broad whitish central stripe, and a narrow one on the basal area ; in the green form again the basal and central areas are occasionally crossed by red bands, and this is one of the prettiest forms of the species and, so far as I know, occurs only in the large sallow-feeding race ;

it possibly represents ab. *fusco-undata*, which is most frequent in the smaller moorland race.

The egg (Plate 87, Fig. 1*b*) when figured, February 8, 1908, was whitish as regards the shell, but the interior was dark greenish. In April the caterpillar appeared to be formed, but it did not leave the shell until early in May.

The full-grown caterpillar (Plate 87, Figs. 1, 1*a*) is brownish, inclining to blackish ; whitish between the rings, white lines along the back and sides, and tinged with red along the spiracular region. It feeds, in May and June, on sallow, willow, poplar, hazel, bilberry, and heather. The moth is out in July and August, but I have seen the small bilberry-feeding form (Plate 86, Figs. 5, 6) on a corner of Exmoor, North Devon, in great profusion in late June, whilst in the same district the sallow-feeding, larger form appeared about a fortnight later, at which time specimens among bilberry were not numerous, and rather shabby in appearance.

Except perhaps in the Shetlands, this species is to be found in all parts of the British Isles. It is very common in hedgerows, and around the margins of woods ; the smaller race frequents woods where bilberry is established, and also occurs on mountains and moors.

Abroad, the range extends to Amurland, China, Japan, and also to North America.

May Highflyer (*Hydriomena impluviata*).

The typical and commoner form of this species is shown on Plate 86, Figs. 7 and 8. The ground colour, usually pale green, is sometimes almost white, but more frequently it is tinged with greyish brown, thus leading up to the blackish ab. *infuscata*, Prout (Figs. 9, 10).

The caterpillar is brownish grey, or purplish grey, dotted with black and dappled with dark brown ; of the three lines along

1. Royal Mantle.   2-4. Shoulder-stripe.   5, 6. Barberry Carpet.
7, 8. The Streamer.   9, 10. The Flame.

1, 1a. **Shoulder-stripe:** *caterpillar and chrysalis*
2, 2a. **Streamer:** *eggs and caterpillars.*

the back, the central one is black and swells out on the middle of each ring, the others are pale ; a clear stripe of the ground colour below the black spiracles, and a slender line above them. The general colour is sometimes pale pinky brown or ochreous. It feeds on alder throughout the summer and autumn, and may be found in its domicile of spun-together dry leaves even in November, and sometimes later. Occasionally, a few caterpillars will feed up quickly, and attain the moth state in July or August, but the bulk do not become chrysalids until later in the year, and the moths emerge therefrom in May and early June. (Plate 87, Fig. 2.)

The species seems to occur, more or less freely, wherever there are alders throughout the greater part of the British Isles.

Abroad, the range extends to Eastern Siberia and Amurland.

Ruddy Highflyer (*Hydriomena ruberata*).

This species is most readily distinguished from the last by the short oblique black streak on the tips of the rather narrower fore wings ; there are also black streaks between the veins and below the tips of the wings, as in the last species, but they are generally shorter and often hardly traceable.

The ground colour ranges from pale grey (sometimes with a green tinge), through brownish grey to reddish brown ; usually central and outer marginal bands of a darker shade are present, but these characters may be very indistinct or entirely lost in the general coloration. (Plate 86, Figs. 11 and 12.)

The caterpillar is pale brown, dappled with grey ; three dark greyish lines along the back ; spiracles and the usual dots black, the latter with fine hairs ; head, reddish brown, plates on first and last rings of the body light brown. It feeds, at night, during the summer and autumn, on sallow and willow, spinning together the leaves at the top of a twig to form a retreat during the day.

The moth is found in hedges, woods, and on heaths, in May and June ; it may be occasionally beaten out of sallow bushes, but flies in the early evening, and is then more readily obtained. The species is widely distributed, but not generally common, in England and Wales, and in Scotland to Perthshire and probably further north, as it is found in Orkney, where specimens are numerous but rather small in size, and the caterpillars, according to McArthur, feed on heather as well as on sallow. Decidedly uncommon in Ireland, but it has been met with, in most instances singly, in Armagh, Tyrone, Westmeath, Kerry, Galway, and Sligo.

Royal Mantle (*Anticlea cucullata*).

This species (Plate 88, Fig. 1) is also known as *sinuata*, Hübner.   The white fore wings have a blackish patch at the base and a blackish mark on the front margins beyond the middle ; the former is separated into two parts by a pale reddish-brown band, and there is a reddish band, most distinct on the front area, beyond the black mark ; in some specimens these bands are greyish.

The caterpillar is green, sometimes inclining to yellowish, with two black or purplish stripes, enclosing a broader pale yellow one, along the back ; head, green, freckled with black. It feeds on the flowers of bedstraw (*Galium mollugo*, and *G. verum*), in July and August, or later in some seasons.

The moth is out in late June and in July, and occasionally may be disturbed from its food plant or the surrounding herbage. About dusk it is on the wing, and later is attracted by light.   It seems to occur in most of the English counties from Kent to Cornwall ; also in Berks., Oxon., Herts, and the eastern counties. Always local, and except in the east, where it is found in the Breck-sand area, most frequent in chalky localities.   Barrett notes a specimen from Knowle, Warwickshire, and there are at least two records from Scotland (Perthshire). In Ireland, Mr. W. F. de V. Kane took one example from a wall in co. Clare, and another has been recorded from Galway.

The range of the species abroad extends to Siberia and Amurland; and it is represented in Corea and Japan by *A. yokohamæ*, Butler.

The Shoulder Stripe (*Anticlea badiata*).

The ground colour of the fore wings is pale ochreous brown, inclining to whitish; there are three dark-edged black cross-lines, the first of them sharply bent below the front margin, the second is rather oblique, and the third is wavy and often not clearly defined towards the inner margin; the outer marginal area is broadly bordered with pale reddish brown or dark purplish brown, there is a black streak from the more or less indistinct, whitish submarginal line to the tips of the wings, and a white mark about the middle of the line; the ground colour is most in evidence on the central area of the wings, but even here it is frequently reduced to a slender band, or occasionally only a patch near the front margin of the wing. (Plate 88, Figs. 2–4.)

The caterpillar (Plate 89, Fig. 1) is green, inclining to yellow between the rings; the spiracles are black, and there is some-times a pinkish brown or purplish stripe along their area. Varies in general colour, and also in marking. It feeds, at night, on wild rose, and may be beaten from the bushes from May to July. When full grown it forms an oval cocoon in the earth, and therein changes to a chrysalis (Plate 89, Fig. 1*a*), which is dark reddish brown, inclining to blackish on the thorax, wing-cases, and the front edges of the body rings.

The moth appears in March and April, and may be obtained from almost any hedgerow, where wild rose is plentiful, through-out the British Isles, except that it seems not to extend north of Moray in Scotland.

Barberry Carpet (*Anticlea berberata*).

The fore wings are greyish or whitish, tinged with grey; there are two dark-edged black lines on the basal half, and a black line beyond the middle of the wings; the latter has a conspicuous tooth in its upper half, but the lower wavy half is indistinct; there is a black streak in the tip of the wing. (Plate 88, Figs. 5, 6.)

The stout and roughened caterpillar is brown, with indistinct darker stripes along the back; the head is brown, checkered with darker brown. It feeds, in June and July, on barberry (*Berberis vulgaris*); there is a second brood in late August and September.

The moth is out in May and early June, and again in August. Although it certainly has been noted from other parts of England, the species seems at present to be confined to the eastern counties. Barrett gives Somerset also.

The Flame (*Anticlea rubidata*).

The markings on the reddish fore wings of this species (Plate 88, Figs. 9 and 10) are somewhat similar to those of the last mentioned, but there is no black streak in the tips of the wings, and the upper part of the outer black line is not toothed. The lower central area is often greyish, and the reddish ground colour is sometimes obscured.

The caterpillar is pale brown, sometimes greyish or greenish tinged, with obscure darker diamond-shaped marks on the back; a black central line, indistinct on the middle rings; under side striped and lined with pale and dark brown; head, with a black V-shaped mark. It feeds, in July and early August, on bedstraw (*Galium mollugo* and *G. verum*), and will eat cleavers or goosegrass (*G. aparine*) in confinement.

Pl. 90.

1. Blomer's Rivulet: *caterpillar.*
2. Small White Wave: *caterpillar.*
3. Haworth's Pug: *caterpillar.*

1, 3. **Dingy Shell.**   2, 4. **Small Yellow Wave.**   5, 6. **Small White Wave.**
7, 9. **Waved Carpet.**   8, 10. **Blomer's Rivulet.**

The moth flies in June and July, and in the daytime may be readily disturbed from hedges in localities on the chalk in the southern half of England and Wales, especially in the seaboard counties from Kent to Cornwall. It has been recorded from Derbyshire and Yorkshire, and once from the Isle of Arran (*Entom.* xv. 250).

The Streamer (*Anticlea nigrofasciaria*).

The two examples of this species depicted on Plate 88 show the ordinary form with the central area of the fore wings greyish brown (Fig. 7, Essex), and a New Forest specimen in which the central area is whitish (Fig. 8).

The long caterpillar is green, inclining to yellowish between the rings; a purplish, or reddish-brown, stripe along the back is broken up into spots on the middle rings. It feeds on the flowers and leaves of wild rose, and can be found or beaten out in May and June. (Plate 89, Figs. 2, larva, 2*a*, ova.)

The moth is out in April and early May, and is often seen at rest on palings, etc., but it occurs chiefly in hedgerows, along which it flies at dusk.

This species (also known as *derivata*, Borkhausen) is pretty well distributed over England, Wales, and Scotland up to Sutherlandshire. In Ireland it seems to be local.

Dingy Shell (*Euchœca obliterata*).

This pale ochreous brown species (Plate 91) is in the male (Fig. 1) more or less sprinkled and shaded with darker brown, and the three brown cross lines are consequently often obscure, and rarely as distinct as in the female (Fig. 3).

The green caterpillar has a yellow line running down the middle of a black stripe along the back, and this stripe is bordered on each side with yellow, and broken up by the yellow ring divisions ; head, with a black spot on each side. It feeds, in July and August, on alder.

The moth is out in June and early July, and will be found in almost every locality in England where the alder flourishes, most plentifully, perhaps, on the eastern and western sides. It has been recorded from North and South Wales, but it does not seem to have been noted from Ireland or Scotland.

The range abroad extends to Amurland and Japan.

Small White Wave (*Asthena candidata*).

The delicately lined white moth shown on Plate 91, Figs. 5 ♂ and 6 ♀, is chiefly a woodland species. It is generally common in the south of England, occurs more or less frequently throughout the northern half, and is widely distributed in Wales. In Scotland, it is said to be locally common in Clydesdale, and to be found in Arran and in Perthshire. It is plentiful at Dromoland, co. Clare, Ireland, not uncommon in parts of Galway, and once recorded from Wicklow.

The caterpillar is found, in July and August, on birch, hazel, and wild rose. In general colour it is green, inclining to bluish at each end, and tinged with yellowish along the ridge on the sides ; the back is marked with crimson. (Plate 90, Fig. 2, after Hofmann.)

The moth is out in May and June, and sometimes July, and individuals of a second generation occasionally appear in August or September.

Small Yellow Wave (*Asthena luteata*).

This pretty little species (Plate 91, Figs. 2 and 4) has the pale yellowish wings marked with ochreous brown lines, which vary in thickness, and a dash of the same colour on the fore

Pl. 92.

1. **Grey Pug:** *egg and caterpillar.* 2. **Lime Speck Pug:** *caterpillars.*
3. **Common Pug:** *caterpillar.* 4. **Netted Pug:** *caterpillar.*
5. **White-spotted Pug:** *caterpillar.* 6. **Currant Pug:** *caterpillar.*
7. **Bordered Pug:** *chrysalids.*

1, 4. **Lime Speck Pug.**   2, 5, 8, 11. **Netted Pug.**   7, 10. **Foxglove Pug.**
3, 6. **Toadflax Pug.**   9. **Marbled Pug.**   12. **Dwarf Pug.**

wings, from the central pair of lines to the middle of the outer margin.

The caterpillar, which feeds in August and September, on maple, and in the northern counties on alder, is green, inclining to whitish between the rings.

The moth is out in June and early July, sometimes from mid May in warm localities. It is widely distributed over England and Wales, and in the southern counties of England it occurs in hedges wherever the maple grows, but in the midlands and northwards it is chiefly found among alder. In Scotland it is local and rare in Clydesdale, and is known to occur in Perthshire.

Abroad, the range extends to Amurland and Japan.

Waved Carpet (*Asthena testaceata*).

The typical, greyish-dusted, white form is depicted on Plate 91, Figs. 7 ♂ and 9 ♀. Mr. E. R. Bankes states (*Entom.*, xl. 33) that in one restricted area in mid-Kent this species varies in the direction of melanism, and he describes two forms as under : ab. *intermedia* has the usual coloration, but the wings are thickly dusted with dusky brown, chiefly along the front edge of the fore wings, and the cross lines are more distinct than in the type. In ab. *goodwini* all the wings have the whitish ground colour largely obscured by dusky brown powdering.

The rather spindle-shaped caterpillar is purplish brown, inclining to greenish on the sides and below at each end ; on the back of the middle rings are whitish V-marks, and the last three rings incline to purplish red above (adapted from Fenn). It feeds on the young leaves of alder, birch, and sallow, in July and August. The moth is out in June, and hides by day among the bushes, but may be seen occasionally on tree-trunks. Its haunts are in damp woods and plantations, and it occurs in most of the English and Welsh counties, although it is rarely common, except in the south of England. In Ireland it has been noted as scarce in counties Wicklow, Kerry, Galway, and Sligo.

The range abroad extends to Amurland and Japan.

Blomer's Rivulet (*Asthena blomeri*).

The earliest British specimens of this species (Plate 91, Figs. 8 ♂ and 10 ♀) were taken in Castle Eden Dean, Durham, and among the first to detect these was Captain Blomer, after whom Curtis named the species in 1832. It is still found in that locality, but is also known to occur in Cumberland, Lancs., Yorks., Derby, Staffs., Merionethshire, Worcester, Hereford, Glamorgan, Gloucester, Somerset, Devon, Wilts., Oxford, and Bucks.

The slender caterpillar is yellowish green, generally marked with pinkish-brown on the back, but most or all such markings may be absent. It feeds, on wych elm (*Ulmus montana*) (Plate 90, Fig. 1), in August and September. The moth is out in June and July, earlier or later in some seasons. As a rule, it sits on the trunks of beech trees, but I have seen it on the stems of cherry and fir, though hardly ever on wych-elm. Occasionally, newly emerged specimens have been noted on the leaves of dog's mercury (*Mercurialis perennis*).

The range abroad extends to Amurland and Japan.

Lime-speck Pug (*Eupithecia oblongata*).

The characteristic features of this white, or greyish white species (Plate 93, Figs. 1 and 4) is the bluish grey blotch or the front margin, in the lower end of which is the black disca spot. Occasionally, the blotch is much reduced in size, but it is usually large, and sometimes there are indications of a dusky stripe from it to the inner margin.

When freshly laid, the egg is whitish, but changes to pale orange. The caterpillar (Plate 92, Figs. 2, 2a) is greenish, with more or less connected reddish marks on the back, or green inclining to yellowish, or bluish, without markings. It feeds through the summer on flowers of ragwort, knapweed, scabious, yarrow, golden rod, and Mr. R. Adkin found it on gladiolus.

The moth, which is often common in gardens, is out from May to August, and specimens of a second brood occur in September and October.

It is widely distributed over the British Islands, but in Scotland it does not, apparently, extend north of Perthshire.

Foxglove Pug (*Eupithecia pulchellata*).

The fore wings are pale ochreous brown with a dusky basal patch limited by a black line ; a greyish central band inclining to blackish near the costa, and clouded with ochreous below the middle ; the black-and-white edges are wavy ; a reddish stripe across the wing before the central band, and a similar, but more irregular, one beyond the band. The hind wings are whitish grey, with several dark-grey bands (Plate 93, Figs. 7 ♂, 10 ♀).

In var. *hebudium*, Sheldon, from the Hebrides, the usual reddish stripes are replaced by narrower dark-brown ones ; the space left by the reduction in width is white, giving the insect a decidedly grey appearance.

The caterpillar lives in the flowers of the foxglove (*Digitalis purpurea*) and feeds therein upon the stamens and the immature seeds. It enters by boring through the side walls, and then secures the longer lobe of the blossom to the shorter upper one with a few silken threads. Tenanted flowers have a rather faded look and are easily detected. July is the best month, but the caterpillar may be found earlier as well as later.

The moth is out in May and June, and is found in almost every part of the British Isles where the foxglove is common.

Toadflax Pug (*Eupithecia linariata*).

Very similar to the last species, but generally smaller, neater and more glossy looking. The central band of the fore wing is blacker, without ochreous clouding below the middle, and the edges are not wavy. The hind wings are darker, and the only distinct band is a whitish one beyond the middle (Plate 93, Figs. 3, 6).

The caterpillar is yellowish green, with a series of dull olive or rust coloured spots or bars along the back, bordered on each side by a dusky olive line ; in some examples the markings are absent (Crewe). It feeds in the flowers of yellow toadflax (*Linaria vulgaris*), and may be reared on flowers of the snap-dragon (*Antirrhinum*). It is hardly necessary to examine each blossom separately to find the caterpillar, except, perhaps, to make sure when doubtful about the quarry being there. Probably, a handful of the flower sprays gathered in August or September in any locality in the southern half of England where the food plant abounds would furnish moths in the following May or June. The *Linaria* should be secured on a dry day for choice, but when brought home it need not be put in water ; just throw it into an airy breeding cage, and hopefully await emergence of the perfect insects in due course. Sometimes caterpillars attain the moth state the same year.

The range of the species in England extends to Durham, but it seems to be rather uncommon from the Midlands north-wards. It is found in Wales, and has been recorded once from Scotland (Inverurie), and once from Ireland (Dublin).

Marbled Pug (*Eupithecia irriguata*).

The fore wings are whitish and rather shining, the discal spot is black and very distinct, but the dark grey-brown markings, which are only well defined on the front and outer marginal areas, vary in intensity (Plate 93, Fig. 9).

The long, slender and roughened caterpillar is dull yellowish green ; three lines along the back, the central one reddish and expanded on the middle rings, the others yellowish, head, reddish. It feeds on oak, in late May and in June. The moth is out in April and May, and is sometimes found on fences or palings in the neighbourhood of oak woods, but may be jarred from the oak boughs, on the undersides of which it usually sits.

The New Forest in Hants is, perhaps, the best British locality for the species, but it has been found in Dorset (Glanville's Wootton), Devon (Exeter district, Tiverton, etc.), Sussex (Abbots Wood, St. Leonard's Forest, etc.), Wilts. (Savernake Forest) ; also oak woods in Surrey, Berks., Gloucester, Hereford and Glamorgan. On the eastern side it occurs in Suffolk (Bury and Needham), and Norfolk.

Dwarf Pug (*Eupithecia pusillata*).

The fore wings of this species (Plate 93, Fig. 12) are pale greyish white, discal spot black, cross lines irregular dark grey inclining to brownish, usually most distinct on the front margin.

The long, slender caterpillar is orange-red or dull ochreous green ; three dusky olive lines along the back, the central one often only distinct on the front rings ; a yellow line low down along the sides. It feeds, in June and early July, on spruce (*Picea excelsa*). The moth is out in May and June, and rests by day among the branches of the spruce.

Series II.

Q

The species is very local, but is found in Kent (West Wickham, etc.), Surrey (Mickleham district), Hants (New Forest), Devon (Exeter district, Plymouth), Wilts. (Watlington district), and Suffolk.

Ochreous Pug (*Eupithecia indigata*).

Captured specimens of this pale greyish-ochreous-brown species nearly always have a washed-out appearance, and even freshly emerged examples are unattractive. In some specimens, cross lines are more or less traceable on the fore wings; in others four or five tiny dusky dots will be noted on the front edge; as a rule, the only clearly defined character is the black discal spot (Plate 96, Fig. 1).

The long caterpillar is greenish-yellow or yellowish-red; three lines on the back, the central one brownish, but often only distinct on the front rings; the others, and also one low down along the sides, yellowish; head, reddish (adapted from Crewe). It feeds, in June and July, on pine and larch, or may be reared on juniper.

The moth is out in May and June, and sometimes there seems to be another emergence in the latter part of the summer. It frequents pine-woods, where it rests upon the trunks and branches of the trees.

Generally distributed over the whole of England; has been found in South Wales, and occurs in Perthshire, in Scotland. In Ireland, it has been noted from Tyrone, Derry, and Galway.

Pinion-Spotted Pug (*Eupithecia insigniata*).

The greyish white fore wings have a blackish basal line, and three slender double lines between this and the outer margin; three blotches on the front margin of the wings, the middle one

Pl. 94.

1. **Plain Pug:** *caterpillars.*
2. **Dark Spinach:** *caterpillars.*

1. Pimpinel Pug.   4. Thyme Pug.   7. Bleached Pug.   3, 6, 10. Wormwood Pu
9. Currant Pug.   2, 12. Ling Pug.   5. Campanula Pug.   8, 11. Jasione Pug.

blackish, the others brown with dashes of the same colour below ; discal spot, black and streak-like (Plate 96, Fig. 2).

The long, slightly roughened caterpillar is green, inclining to yellowish, especially between the rings ; reddish marks on the back connected by a slender line of the same colour ; head, green, flecked with reddish. It feeds, on apple, eating flowers and leaves, in May and June. Also said to eat hawthorn and sloe. The moth is out in April and May, but it is rarely met with in the open. If, however, one is lucky enough to capture a female, and fertile eggs are obtained, moths should hardly fail to result. From these the stock might go on increasing year by year for quite a long period. Ten specimens presented to the National Collection of British Lepidoptera in 1904, by the late Mrs. Hutchinson, were bred in April of the previous year, and were the direct descendants of a female captured in 1874, at Grantsfield, Herefordshire.

Other counties in England from which the species has been recorded are—Worcester (Birchwood), Gloucester, Somerset, Wilts., Hants (Hayling Island), Sussex, Surrey, Kent, Berks., Bucks., Huntingdon, Cambridge (once bred from mixed larvæ beaten from hawthorn on the "Gogs"), Suffolk (beaten from hawthorn at Brandon, Tuddenham, etc.), and Norfolk.

As *insigniata*, Hübner, is claimed to be at least two years older than *consignata*, Borkhausen, the former name will have to be adopted for this species.

Netted Pug (*Eupithecia venosata*).

This moth has also been named by the old authors "the Pretty Widow Moth." On Plate 93 are shown four examples ; the typical form (Fig. 2), in which the fore wings are pale greyish, with black cross lines, two of which are edged with whitish ; var. *fumosæ*, Gregson = *nubilata*, Bohatsch (Fig. 5)—the Shetland race—is brownish grey, with the markings obscure ; Fig. 8

represents a variegated modification of the last form, for which the name *bandanæ* was proposed by Gregson; Fig. 11 depicts another specimen, which in its light-brown colour closely approaches the Orkney form var. *ochracæ*, Gregson = *orcadensis*, Prout.

Specimens from North Devon have a rather darker tone of the typical coloration, and those from North Wales and from Ireland incline to brownish.

The rather stumpy caterpillar is greyish brown above, and pale greenish or yellowish below; three darker brown lines along the back; head, blackish. It is found from late June to early August, in the seed capsules of catchfly (*Silene inflata*, *S. maritima*, etc.). Plate 92, Fig. 4, from a coloured drawing by Mr. A. Sich.

The moth is out in May and June, and is widely distributed over the British Isles.

Pimpinel Pug (*Eupithecia pimpinellata*).

A portrait of this species, which, as a British insect, was first noted in Suffolk nearly sixty years ago, will be found on Plate 95, Fig. 1. The fore wings are pale brownish, except on the front edge, which is greyish; the black discal spot is distinct and rather long; the median vein and its branches are dotted with black, and most of the cross lines are only distinct on the front margin, where they are blackish; the rather wavy whitish sub-marginal line is sometimes marked with blackish. In some specimens the costal half of the fore wings is greyish, and the other portion only tinged with pale brownish.

The long caterpillar is green, with three purplish lines along the back, the central one wider and more distinct than the others; the head is purple. Sometimes purple, with two lines of a deeper shade on each side of the back (Crewe). It feeds, in the autumn, on flowers of burnet-saxifrage (*Pimpinella*).

The moth is out in June and July, and in the late afternoon is occasionally put up from among its food plant or the herbage around, but such specimens are rarely worth keeping, unless of the female sex, when eggs may be obtained.

The species has a wide distribution in England, especially in the southern half; it occurs in Wales, and also in Ireland, but not in Scotland.

Thyme Pug (*Eupithecia distinctaria*).

This delicately marked species, better known, perhaps, as *constrictata*, Guenée (Plate 95, Fig. 4), has the fore wings whitish grey, with three slender blackish curved cross lines, and some less distinct greyish ones; the outer margin is slightly darker, and traversed by a wavy whitish line; discal spot black and conspicuous.

I have not seen specimens from the Hebrides, but, according to Barrett, these have a more decided grey tint.

The rather long, wrinkled caterpillar is dark green, inclining to yellowish between the rings, with a broad purplish red line along the back. It feeds on the flowers of wild thyme (*Thymus serpyllum*), in August and September.

The moth is out in June and July, and inhabits dry places where there is an abundant growth of wild thyme. It is easily alarmed, and quickly rises on the wing from its hiding-place among the herbage.

The species is, or has been, found in most of the southern counties of England, from Sussex to Cornwall, on the western side from Somerset to Westmorland, including North Wales and the Isle of Man; also recorded from Buckinghamshire, Yorkshire (Richmond), and Northumberland. In Scotland it occurs chiefly on the west to Ross, and in the Hebrides; in Ireland it is widely spread, but most frequently met with on the coast.

Bleached Pug (*Eupithecia expallidata*).

The ample wings light brown in colour, with large black discal spot, and smaller black marks on the front edge of the fore wings, distinguish this species (Plate 95, Fig. 7) from its closest British allies.

The caterpillar feeds, in September and October, on flowers of golden rod (*Solidago virgaurea*), but it will thrive on those of michaelmas daisy, and probably the asters of the garden. It varies in ground colour, but this is usually some shade of green, and there are brownish spots and lines on the back.

The moth is out from late June until August, and may be put up from among golden rod during the day, or netted as it flies about the plant in the gloaming.

It is rather local, but occurs in most of the southern counties of England, from Kent to Devonshire, and westward from Somerset to Hereford and South Wales ; also recorded from North Lancashire. Rare in Scotland, and only noted from Perthshire and Aberdeenshire. Reported from a few localities on the coast in Ireland.

Currant Pug (*Eupithecia assimilata*).

This species (Plate 95, Fig. 9) is similar in marking to that next mentioned, but the wings are shorter and rounder ; the fore wings are a trifle redder in tint, and the white mark at the termination of the submarginal line is usually more conspicuous.

The rather slender caterpillar, figured on Plate 92, Fig. 6, from a coloured drawing by Mr. A. Sich, is yellowish green, inclining to yellow between the rings ; three darker green lines on the back, the central one most distinct, the others rather broad and not well defined ; sometimes the central line is tinged with brown, as also is the front edge of each ring. It feeds on

1. **Ochreous Pug.**   2. **Pinion-spotted Pug.**   3, 4. **Edinburgh Pug.**
5-8. **Satyr Pug.**   9. **White-spotted Pug, var.** *angelicata.*

1. White-spotted Pug.   2, 5. Bordered Pug.   3. Larch Pug.
4, 7. **Common Pug.**   6. Grey Pug.   8, 11. Tawny Speckled Pug.
9. **Plain Pug.**   10. Golden-rod Pug.   12. Scarce Pug.
13. **Triple-spotted Pug.**   14. Shaded Pug.

currant and hop, and is said to eat the leaves of gooseberry also. The first brood is in June and July, and the second in the autumn. The moth is out in May and June and in August. It frequents gardens, and hides among the foliage, or occasionally sits on walls or palings; from hedges where the wild hop grows freely it may be beaten out in the daytime, but it flies in the twilight, sometimes in numbers, around the hop bines.

Widely distributed over England, Wales, and Scotland up to Ross; in Ireland it has been noted from Tyrone, Dublin, Cork, Galway, and Sligo.

Wormwood Pug (*Eupithecia absinthiata*).

The fore wings are reddish or purplish brown; cross lines indistinct, but represented on the front edge by black marks; discal dot black, submarginal line whitish interrupted, often indistinct, except above the inner margin (Plate 95, Figs. 3, 6, 10). The short, stout, and roughened caterpillar varies in colour, and may be yellowish green, deep rose colour, or dirty reddish brown; a series of lozenge-shaped reddish spots on the back, faint towards each end (often absent in green forms); oblique yellow stripes on the sides form borders to the marks on the back (adapted from Crewe). It feeds, in the autumn, on the flowers of ragwort, golden rod, aster, yarrow, hemp agrimony, etc. The moth is out in June and July.

The species is generally common in the south of England, and is widely distributed over the rest of that country, Wales, and Ireland. In Scotland its range extends to Moray.

Abroad, the distribution spreads to Amurland.

Ling Pug (*Eupithecia goossensiata*).

The fore wings are rather narrower and more pointed at the tips than those of the last species; the ground colour of the fore wings is of a paler reddish brown, and frequently tinged

with greyish; the hind wings are usually greyish-brown (Plate
95, Figs. 2, 12). The caterpillar, which feeds in August and
September on the flowers of heath (*Erica*), and ling (*Calluna*),
is pinkish with dusky marks on the back, most distinct on the
middle rings; a yellowish line low down along the side has
dusky marks upon it; head, dusky olive, marked with white
(adapted from Crewe).

It may be mentioned here, that *knautiata*, Gregson, which
was described as a distinct species, is by some authorities
considered to be a form of this species, whilst others refer it to
absinthiata. The caterpillar is stouter than that of *goossensiata*,
varies in colour from whitish to green, and even purplish-brown,
but not to pinkish; it feeds on the flowers and seeds of *Knautia
arvensis*. The moth is out in June and July, and occurs on
heaths and moors throughout England, Wales, and Ireland.
In Scotland, it is obtained freely in some parts of the south,
and its range extends to the Orkneys.

This species is the *minutata* of Guenée and other authors,
but this name, being a synonym of *absinthiata*, will have to be
discarded in favour of *goossensiata*, Mabille (1869).

Campanula Pug (*Eupithecia denotata*).

The faint reddish tinged pale-brown fore wings distinguish
this species (Plate 95, Fig. 5). The blackish marks on the
front edge are minute, the cross lines are usually indistinct
and often absent; the discal spot, however, is black and
conspicuous, and the whitish submarginal line is very wavy.
In general colour, the caterpillar is pale brownish; lines and
marks on the back, dark brown or blackish. It feeds on the
seeds of the nettle-leaved bell-flower (*Campanula trachelium*),
and may be reared on the flowers of the various kinds of
Campanula grown in gardens: August and early September.

The moth is out in July, but is rarely seen in a state of nature. Caterpillars, however, are not uncommon, where the food plant is plentiful, in several of the English counties from Worcester-shire southwards to Kent and Cornwall ; also in Norfolk.

This species is the *campanulata* of most British authors.

Jasione Pug (*Eupithecia jasioneata*).

Except that the ground colour inclines to dark greyish brown, and the cross markings are rather more in evidence, this species is somewhat similar to that last mentioned, pale specimens especially (Plate 95, Figs. 8, 11). The caterpillar feeds in the seed heads of sheep's bit (*Jasione montana*), is very like that of *denotata* (*campanulata*), and occurs in the same months. Possibly this insect, which is regarded as purely British, may eventually be reduced to varietal rank. As pointed out by Mr. Prout, it is in its paler form not easily separable from *atraria*, Herrich-Schaeffer, a mountain form of *denotata*, Hübner. Whether species or variety, it is equally interesting to the student of British Lepidoptera from the fact that, up to the year 1878, it seems to have been unknown to entomologists. From its close allies, it stands out more distinctly than do *absinthiata* and *goossensiata* from each other, and the latter can hardly escape a similar fate if *jasioneata* is degraded.

The moth is out in May and June, but it is very rarely seen at large, though caterpillars are found locally in Devon and Somerset, England ; at Barmouth, in Merionethshire, North Wales ; and in Cork and Kerry, Ireland. Possibly, it awaits discovery in several other parts of the British Isles, and almost certainly in the west of England. In ascertaining new localities for the species, the best method of investigation would be to search for the caterpillars.

White-spotted Pug (*Eupithecia albipunctata*).

This greyish brown species (Plate 97, Fig. 1) will be recognised by the white spot at the lower end of the whitish submarginal line on the fore wings; not infrequently there is a second white spot placed on the line about the middle, and sometimes a third near the front margin; the hind wings have a white dot at the anal angle, and, occasionally, a second is placed a little beyond. Ab. *angelicata*, Barrett, occurring with the type in the north of England, is blackish with the discal spot and the veins showing blacker, but without white spots. (Plate 96, Fig. 9.) The caterpillar is pale lemon yellow, or yellowish green; three brown lines along the back, the central one with brown marks upon it; some brownish marks on the sides. Variable in general colour, and the markings sometimes absent. It feeds on the flowers of angelica (*Angelica sylvestris*), hogweed (*Heracleum sphondylium*), and other Umbelliferæ. It has also been reared on a diet of elder leaves: August, September, or even later. Our figure (Plate 92, Fig. 5) is from a coloured drawing by Mr. A. Sich. The moth emerges in May and June, sometimes earlier in confinement, and then a second generation has resulted in July.

Widely distributed in England, in many localities the caterpillars are not uncommon, although the moth may never be seen at large. Also occurs in South Wales, in Scotland to Aberdeenshire; and in Ireland it has been found in Sligo and Cork.

Common Pug (*Eupithecia vulgata*).

This pug varies in colour from pale grey brown through reddish brown to blackish. In some of the lighter coloured specimens, the darker cross lines and the whitish submarginal lines are all well defined; more frequently, perhaps, most of

1. Lead-coloured Pug.   2. Haworth's Pug.   3. Valerian Pug.   4. Marsh Pug.
5. Slender Pug.   6. Maple Pug.   7. Angle-barred Pug.
8. Ash Pug.

1, 2. **Narrow-winged Pug.**   3. **Brindled Pug.**   4. **Mottled Pug.**
      5. **Oak-tree Pug.**   6, 7. **Juniper Pug.**   8-10. **Double-striped Pug.**
                        11-12. **Cloaked Pug.**

the markings are indistinct or absent, but the small black discal dot and a white spot above the outer angle of the fore wing remain fairly clear. (Plate 97, Figs. 4, 7, ab. *subfuscata*, Haw.) The caterpillar (Plate 92, Fig. 3) is brownish, inclining to reddish, dotted with white ; a series of dirty green marks along the back, and a pale yellow wavy line low down along the sides. It feeds on the leaves of sallow, hawthorn, bramble, bilberry, ragwort, golden-rod and various other plants. There are at least two broods in the year, one in June and July, and the other in the autumn. The moth flies in May and June, and again in August, and is often common, almost everywhere, over the greater part of the British Isles.

The range abroad extends to Eastern Siberia and Amurland.

Golden-rod Pug (*Eupithecia virgaureata*).

The fore wings of this obscurely marked species (Plate 97, Fig. 10) are pale greyish brown inclining to ochreous ; the discal spot is black, the veins are marked with dark brown and white, and the whitish submarginal line terminates in a white spot above the inner angle.

The caterpillar varies in colour from grey brown or purplish grey to reddish brown ; a series of blackish triangular spots on the back, and yellowish oblique stripes on the sides. It feeds on the flowers of the golden-rod (*Solidago virgaurea*), in the autumn ; also on ragwort (*Senecio*). The moth is out in May and early June, but in captivity there is apparently a second emergence in July and early August. The caterpillars from which these smaller and rather darker specimens result, hatch from the egg in May and feed on the flowers of beaked parsley (*Anthriscus sylvestris*).

Widely distributed in England, Wales and Ireland.

The range abroad extends to north-east Siberia ; and the species has been recorded from Japan.

Triple-spotted Pug (*Eupithecia trisignaria*).

The most noticeable markings on the rather shiny, pale-brown fore wings of this species (Plate 97, Fig. 13) are the black discal spot and two blackish clouds above it on the front margin.

The stoutish caterpillar is green, with three darker green lines along the back, and a wavy yellowish line low down along the sides ; head, black. It feeds, in the autumn, on flowers and seeds of angelica and cow-parsnip, but the former is its chief food.

June and July are the months for the moth, but it is rarely met with in the open. The only English counties in which the species has been noted are Surrey, Sussex, Dorset and Devon in the south ; from Herefordshire in the west its range extends through Worcester, Warwick, Leicester, and Derby to Lancashire and York. In Scotland, Renton records it as common at Hawick, in Roxburghshire; and it was recorded from Argyllshire in 1902. Hardly known in Ireland.

Larch Pug (*Eupithecia lariciata*).

This species (Plate 97, Fig. 3) is very like that next referred to, but the fore wings are rather longer, the ground colour is whiter, and the dark-grey or blackish cross lines are rather more angled and slanting; the hind wings are paler, and especially so on the front margins.

The long caterpillar is bright green, with a darker green line along the back, merging into reddish on the last ring ; sometimes reddish ochreous with the line along the back brownish. It feeds, in June and July, on larch, and will also eat spruce.

The moth is out in May and early June, and may be jarred from larch trees, or sometimes be found at rest on their stems.

As a British species, it was first met with in Surrey, in 1862, then it was noted in Sussex, and shortly afterwards in Yorkshire. At the present time, it will probably be found in any locality where larch is plentiful.

Grey Pug (*Eupithecia castigata*).

Although, as the English name suggests, this insect is greyish, there is always a tinge of ochreous in the composition of its general colour (Plate 97, Fig. 6). Not infrequently the ground colour is decidedly brownish in tint. The markings vary in clearness, but are most distinct in the paler forms. A blackish form occurs in the north of England, and in the Clydesdale district of Scotland, and was formerly known as the " Paisley Pug."

The longish caterpillar (Plate 92, Fig. 1) is pale or dusky olive, varying to reddish brown, with a series of darker marks on the back. It feeds, from August to October, on the foliage of almost any plant.

The moth is out in May and June, and occasionally a few specimens emerge in the autumn. Generally distributed over the British Isles, but apparently not noted in the Orkneys and Shetlands.

Abroad, the range extends to Amurland.

Plain Pug (*Eupithecia subnotata*).

The fore wings of this species are pale ochreous brown, inclining to pale reddish on the outer marginal area; the most distinct markings are a pale cross band beyond the black discal dot, and a pale winding submarginal line. The hind wings are smoky grey, with whitish wavy cross lines, the most distinct being the outer (Plate 97, Fig. 9). The stoutish and somewhat stumpy caterpillar is green, or pale yellowish brown, with three darker lines and marks on the back ; a yellowish line low down on the sides.   It feeds on flowers and seeds of orache (*Atriplex*), and goosefoot (*Chenopodium*): August and September.   Figured on Plate 94, Figs. 1, 1*a*, from coloured drawings by Mr. A. Sich. In July, the moth may be disturbed from its food plant or adjacent herbage, or it may be seen resting on palings or fences.   It flies at night, and will come to light.

Not uncommon in many places in the southern half of England, and found in the rest of the country, chiefly on the coast, to Hartlepool in Durham, also in Wales.   Once recorded from south Scotland, and only noted from the coast near Dublin, in Ireland.

Scarce Pug (*Eupithecia extensaria*).

The conspicuously marked insect represented on Plate 97, Fig. 12, is, so far, only known to occur, in Britain, on the coasts of Norfolk and Yorkshire.   It was first discovered in the latter county more than thirty years ago ; about twelve years later it was found on the Norfolk coast, and caterpillars were also obtained from the sea wormwood (*Artemisia maritima*) in the autumn.

The long caterpillar, which feeds on the flowers and foliage of its food plant, is green, with three lines along the back, the central one dusky and the others whitish ; a white stripe low down along the sides is edged below with rosy brown.   It will thrive on the cultivated southernwood or "lad's love" (*Artemisia abrotanum*).

The moth is out in June and July, and may be found in its haunts among the sea wormwood, not only on the coast of Norfolk, but quite possibly, here and there, in suitable places on the east coast from Essex to the Humber.   Caterpillars may be obtained in August and September.

1. **V. Pug.**   2-6. **Green Pug,** *and vars.*   7, 8. **Bilberry Pug.**

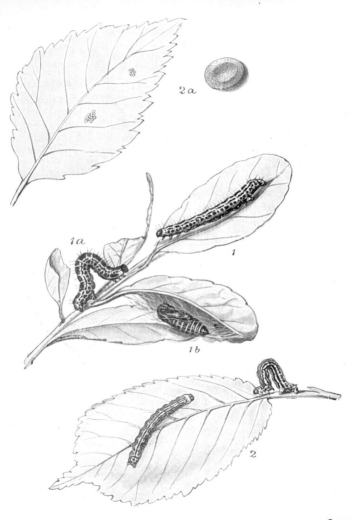

1. **Magpie**: *caterpillars and chrysalis.*
2. **Clouded Magpie**: *eggs, natural size and enlarged, and caterpillars.*

Edinburgh Pug (*Eupithecia helveticaria*).

The two examples of this species on Plate 96, Figs. 3, 4, are from the Pentland Hills, Scotland, and are referable to *anglicata*, Millière. In this form, which is smaller than the type, the fore wings are grey brown, more or less tinged with reddish, and sometimes inclining to purplish ; the whitish edged dark cross lines, especially the basal first and second, are usually distinct, and the veins are often marked with black and white. Ab. *arceuthata*, Freyer, a paler grey form, occurs in Buckinghamshire, and has also been reported from Surrey. The specimens from the latter county, at least those from the Dorking district, were subsequently referred to *E. satyrata*.

The stoutish and rather rough caterpillar is green, with three lines along the back, the central one dark green, and the others white ; a broad yellowish stripe low down along the sides. It feeds on juniper, in June and July, and sometimes again in September and October. The moth is out in April, May, and June, and a second brood may appear in August and September. The species seems to occur among juniper, in Scotland, from Roxburghshire to Sutherland. It is local in North Lancashire, has been reported from near Llandudno, North Wales, and, as adverted to above, occurs in Bucks.

Satyr Pug (*Eupithecia satyrata*).

Four specimens are depicted on Plate 96. Fig. 5 represents the typical pale brownish grey form, in which the cross lines are indistinct, and the veins are marked with white and dusky. Fig. 6 shows the rather browner, moorland ab. *callunaria*, Doubleday, and Figs. 7 and 8 depict two forms of the Shetland race, known as var. *curzoni*, Gregson. A much rarer form than any of the above is the pale brownish ab. *pernotata*, Guenée (*cauchyata*, Meyrick).

The caterpillar is greenish with a series of purplish-brown edged, dusky green, Y-shaped marks along the back; above the yellow spiracular line is a row of slanting purplish blotches; sometimes the general colour is paler, and the markings on the back and sides rosy; occasionally, the whole of the back is rosy (adapted from Crewe). It feeds on the flowers of knapweed (*Centaurea nigra*), scabious, hawkweed (*Hieracium*), heath, sallow, etc., etc.: August and September.

The moth is out in May and June, and is found in woodlands, and on heaths and moors. It is widely distributed over the British Isles.

Bordered Pug (*Eupithecia succenturiata*).

The fore wings are white, clouded and suffused with dark grey on all the margins. The greyish clouding sometimes covers the whole area of the wings, except a very limited space under the black discal spot (ab. *disparata*, Hübner). Plate 97, Figs. 2, a specimen from Lancs., 5, one from Surrey.

The caterpillar is reddish brown, paler in some specimens than in others; a series of blackish spear-head marks along the back, connected by a blackish line, and a dusky line on each side; a whitish line along the spiracles. It feeds, in September and October, on mugwort (*Artemisia vulgaris*), tansy (*Tanacetum vulgare*), and yarrow (*Achillea*). It may be reared on garden Chrysanthemum. Chrysalis, dark buff, inclining to brown; wing cases olive green; figure 7 on Plate 92 is from a photo by Mr. Main, and is enlarged to twice the natural size.

The moth is out in July and early August; it is not readily put up from its hiding-place among herbage, but at night, when on the wing, it will come to light.

The species is most frequent, perhaps, on the coast, but it is widely distributed over England and Wales. Rare in Ireland, and only noted from counties Armagh, Louth, and Dublin; Kane states that he met with it in some numbers on Lambay Island. Once reported from Ayrshire, Scotland.

The Surrey specimen (Fig. 5) appears to be referable to *exalbidata*, Staudinger, a form occurring chiefly in Asia, but occasionally found in Germany and elsewhere in Europe.

Tawny Speckled Pug (*Eupithecia subfulvata*).

Two forms of this species are shown on Plate 97. Fig. 8 represents the reddish typical form, and Fig. 11 (from Lancs. coast) the dark ab. *oxydata*, Treitschke. Between these two extremes, there are various intermediate forms, showing more or less distinct cross lines.

The caterpillar is reddish brown, with a chain of oval, olive-brown spots along the back; there are also two brownish interrupted lines; the spiracular line is white. Sometimes the general colour is ochreous brown, or grey brown. It feeds, in September and October, on yarrow, and will thrive on tansy, and the flowers of garden chrysanthemum.

The chrysalis of this species is said to differ from that of *E. succenturiata* in being of a rich red colour, inclining to buff on the wing cases.

In July and August, the moth may sometimes be seen resting on fences, but it is more frequently hidden away among herbage. At night it will visit flowers, especially those of the ragwort.

The species is widely distributed over England and Wales, and in Scotland up to Moray. In Ireland, it is found on the coast from Louth to Cork.

By some entomologists, *subfulvata*, Haworth, and its variety, *oxydata*, are set down as forms of the preceding species.

Series II.

R

Shaded Pug (*Eupithecia scabiosata*).

The grey, or greyish-brown lined, whitish species shown on Plate 97, Fig. 14, has been known by three names in Britain. It was named and described by Stephens, in 1831, as *piperata* (The Speckled Pug), from a specimen, or specimens, taken at Riddlesdown, near Croydon, Surrey; later, it was supposed to be the *subumbrata*, of the *Vienna Catalogue* (1776), and certainly of Guenée. The name given to it by Borkhausen, in 1794, appears to be the correct one, and is here adopted.

Crewe describes the caterpillar as yellowish green, with three dark lines on the back, the outer one not clearly defined; a yellow line on each side of the head, and of the last ring of the body.

It feeds on flowers of one of the hawkbits (*Leontodon hispidus*), and hawk's-beard (*Crepis taraxacifolia*), etc., from July to September. In June and early July, the moth may be started up from the herbage, as the collector walks over rough ground inland, or more frequently on the coast. It also occurs in fens, marshy places in woods, etc.

The species occurs in Bucks., Berks., Surrey, and in the seaboard counties from Norfolk in the east to Gloucestershire in the west, also in South Wales; in the north it is found in Lancashire, Yorkshire, Durham, and Northumberland. It is not common in Scotland, but has been reported from various parts, extending from Wigtown to Argyll and Aberdeen. In Ireland it is also a coast insect, from Donegal to Cork.

Haworth's Pug (*Eupithecia haworthiata*).

The fore wings of this species (Plate 98, Fig. 2) are pale greyish, with dark cross lines, and still darker narrow bands; hind wings, similar, but markings less distinct. Resembles the last species in size, but the wings are somewhat rounder, darker, and not so silky in appearance ; the body, near the thorax, is ochreous brown. Also known as *isogrammaria*, Herrich-Schaeffer, but *haworthiata*, Doubleday, is stated by Prout to be the older name.

In July and August the caterpillar (Plate 90, Fig. 3) may be found in the flower-buds of the traveller's joy or old man's beard (*Clematis vitalba*). It is green, with a bluish or pinkish tinge, and there are generally three darker stripes along the back, but these are sometimes absent ; occasionally the ground colour is yellowish.

The moth is out in June and July, and may be seen flying about clematis in the sunshine, but such specimens are not often worth taking. It is easily reared from caterpillars, which will thrive on flowers of garden *Clematis*, and may be obtained by the score, either by beating, or by searching for discoloured or black-specked flower buds of the traveller's joy.

The species is most frequent in the south of England, but it occurs in all the eastern, some of the midland, and also in the northern counties to Lancashire and Yorkshire ; in the last-named county, Porritt states that the caterpillars were found in profusion on *Clematis* near Wadworth, Doncaster, in 1901. It inhabits South Wales and Ireland.

Abroad, the species ranges to Amurland and China.

Valerian Pug (*Eupithecia valerianata*).

The fore wings of this species (Plate 98, Fig. 3) are brownish grey, with indistinct darker cross lines, and a wavy whitish sub-marginal line ; the latter is sometimes not clear, except towards the inner angle.

Caterpillar, rather short, bright green, with three darker green lines along the back ; a whitish line low down along the sides, and the ring-divisions are yellow. It feeds, in July and August, on flowers and seeds of all-heal, or cat's valerian (*Valeriana officinalis*).

The moth is out in May and June ; its haunts are in fens, marshes, and damp spots affected by its food plant, but, as a rule, is only found in the caterpillar state. A local, but widely distributed species in England ; occurs also in Wales and in Ireland.

Lead-coloured Pug (*Eupithecia plumbeolata*).

The small, obscurely marked species, represented on Plate 98, Fig. 1, has the fore wings whitish grey, sometimes assuming a yellowish tinge ; a number of rather wavy, darker cross lines, and a more or less clearly defined pale band beyond the middle ; discal spot always tiny and rarely distinct.

The stumpy caterpillar is yellowish green, with three purplish-red lines along the back, the central one swollen on each ring, and the others irregular ; sometimes the back is suffused with purplish-red. It feeds on the flowers of cow-wheat (*Melam-pyrum*) in July and August.

The moth is out in May and June, and is readily induced to fly out from among cow-wheat, or the other herbage around. It may be found in most of the English counties, wherever its food plant abounds ; in South Wales ; in Scotland to Argyll and Aberdeen, and in Ireland from Cork to Donegal.

The range abroad extends to Amurland.

Marsh Pug (*Eupithecia pygmæata*).

This species (Plate 98, Fig. 4) may be distinguished from *haworthiata*, which it approaches in size and general appearance, by its more pointed fore wings and the white dot at the inner angle of these wings.

The long, thin caterpillar is yellowish green; a pale olive line along the middle of the back, connecting a series of urn-shaped blotches of the same colour; two pale olive, irregular lines on each side. It feeds, in June and July, on flowers of stitchwort (*Stellaria holostea*).

The moth is out in May and June, sometimes later; examples of a second brood have been obtained in August and September. It flies in the afternoon, but only when the sun shines, and where the food plant grows freely.

The species occurs in all the eastern counties of England, in Bucks., and in the northern counties to Cumberland and Northumberland. In Wales it has been recorded from Colwyn, Denbighshire; in Scotland it is widely spread to Perthshire; it is local and scarce in Ireland.

Slender Pug (*Eupithecia tenuiata*).

The fore wings are rather rounded; grey, more or less tinged with brownish, and with ochreous or reddish brown along the front edge; the latter with dusky clouds upon it; the cross lines are dark grey brown and fairly distinct, and the discal spot is black (Plate 98, Fig. 5). A large grey form from Moray, in Scotland, has been named *cineræ*, Gregson.

Caterpillar, rather stumpy, and dingy yellowish green in colour, the sides and middle of the back rosy; a series of dusky spots, edged by black lines or short streaks, along the back; and a row of pinkish oblique stripes on the sides. It feeds, in the spring, in sallow catkins, and the moths may often be bred in numbers, in June and July, from those catkins which fall most readily from the bushes when we go "a sallowing." Moths frequently rest on the stems, and where there is a clump of well-grown sallows, a good series may be obtained.

The species is partial to fens and marshy places, and is found in such situations over the greater part of the British Isles.

Maple Pug (*Eupithecia inturbata*).

The fore wings are greyish brown, with many darker cross lines; the outer margin is darker and traversed by a pale line; discal dot, dark grey and not very distinct (Plate 98, Fig. 6). This species was long known as *subciliata*, Guenée, but is now referred to *inturbata*, Hübner.

In May and June the caterpillars may be beaten from maple, which is apparently the only food plant, and of which they have a decided preference for the flowers. When full grown the larva is yellowish green with a purplish stripe along the back, and whitish lines along the sides.

The moth may be jarred from the branches of the maple in July and August; it is occasionally seen resting on fences, etc. It seems to be found in England and Wales, in most places where there is a mature growth of maple.

The Angle-barred Pug (*Eupithecia innotata*).

The greyish-brown fore wings of this species (Plate 98, Fig. 7) are crossed by darker oblique lines, which are angled on the front margin; the submarginal line is white and irregular, especially at each end.

Caterpillar, ochreous grey, inclining to pinkish, marked on the back with white-edged, purplish- or reddish-brown blotches, and on the sides with reddish or purple spots; a whitish line low down along the sides. It feeds on the flowers of wormwood and mugwort (*Artemisia*), from August to October.

The moth, which is uncommon and very local in England, is out in July. It occurs in Devonshire (Exeter district), Kent (Wye), Essex (Shoeburyness), Lincolnshire (Skegness, etc.), Lancashire and Cheshire (coast sand-hills, Macclesfield, etc.), and Durham (Hartlepool).

Ash Pug (*Eupithecia fraxinata*).

Very similar to the last mentioned, but smaller, and the markings are less distinct (Plate 98, Fig. 8).

The caterpillar is variable, but generally some shade of green, occasionally purplish red ; lines on the sides yellowish, and sometimes there are dusky purplish marks on the back. It feeds, in August and September, on ash, and is said to eat *Artemisia*, *Laurustinus*, and the flowers of scabious. The moth is out in late June and July, and sometimes a second generation appears in the autumn.

This species, which by some entomologists is considered to be a form of *E. innotata*, is widely distributed over England, south Scotland, and Ireland. *Tamarisciata*, Freyer, is also considered by some authorities to be a form of *E. innotata*.

Some moths reared from larvæ obtained, in 1905, from Tamarisk, in Cornwall, have been referred to *tamarisciata*.

Narrow-winged Pug (*Eupithecia nanata*).

The rather variable species represented on Plate 99, Figs. 1 and 2, will easily be recognised by its long pointed fore wings, which in colour are whitish grey, darkened by brownish cross-stripes ; a whitish spot before the small, black discal dot.

The long, thin, caterpillar, which feeds on ling or heather in the autumn, is whitish with a greenish tinge : the sides are marked with red, and there are some reddish spots on the back.

On almost all heather-clad ground throughout the British Isles, this pretty little moth will be found, more or less commonly, during the months of May and early June, and sometimes there is a second flight in July and August.

Brindled Pug (*Eupithecia abbreviata*).

The ochreous grey fore wings of this species (Plate 99, Fig. 3) are crossed by dark, bent lines, and marked with black on the veins ; the central area is sometimes whitish, and generally paler than the ground colour.

Caterpillar, slender, ochreous brown in colour, with browner lines and redder V-shaped marks on the back. It feeds on oak, in June and July. The moth is not uncommon in oak woods, in April and May, and may be beaten from the boughs in the daytime, and not infrequently found resting on the trunks. Generally distributed, but in Scotland not noted north of Perthshire.

Oak-tree Pug (*Eupithecia dodoneata*).

This species (Plate 99, Fig. 5) differs from the last in being smaller, paler in colour, more distinctly marked, and with a rather larger and more conspicuous discal spot.

The caterpillar feeds, in June and July, on young leaves of oak, the flowers of the evergreen oak (*Quercus ilex*), and hawthorn. It is orange, or ochreous red, with blackish marks connected by a line of the same colour along the back, and yellowish stripes and lines on the sides.

The moth is out in May and early June, and occurs in some of the woods in most of the southern counties of England, and on the west to Worcestershire. It has been recorded from Yorks. and Cumberland ; from Glamorganshire, South Wales ; and from counties Armagh, Dublin, Wicklow, and Sligo, in Ireland.

Mottled Pug (*Eupithecia exiguata*).

In some respects this species (Plate 99, Fig. 4) is not unlike *E. abbreviata*, but the general colour of the fore wings is pale grey inclining to brownish ; a good character is the blackish band before the submarginal line, which is interrupted by patches of the ground colour, one above, and the other below, the middle ; the submarginal line is whitish towards the inner margin.

Caterpillar, long and thin ; dark green ; a series of yellow dotted reddish marks on the back, and a yellow-edged reddish line low down along the sides. It feeds, in the autumn, on hawthorn, sloe, currant, sallow, ash, etc.

The moth is out in May and June, and is sometimes seen at rest on the stems and branches of trees, fences, etc., and may be beaten out of hedgerows.

Widely distributed throughout England, Wales, Scotland to Perthshire, and Ireland.

Juniper Pug (*Eupithecia sobrinata*).

Two specimens are shown on Plate 99 : Fig. 6 represents a more or less typical example from the Surrey downs, and Fig. 7 a pale form from Forres in Scotland. The species varies in tint of ground colour, and in the strength of marking, in all its localities ; but in Scotland there is a greater tendency to pale forms than in England. Mr. H. McArthur, during the present year, obtained an extensive and most variable series from heather, at Aviemore, in Inverness. A pale-brownish tinged white pug found in Kent and the Isle of Wight, at one time referred to *E. ultimaria*, Boisduval, and afterwards known as *stevensata*, Webb, is really, according to Prout, *anglicata*, Herrich-Schaeffer. Whether this is a form of the present species or specifically distinct is still left in doubt, but personally I believe it to be a variety.

The dark-green, sometimes reddish marked, caterpillars may be beaten from juniper bushes, from April to early June. The moth is out from late July to early October, and may be found in nearly all parts of the British Isles where the food plant occurs, and occasionally in localities from which juniper appears to be absent.

Double-striped Pug (*Gymnoscelis (Eupithecia) pumilata*).

This species varies a good deal in the tint of the ground colour and the cross markings. Three forms are depicted on Plate 99 : Fig. 8 is a typical male, and Fig. 9 shows a female

FIG. 5.
Double-striped Pug, at rest.
(Photo by W. J. Lucas.)

with distinct red bands (ab. *rufifasciata*, Haworth); both specimens are from Surrey. The greyish example without red markings (Fig. 10) is from Ireland, and approaches ab. *tempestivata*, Zeller, in form.

The caterpillar ranges in colour from yellowish-green to reddish ; on the back there is a dark-green or blackish line, and often a series of marks of the same colour ; the lines on the sides are yellowish. It feeds chiefly in or on the flowers of furze, broom, holly, clematis, hawthorn, etc., from May to September. There are certainly two broods, possibly more. The specimens of the first, or spring, generation are usually larger in size and more strongly marked than those of the summer brood.

The moth is most frequent, perhaps, in April, May, July, and August, but it may be met with in either of the months from April to November. Pretty generally distributed over the British Isles, including the Hebrides and the Orkneys.

Cloaked Pug (*Eucymatoge togata*).

Over sixty years ago, this fine pug (Plate 99, Figs. 11 and 12) was detected in England. It was first noted in a plantation of spruce fir at Black Park, Buckinghamshire, in mid-June, 1845, and for many years this was the only known British locality. At the present time it is obtained more or less regularly in the New Forest, and has been recorded, chiefly in single specimens, from Wiltshire, Essex, Cambridgeshire, Suffolk, Yorkshire, and Durham. It is not uncommon in Scotland up to Inverness, but is most plentiful in Perthshire.

Kane (*Catalogue of the Lepidoptera of Ireland*) states that it is spreading over an extensive area in Ireland, as a result of the planting of spruce fir.

The caterpillar, which feeds in the spruce cones, and eats the immature seeds, is dingy white with a pinkish tinge, and suffused with blackish above; the lines along the back and sides, when present, are whitish but not distinct ; head, and raised dots on the body, black ; a brown plate on the first ring : July and August. Cones containing caterpillars may be secured by visiting a known locality for the species towards the end of August, especially immediately after a gale.

The moth may be dislodged from its resting place among the branches of the spruce in June, sometimes earlier or later.

V-Pug (*Chloroclystis coronata*).

This is " *Phalæna*" *v-ata*, Haworth, and also the V-Pug of that author. A later English name for the species is " The Coronet Pug," an Anglicism for the Latin specific name, and has reference to the black upper part of the outer cross line which is twice angled and bears a fanciful resemblance to a coronet; the lower angle is, however, most distinct, therefore Haworth's English name seems most suitable as it indicates the V-mark, which is a noticeable character of this delicate green species. (Plate 100, Fig. 1.)

The caterpillar is yellowish green, with three reddish lines along the back, the central one most distinct and sometimes forming triangular marks, or lozenges. The ground colour varies, and may be greener, yellower, or occasionally greyish; and the markings are not always present.

There are two generations, the first in June and July, and the second in the autumn, and in confinement a third brood is sometimes obtained. The blossoms of various plants are eaten, but those of hemp-agrimony (*Eupatorium cannabinum*), golden-rod (*Solidago*), clematis, and purple loosestrife (*Lythrum salicaria*), are perhaps favourites. Hawthorn and bramble have also been mentioned as food plants.

The moth is out in most of the months from May to August, but seems to be most frequent in the first named.

Generally distributed in the southern half of England, extending into South Wales, rare in Yorkshire and in Roxburghshire, Scotland. Widely distributed in Ireland. The range abroad extends to Japan.

Green Pug (*Chloroclystis rectangulata*).

Of this variable species five examples are shown on Plate 100. Figs. 2 and 3 represent the typical and more usual forms; 3 varies in the direction of ab. *subaerata*, Hübn., and Fig. 4 is the greyish ab. *cydoniata*, Bork. Ab. *nigrosericeata*, Haworth (Fig. 6), is blackish with white submarginal line; and an intermediate form (Fig. 5) may be referable to ab. *sericeata*, Haworth.

The stumpy caterpillar is of a pale yellow green colour, with a more or less distinct reddish or dark-green line along the back, and reddish ring-divisions. It feeds in flowers of the wild apple or crab, and of apples and pears grown in orchards and gardens. It is found in April and May, and the moth is out in June and July.

The species is common throughout the greater part of England and Wales, and its range extends to Ross in Scotland. It has a wide distribution in Ireland.

Bilberry Pug (*Chloroclystis debiliata*).

As a British insect, this species (Plate 100, Figs. 7 and 8) was first found in Devonshire, and was then known by the English name of "The Devon Pug." As the yellowish green caterpillar, marked with a darker line along the back and a yellowish one low down on the sides, feeds on bilberry, in April and May, and is by no means confined to Devonshire, the popular name here adopted is more suitable.

When quite fresh the moth, which is out in June and July, has a very delicate tinge of green, but this quickly fades out, leaving a pale greyish white insect. In the typical form (Fig. 7) the black central lines are fairly well defined, but in ab. *nigropunctata*, Chant (Fig. 8), the lines are represented by a series of dots.

The species is common in some of the sheltered hollows among the hills in Devon and Somerset, and I used to find it in abundance in the Martinhoe district, in the former county. The moths were rarely disturbed from the food plant during the day, but towards dusk they flew in numbers around small trees of mountain ash. Other counties in which it is known to occur are — England : Cornwall, Worcester, Staffordshire, Leicester, and Lancashire (formerly on Chat Moss). Wales : Glamorgan and Pembroke. Scotland : Aberdeen. Ireland : Wicklow, Waterford, Cork, Kerry, and Sligo.

Dentated Pug (*Collix sparsata*).

At one time this greyish brown species (Plate 102, Figs. 1, 2) was known by the English name of " Broom Scallop," but it is now usually referred to, in the vulgar tongue, as the Dentated Pug. The hind wings have their outer margins toothed rather than scalloped, and the insect has nothing to do with broom.

The rather long caterpillar is pale green, with four white lines along the back, and one on each side ; a whitish stripe along the black spiracles. Head, pale brown, rather flat above. (Adapted from Porritt.) It feeds on the yellow loosestrife (*Lysimachia vulgaris*), in July and August, or even later. Fens and marshy woodlands are the haunts of the moth, which is out in June and early July. It hides among the coarser vegetation, and is not always easily disturbed therefrom ; neither is it often noticed when on the wing at night, although it is sometimes found at the flowers of buckthorn.

Localities for the species are the fens of Cambridge and Norfolk, the boggy parts of the New Forest, Hants ; Dorset (Bloxworth and Hyde, etc.) ; Cheshire (Delamere Forest) ; Yorkshire (bogs near York, and Thorne Waste).

The range abroad extends to Japan.

Dark Spinach (*Pelurga comitata*).

The darker banded, pale ochreous species shown on Plate 102, Figs. 3 ♂, 4 ♀, varies in the colour of the band to brownish ; the central area of this band is almost always pale ochreous or whitish, to a greater or lesser extent.

Caterpillar, stout and roughened ; ochreous inclining to reddish, and tinged above with greenish ; a series of V-shaped marks along the back, yellow oblique darker on the sides, and a greyish edged pale wavy line low down along the sides.

The figures 2, 2a, on Plate 94 are from coloured drawings by Mr. A. Sich.

It feeds in the autumn on the flowers and seeds of various kinds of goosefoot (*Chenopodium*), also on Orache (*Atriplex*). The moth is out in July and August, and may be found among its food plants and other low herbage growing in waste places, more particularly those on sandy coasts. Around the borders of market gardens, especially those in the south of London, and in Kent and Surrey, it is often very common. The species probably occurs more or less freely in suitable places almost throughout the British Isles.

Its range abroad extends to East Siberia.

Slender-striped Rufous (*Phibalapteryx lapidata*).

The rather pointed fore wings are pale brownish, and are crossed by several fine wavy and rather darker lines, and three more distinct, slightly curved lines, one of which is at the base and two are on the central area. The outer margin of the hind wings, which are pale brown, more or less shaded with dusky, is irregular. (Plate 102, Fig. 6.)

Caterpillar, whitish-yellow above, inclining to pale buff below; lines of grey freckles along the back and sides, the lower one broader and darker; head, grey, freckled with darker. According to Hellins, who reared it from the egg, it feeds in May and June, on traveller's joy (*Clematis vitalba*). The natural food is doubtful, but is said to be grass, whilst Kirby states that in the South of France the caterpillar eats evergreen oak.

The moth is out in September and early October, and is found in Scotland on the hills, in rough grassy and rush-covered spots, at elevations ranging from 300 to 800 feet. In Ireland, it is not uncommon in Antrim, Donegal, Sligo, Mayo, Galway, and Limerick.   Barrett states that a specimen has been taken at Shap Fell in Westmorland.

Abroad, the range extends to East Siberia.

Many-lined Moth (*Phibalapteryx polygrammata*).

The female example of this species, represented on Plate 102, Fig. 5, is from Germany ; the male is somewhat paler and the central markings less distinct.   This form is var. *conjunctaria*, Lederer, and most of the specimens formerly obtained in the Cambridgeshire fens, chiefly Burwell and Wicken, were referable to it.   The species has not been seen in its old fenland haunts for very many years, and it is probably now extinct in Britain.   Specimens have been in the past (and still continue to be) recorded from other British localities, but these on investigation are found to be cases of mistaken identity. *C. vittata = lignata* bears a strong likeness to *P. polygrammata*, and is often confused with it, but in the latter the outer band does not run to the tips of the fore wings, as it does in the former species.

Small Waved Umber (*Phibalapteryx (Coenocalpe) vitalbata*).

At first sight this moth (Plate 102, Fig. 7) might be mistaken for a small specimen of the Waved Umber (*Hemerophila abruptaria*), but it will be noted that the dark stripe on the fore wings starts from the middle of the inner margin, and runs to just below the tips of the wings ; the outer margin of the hind wings is not wavy, and the antennæ of the male are not pectinated.

The caterpillar, which feeds on traveller's joy (*Clematis vitalba*), in June—July, and in September—October, is greyish brown, with three blackish lines along the back, the central one broader than the other two, especially on the middle of each ring, where it swells out into a black spot.

In May and June, and again in August, the moth may be disturbed from the food plant growing in masses in hedgerows, etc. It occurs in most of the southern counties of England, westward to Herefordshire and South Wales, and eastward to Suffolk. Forsythe states that it is local in the Lancaster district.

The range abroad extends to Amurland and Japan.

The Fern (*Phibalapteryx* (*Coenocalpe*) *tersata*).

The general colour of this species (Plate 102, Fig. 8) is pale brown, with a tendency to reddish in some specimens, and to greyish in others.

Caterpillar, pale brownish inclining to ochreous ; on each side of an irregular blackish line along the centre of the back is a pale yellowish line, and there are white spots on the back of the middle rings. It feeds on *Clematis*, in August and September. The moth is out in June and July, and will be found in similar localities to those mentioned for the previous species, and, except that it has not been recorded from Lancaster, its range in England is much about the same.

The distribution abroad extends to Japan.

Oblique Carpet (*Coenocalpe vittata*).

This species, also known as *lignata*, Hübner, is usually pale brown in ground colour, tinged with ochreous or pinkish ; the darker oblique stripes vary in width and in intensity. (Plate 102, Figs. 9 ♂, gen. 1 ; 10 ♂, gen. 2.)

The caterpillar is of a yellow-green colour, inclining to

Series II. S

ochreous brown on the upper portions of the middle rings ; a
darker irregular line along the back, and a whitish line on each
side, the latter edged above and below with a fine black line ;
below the spiracles is a pale pinkish brown stripe.   Varies in
the tint of ground colour and in the markings.   It feeds, after
hibernation, on bedstraw (*Galium palustre*, *G. saxatile*, etc.),
and caterpillars from eggs laid in June may be reared on
clematis, wild or cultivated.

The moth is out in May and June, sometimes later, and a
second generation appears in August and September; the
individuals of the later brood are often smaller than those of
the first brood.   Its haunts are fens, marshes, and water-meads,
but in Middlesex I have taken a specimen or two flying along a
weedy ditch.   Widely distributed throughout the British Isles,
but not noted in Scotland north of Moray.

The Gem (*Percnoptilota fluviata*).

Also known in the vulgar tongue as "The Narrow-barred
Carpet."   As will be seen on reference to Plate 102, the male
(Fig. 12) is pale brown with a dark central band ; and the
female (Fig. 11) is purplish brown, the central band rather
blackish, and on it is the discal mark, a black centred white
spot.   The specimens figured are rather small.

The following aberrations have been named—ab. *marginata*,
Mathew, with the fringes of all the wings conspicuously pinky-
grey ; ab. *olivacea*, Mathew, a form of the female with olive
brown fore wings ; ab. *obsoleta*, Mathew, a form of the male
with the dark central band nearly or quite absent.

The caterpillar is greyish, sometimes tinged with pink, and
sometimes with green ; three dusky lines on the head and first
three rings of the body, a series of blackish outlined, whitish
marks on the middle rings, and blackish marks on the other

1, 2. **Dentated Pug.**   3, 4. **Dark Spinach.**   5. **Many-lined.**
6. **Slender-striped Rufous.**   7. **Small Waved Umber.**   8. **The Fern.**
9, 10. **Oblique Carpet.**   11, 12. **The Gem.**

1-5. **Magpie Moth.** 6-8. **Clouded Magpie.**

rings, which are pale in colour ; a blackish line above the black-edged spiracles is broken up into dashes on the middle rings. Several other forms of the caterpillar, which is a variable one, have been described by Hellins. The food comprises groundsel, knotgrass, chrysanthemum, and various other plants. There are several generations during the year, and in hot weather the caterpillars feed up rapidly, so quickly indeed that in about a month the whole round of changes from egg to moth is effected. The species is migratory in habit, and there is little doubt that the specimens taken in this country in late spring or early summer are immigrants ; those examples obtained later in the year are probably the descendants of such aliens. It is more frequently noted from southern England, chiefly from the seaboard counties, but it has been recorded from Lancashire and Yorkshire ; also from Wales, and from several parts of Ireland: April to November.

BOARMIINÆ.

Clouded Magpie (*Abraxas sylvata*).

A more or less typical example of each sex of this variable species will be found on Plate 103. Fig. 7 represents a male, and Fig. 8 a female ; the slightly marked specimen (Fig. 6) somewhat approaches the continental species *A. pantaria*, L., in appearance, and it is probable that such individuals have done duty for the species just named in some of the older collections of British lepidoptera. On Plate 104 are shown the leaden tinted form (Fig. 6), sometimes not infrequent in certain Yorkshire localities ; a specimen with smoky fore wings (Fig. 7), taken with a few other examples of the same form in a wood in Buckinghamshire, in 1907, when also the strongly banded form (Fig. 8) was secured by Mr. A. J. Scollick. Between these extremes and the more typical forms all kinds of intergrades occur, but it is not possible here to discuss these in detail.

The pale greenish yellow eggs and two caterpillars are figured on Plate 101, Figs. 2, 2a. The latter are whitish, inclining to yellowish on the back, and lined with black ; stripe below the black spiracles, yellow ; head, black and glossy. The food is wych-elm (*Ulmus montana*), but beech and hazel are said to be eaten at times : August to October. The moth is found in May and June, sitting about on the leaves of dog's mercury, and other vegetation in its woodland haunts. Although it sometimes occurs sparingly in the southern seaboard counties, it is far more frequent in the west, ranging from North Devon to Cumberland, and including Wales. It is common in Bucks., and northwards to Northumberland, and extends into South Scotland. In Ireland, not uncommon at Killarney, and reported from a few other localities.

The Magpie (*Abraxas grossulariata*).

Except that the specimen represented by Fig. 2 has traces of a yellow band on the hind wings, Figs. 1—3 on Plate 103 show this highly variable species in its typical and most frequent form. Figs. 4 and 5 depict examples of the ordinary darker forms leading up to ab. *hazeleighensis*, Raynor, in which the whole of the fore wing area between the orange bands is blackish, except two tiny white specks near the front margin. Not infrequently the black spots on the outer margin of the fore wings exhibit a tendency to spread inwards, as in Figs. 2 and 5, and very occasionally they unite with the series of spots outside the orange band, as in Plate 104, Fig. 1, which represents a specimen (kindly lent by Mr. R. Adkin) with blackish tinged hind wings. Sometimes the ground colour of all the wings is yellowish (ab. *lutea*, Cockerell), but the markings are of the usual pattern. The example of this form (Plate 104, Fig. 3) was reared from a large number of caterpillars I collected at Purley, in Surrey, a year or two ago, and was the only example among the moths resulting therefrom that was worth retaining. The very fine variety shown on Plate 104, Fig. 5, is ab. *varleyata*, Porritt, which occurs in Yorkshire, but is mostly reared in captivity from eggs obtained from a wild female in the first place, and subsequent pairings ; the specimen figured is an especially fine example of the female sex, raised among others of the same form by Mr. G. T. Porritt of Huddersfield, who has been good enough to lend it for the purpose. Several other varieties of this species have been named and described by the Rev. Gilbert H.

Fig. 6.
Magpie Moth, drying wings.
(Photo by H. Main.)

Raynor, but reference can only be made here to two of these ; one is ab. *melanozona*, a Scottish form, in which there is a black blotch with traces of yellow in it at the base of the fore wings ; a large black discal spot in the white central area ; a black band, widening towards the front margin, before the faint yellow band, the latter followed by four black spots ; hind wings with central black spot, and two series of black spots beyond, seven in each series, separated by a well-defined white area. Fig. 2 on Plate 104 represents a specimen that approaches this variety. The handsome cream-coloured specimen (Plate 104, Fig. 4) is ab. *lacticolor*, Raynor, and I am obliged to Mr. Adkin for the loan of these insects also.

The caterpillar and chrysalis are figured on Plate 101, Figs. 1, 1*b*; the former is creamy white, marked on the back with black blotches and dots, and lines of black dots on the sides ; between the lower two rows is a broad reddish line ; head, black ; sometimes the whole body is black. It occurs in gardens, and sometimes is a serious pest where currants and gooseberries are cultivated ; it frequently abounds on *Euonymus japonicus*. In the open country it feeds on sloe and hawthorn ; sometimes it is found on elm (low growth in hedges), apple, navelwort (*Cotyledon umbilicus*), orpine (*Sedum telephium*), and in the Hebrides, on ling (*Calluna*). August to May, or early June, are the months in which it is found as a rule ; occasionally it does not hibernate, but feeds up and attains the moth state in the autumn of the year that it hatches from the egg. The moth is out, normally, in July and August, and is generally distributed over the greater part of the British Isles.

The range abroad extends to East Siberia, China, and Japan.

Clouded Border (*Lomaspilis marginata*).

Figs. 1 and 2 on Plate 107 represent the more usual forms, in both sexes, of this rather common, but pretty, little moth. Occasionally, specimens are obtained in which, with the exception of a dark patch or two on the front margin, the wings are entirely white or slightly tinged with pale yellowish (ab. *pollutaria*, Hübner) ; a modification of this form is shown in Fig. 3.

1-5. **Magpie Moth varieties.**   6-8. **Clouded Magpie varieties.**

1. **Scorched Carpet :** *caterpillar.*
2. **Clouded Border :** *caterpillar.*
3. **Common White Wave :** *caterpillar.*

Ab. *nigrofasciaria*, Schöyen, has a rather broad blackish band across the central area of each wing, and indications of such bands, in the shape of spots or dots, are seen in many examples of the species ; occasionally, the irregular dark border of the outer margin of the wings is traversed by an interrupted whitish line.

The caterpillar is yellowish-green, with three dark-green double lines on the back, the central one blotched with purplish brown on the last ring ; head, green, marked with purplish brown. The figure (Plate 105, Fig. 2) is from a drawing in colour by Mr. Sich. It feeds on sallow, willow, and aspen, and may be found almost throughout the summer from June. The moth is also met with during the summer months, but seems to be most frequent in May and June. The species prefers moist localities where sallows abound, and in such places seems to occur pretty generally over the British Isles. In Scotland, however, it has not, apparently, been noted north of Moray.

The range abroad extends to Amurland and Japan.

The Scorched Carpet (*Ligdia adustata*).

The bluish-grey band on the outer third of the fore wings varies in width, and the velvety black marking thereon varies in amount ; this area of the wings is also more or less clouded with reddish brown, and the underside of all the wings is much suffused with reddish brown, which gives the insect the burnt or scorched appearance to which both Latin and English names refer. (Plate 107, Figs. 4 ♂ and 5 ♀.) In June and early July, and again in late August and September, the red-spotted, bright-green caterpillar may be beaten from the spindle bushes (*Euonymus europæus*) in hedgerows. (Fig. 1, Plate 105, is from a coloured drawing by Mr. Sich.)

The moth is out in late April sometimes, but it is more frequent in May and June, and as a second generation in August, earlier or later in some seasons. It may be knocked out of hedges in which spindle is growing. The species is not uncommon in most of the southern English counties, but in the northern ones its occurrence is more casual. It has been recorded from North Wales ; in Ireland it is fairly common in some western and southern counties, and rare in the east and north ; in Scotland, only noted from the south-east, Arran, and the Hebrides.

Abroad, its range extends to Japan, where it is represented by var. *japoniata*, Staudinger.

The Sloe Carpet (*Aleucis (Bapta) pictaria*).

This blackish-grey species (Plate 107, Fig. 6) has been confused in the past with *pictaria*, Thunberg, which is referable to *Cleora lichenaria*, and it was then known by the popular name of " The Grey Carpet." As the caterpillar feeds on the foliage of the sloe, and the moth is fond of resting on the stems and twigs, and appears at the time the bushes are wreathed in their snowy blossoms, the sloe carpet seems to be rather more suitable than are most of the names by which our moths are popularly known.

The caterpillar is dusky brown, with blackish V-shaped marks upon the back, white marks on rings 7 and 8, and a black line on the last ring. It feeds at night, in June and early July, and as it remains on the bushes during the day, it may be obtained by beating. At night the moths fly about the bushes for a short time, and then sit on the twigs, when they may be secured. Of course, a lantern will be a necessity.

Barrett states that stunted bushes on open heaths and hillsides are preferred to hedgerows.

The species is very local, but generally not uncommon where it occurs, as, for example, in the New Forest, Hampshire; the Loughton and Colchester districts, Essex; and in some parts of Kent. It has been noted from Tilgate Forest, and other localities in Sussex; and also from Surrey, Berkshire, and Suffolk.

White-pinion Spotted (*Bapta bimaculata*).

The two cross lines on the fore wings of this silky white species (Plate 107, Fig. 9) commence in blackish spots on the front margin; often they are only indicated by series of dots, and are rarely really distinct. Occasionally, a greyish submarginal line or band is present.

The darkish green caterpillar has a series of purplish marks on the back; head, inclining to yellowish, and powdered with purplish. It feeds, in June and July, on the leaves of wild cherry and plum, and will eat hawthorn; it may be beaten from its food plant in the daytime. The moth is out in May and June, and shelters in bushes, etc., in woods and hedgerows. During the day it is frequently put up from its hiding-places, but its usual time of flight is the evening, when it is readily seen and not difficult to capture. It is local, and perhaps most frequently met with in those parts of South England where the wild cherry flourishes. Occurs more or less commonly in most of the southern counties, but north of Gloucester, Oxford, and Norfolk it has only been noted from North Lancashire, West-moreland, and Cumberland. In Wales the late Mr. C. G. Barrett found the moth rare in Pembrokeshire, and there is also a record from Anglesey.

The range abroad extends to China, Corea, and Japan.

Clouded Silver (*Bapta temerata*).

In its silky, white wings this species (Plate 107, Figs. 7 ♂, 8 ♀) is similar to the last mentioned. It is, however, rather larger, and there are greyish clouds on each side of the outer cross line, but there are no blackish spots on the front edge of the fore wings. The clouding referred to is heavier and darker in some specimens than in others, but occasionally, chiefly in the female, is almost absent.

The green caterpillar, when full grown, is ornamented with brown-bordered reddish spots on the back, but these markings are absent in its earlier stages. The head is paler than the body, and has a reddish spot on each side. It feeds, in July and August, on sloe, plum, and bird cherry in this country, but the continental authors give birch, willow, rose, etc. The moth is out in May and June, and occurs throughout England and Wales, to Cumberland; but it is far more frequent in the south than in the north. Barrett mentions a single specimen from Wigtownshire in Scotland. In Ireland, Kane states that it is abundant at Clonbrock, Merlin Park, and in several other localities in Galway; it is not uncommon at Killarney, Kerry; and a few specimens have been taken at Powerscourt, Wicklow, and Sligo.

The range abroad extends to Amurland and Japan.

Common White Wave (*Cabera pusaria*).

In its typical form (Plate 107, Figs. 10, 11) this white species has three dark-grey almost parallel cross lines on the fore wings and two on the hind wings. The first or the second of these lines on the fore wings may be absent, occasionally both may be missing and the third very faint. Not infrequently in undersized bred specimens the first line approaches the second line either

Pl. 106.

1. **Barred Red** : *caterpillar.*
2, 2a. **Barred Umber** : *egg, natural size and enlarged, and caterpillar.*
3. **Light Emerald** : *eggs, natural size and enlarged.*

1-3. **Clouded Border.**   4, 5. **Scorched Carpet.**   6. **Sloe Carpet.**
7, 8. **Clouded Silver.**   9. **White-pinion Spotted.**
10-12. **Common White Wave.**   13, 14. **Common Wave.**

throughout its length or near the inner margin, and more rarely the two are united ; in most of such aberrations the tips of the fore wings are rather more rounded than in typical specimens, and these are referable to ab. *rotundaria*, Haworth (Round-winged Wave). I have over a dozen examples of this form, all of which were reared from caterpillars which had been kept on short rations when nearly mature ; in some, the outer margin of the fore wings is distinctly rounded, but in others it is much the same as in the larger typical form, and one of these is shown on Plate 107, Fig. 12. The ground colour occasionally assumes a greyish tint, and sometimes this is tinged with pink ; more rarely the general colour is leaden grey.

The caterpillar, of which there are two broods, one in July and another in September, feeds on birch, alder, sallow, etc. It is purplish brown, spotted with white above, and greenish below on the first three rings. There is also a green form with purplish brown marks on the back. (Plate 105, Fig. 3, from a coloured drawing by Mr. A. Sich.) The moth is out in May, June, and August, and is generally common throughout the greater part of the British Isles.

Abroad, the range extends to East Siberia and Amurland.

Common Wave (*Cabera exanthemata*).

Somewhat similar to the last species, but sprinkled with ochreous grey ; the fore wings have three greyish cross lines, the first two less regular than those of *pusaria*, and the outer one distinctly curved; variation in the lines is pretty much the same as in *pusaria* and its small form ab. *rotundaria*. Of the form showing the first and second lines more or less confluent, I have seven examples reared from collected caterpillars ; six are undersized, but the other is of quite ordinary size (ab. *approximata*, Haworth); another specimen, also bred, is thinly powdered with ochreous grey, and the lines are very indistinct The more usual forms are shown on Plate 107, Figs. 13, 14.

The caterpillar is green, inclining to yellowish or to brownish; some purplish-red marks and white-edged black spots on the back; the ring divisions are yellow, and there are reddish-brown or purplish-red marks on the sides; the markings vary. It feeds on birch, alder, and sallow, and may be beaten out at any time from July to September. The moth is out through the summer from May; its range in the British Isles is very similar to that of the last species, but it seems to have a preference for moist places.

The distribution abroad extends eastward to Amurland, and a form known as ab. *schæfferi*, Bremer, occurs in the last-named country, and also in Corea and Japan.

Barred Umber (*Numeria pulveraria*).

Pale ochreous or reddish brown freckled with darker; the central dark reddish brown band is sometimes much narrowed below the middle; sometimes only the edges of the band are dark, the enclosed space being but little darker than the ground colour, or occasionally tinged with greenish; one example of the latter and two of the former were reared this year (1908) from larvæ received in July, 1907, from Mr. F. Pope of Exeter; a male specimen bred from the same batch of larvæ, but which emerged in August of the year last mentioned, is distinctly tinged with rosy over all the wings; the narrow band on the hind wings, not usually extended to the front edge, is in this specimen entire, whilst the greenish-banded specimen referred to above is without trace of a band on the hind wings. Two examples which are without locality, but which, I believe, came from the New Forest, have pale greyish-brown fore wings banded with brown in which there is a tinge of olive. Two examples of the male are figured on Plate 108. The eggs (Plate

106, Fig. 2*a*) were pale greenish yellow when laid, May 17 to 20 ; the larvæ hatched out from May 31 to June 2.

The caterpillar, which is also depicted on the plate, is reddish brown, mottled with yellowish brown. It feeds on birch, sallow, ash, etc., from June to August.

The moth, as a rule, does not emerge until the following spring, but sometimes specimens will come out the same year.

Although widely distributed over nearly the whole of the British Isles, the species seems to be rarely met with in large numbers. The range abroad extends to Amurland, Corea, and Japan.

Barred Red (*Ellopia* (*Hylaea*) *prosapiaria*).

The typical form of this species is depicted on Plate 108, Figs. 4 ♂, 5 ♀, and Fig. 3 on the same plate represents ab. *prasinaria*, Hübner, a form not uncommon in Germany (whence came the example figured), Switzerland, and other parts of the continent, but which is very rare in Britain, and has been recorded from Kent and Suffolk. Sometimes, but chiefly in Scotland, the colour varies to a greyish or even yellowish tint ; the cross lines are often parallel or nearly so, and frequently approach each other about the middle ; the usual white edging to the cross lines is occasionally absent, and the enclosed space in such specimens is hardly darker than the general colour.

On Plate 106, Fig. 1, will be found a figure of the caterpillar, which is tawny brown with white-edged, connected reddish marks along the back. It feeds, from September to May, on Scots pine (*Pinus sylvestris*), and occasionally on larch. The moth is out in June and July, and sometimes in September. It may be jarred from the pine boughs, and is not infrequently seen resting on foliage of the undergrowth. Generally distributed in fir-woods throughout Great Britain, and widely spread in Ireland.

The range abroad extends to East Siberia.

The Light Emerald (*Metrocampa* (*Eudalimia*) *margaritaria*).

When quite fresh, this species (Plate 108, Fig. 6) is of a delicate whitish-green colour, but the green tint is apt to fade or to change colour, so that the wings are almost ochreous white sometimes.

The eggs shown on Plate 106, Fig. 3, were kindly supplied by Mr. Norman Riley.

The caterpillar ranges in colour from greenish brown to purplish brown, and is frequently freckled with a darker shade of the general colour ; there is sometimes a pale patch on rings 6 and 7, and the sides are fringed with fine bristles along the spiracle area. It feeds, from September to May, on the leaves of oak, birch, beech, elm, etc., and during the winter will nibble the bark of the younger twigs, and also eat the buds.

The moth, which is partial to the woodlands, is out in June and July, and is pretty generally distributed over the British Isles, except the Hebrides, Orkneys, and Shetlands.

Large Thorn (*Ennomos autumnaria*).

This fine species was first definitely ascertained to occur in Britain in 1855, but it had been reported as British at a much earlier date, and was figured by Wood in 1839. Up to 1859 it had only been recorded from the North Foreland and Margate in Kent, and from Brighton, Sussex. In 1862, a specimen was taken at Brighton and one at Deal, the latter a female. Two examples were secured at Gosport, Hampshire, in 1865, and one at Deal in 1867. Then, after an interval of ten years, three were captured in Hants (Alverstoke), and two years later a round dozen were obtained at Gosport. During the last thirty years specimens have been recorded from Margate, Deal,

Pl. 108.

1, 2. Barred Umber.   3. Barred Red (green var.).
4, 5. Barred Red.   6. Light Emerald.

1, 3. **Large Thorn.**   2, 4, 5. **August Thorn.**

Dover, Folkestone, Hythe, and Ashford (1907), in Kent, from Chichester, Sussex, and from Shoeburyness, Essex (1898). It has been reared on several occasions from eggs obtained from captured females, and is still more frequently bred from eggs deposited by the descendants of wild parents.

The eggs are deep olive, with a white ring at one end; and the caterpillar is brownish in colour, rather shining, and very twig-like. It feeds on birch, alder, hawthorn, sloe, plum, etc., and has been found on sycamore and cherry; May to August. The early stages are figured on Plate 110, Figs. 1, 1a, b, c. The moth (Plate 109, Figs. 1 ♂, 3 ♀), which varies in colour from pale to deep ochreous yellow, and also in the amount of purplish brown freckling, usually has the upper part of the outer marginal area some shade of tawny brown. Specimens of a greyish chocolate tint have recently been reared by Mr. Newman, of Bexley (Plate 134, Fig. 9). Most of the specimens captured in England have been obtained at light in the autumn. The range abroad extends to Amurland, Japan, and North America.

August Thorn (*Ennomos quercinaria*).

The male (Plate 109, Fig. 2) is generally yellower than the female (Fig. 4), and it is in the former sex that brownish or red-brown clouding on the outer area beyond the second cross line appears most frequently, but it occurs also in the female (Plate 109, Fig. 5). Sometimes the wings are partly or entirely dull reddish brown. Two other examples of the type form showing modification of the cross lines will be found on Plate 111, Figs. 5 ♂, 6 ♀. In ab. *carpinaria*, Hübner, the wings are of a reddish ochreous colour. A hybrid resulting from a crossing of *E. alniaria* ♂ and *E. quercinaria* ♀ has been named *dartfordi*, Tutt.

The caterpillar (Plate 113, Fig. 3) is generally grey brown, mottled with reddish or olive; but, according to Fenn, it is sometimes greenish, without humps or projections. It feeds, in the summer, on lime, birch, oak, hawthorn, etc. A chrysalis which I took out of its puparium (two leaves spun together with silk) on July 9, 1907, was green, with the upper surface tinged with yellowish ; a dark-green central line, and a series of dark-green irregular marks on each side ; the tail pointed and furnished with reddish hooks.

The moth is out in August and September, and may often be seen sitting on the boles of trees, generally low down. The species is widely distributed over England, but is much more frequent in the south than in the north. It has been recorded from Swansea in Wales; from Dumfries, Dunoon, and Monteith, in Scotland; and from near Derry, Hazlewood (Sligo), Mote Park (Roscommon), and Clonbrock (Galway), in Ireland.

Canary-shouldered Thorn (*Ennomos alniaria*).

This species (Plate 111, Figs. 1, 2) is generally easily recognised by the canary yellow coloured hairs of the thorax. The fore wings are yellowish, sprinkled with purplish grey, and crossed by two curved greyish-brown lines, which not infrequently fall close together on the inner margin. In some female specimens that I reared from eggs, received from York, the wings are more or less tinged with dull tawny brown, especially on the outer area, and in two of them the thorax is also brownish tinged.

The at first green, and afterwards blackish slate-coloured, egg, with whitish ring, and the caterpillar are shown on Plate 110, Fig. 2, 2*a*. The latter is brownish, mottled with purplish above, and inclining to greenish below; head, rather paler brown. It feeds, from May to July, on birch, alder, etc. The moth is out in the autumn, and occurs in suitable woodland and marshy places over England, Wales, and Scotland to Moray. It has been found in many parts of Ireland.

1 1*a*, 1*b*, 1*c*. **Large Thorn :** *eggs, natural size and enlarged ; caterpillar, chrysalis and puparium.*

    2, 2*a*. **Canary-shouldered Thorn :** *eggs, natural size and enlarged, and caterpillar.*

    3, 3*a*. **Dusky Thorn :** *caterpillar and chrysalis.*

1, 2. **Canary-shouldered Thorn.**   3, 4. **Dusky Thorn.**   5, 6. **August Thorn.**

Dusky Thorn (*Ennomos fuscantaria*).

Figs. 3 ♂, 4 ♀, Plate 111, represent the usual form of this species; in some specimens the outer marginal pale purplish-brown shading spreads inwards over the fore wings to the base; in other examples it is only seen on the upper part of the outer area.

The caterpillar (Plate 110, Fig. 3) is green, pretty much of the same tint as the underside of the ash leaf upon which, and the stalks, it rests by day. In some examples the general colour inclines to pale brown, or reddish brown. It may be found during the summer, and where the leaves are seen to have neat round holes in them, these should be examined, when this caterpillar will probably be found somewhere adjacent. Ash (*Fraxinus excelsior*) is the usual food, but possibly privet might answer as a substitute. The moth is out in August and September, and occurs in most parts of Southern England where the ash flourishes; its range extends into South Wales, and northwards to Durham and Northumberland. Only doubtfully recorded from Ireland, and apparently unknown in Scotland.

September Thorn (*Ennomos erosaria*).

This species, shown on Plate 134, Fig. 6, varies in ground colour from pale ochreous to pale fulvous; the cross lines approach towards the inner margin, and sometimes the second line is bent inwards below the middle. The central spot is generally absent, and when present is exceedingly faint. The twig-like caterpillar is brownish, with a greenish or purplish tinge. In its infancy it is a smooth-looking creature, but as it advances in growth knobs and humps appear, the most prominent of which are on rings 2, 5, 8, and 11; on the last ring there are two points. It feeds on oak chiefly, but will eat birch, lime, etc.: May to July. The moth is out in August and September, and occurs more or less frequently in most of the southern counties of England, but is rather scarce in the Midlands and northwards. It occurs in South Wales, and has been recorded from the south of Scotland. Very rare in Ireland.

NOTE.—The species of *Ennomos* are fond of light, and in suitable spots, gas and electric lamps, in the streets, or even in the house when windows are open, will attract these moths. Most of the specimens of *autumnaria* that have been captured in Britain have occurred at light. *Quercinaria* is, perhaps, less often noted at light than its allies; but, curiously, this species is more frequently seen at rest on tree trunks, etc., than are either of the other kinds. Female moths taken at light may not always be in first-rate condition, but they will probably lay eggs, and should be kept for that purpose in a chip box. The caterpillars do not hatch out until the following spring. Put the eggs in a cool place.

Early Thorn (*Selenia bilunaria*).

The sexes of the spring or typical form are depicted on Plate 112, Figs. 1 ♂, 2 ♀, and the paler summer form var. *juliaria* (July Thorn), Haworth, is represented by Fig. 3. The underside is shown in Mr. H. Main's photo of the moth in its natural resting attitude.

The caterpillar is orange or reddish brown, sometimes inclining to purplish; there are pairs of reddish raised points on the back of rings 7 and 8; as will be seen from the accompanying illustration, which is from a photograph by Mr. Main, the creature, when resting, is very like a twig. It feeds on birch, alder, sallow, hawthorn, sloe, etc., in May and June, and again in August and September. The moth is out in April and

early May.   In 1905, a male occurred at Carnforth, Lancs., on
June 8; the second generation appears in July and August.
A third has been obtained in captivity, and the moths of this
brood are similar to those of the second.   It has happened that
the emergence of some moths of the second, or summer, form
has been delayed until the
following February, but these
remained true to their race
and did not assume the spring
form.

Generally distributed
throughout England and
Wales, and often abundant,

FIG. 7.   FIG. 8.
Early Thorn at rest.   Caterpillar of Early Thorn.
(Photos by H. Main.)

especially in the south.   In Scotland, Renton states that it is
common in Roxburghshire, but there is only one brood; the
range extends to Sutherlandshire.   Widely spread in Ireland
and plentiful in some parts.

Lunar Thorn (*Selenia lunaria*).

A female of this species is shown on Plate 112, Fig. 4 ; the male is usually more clouded with reddish. A second generation is sometimes raised in captivity, and the males of this brood (var. *delunaria*, Hübner) are somewhat paler, whilst the females incline to a yellowish tint. In Scotch specimens, the reddish markings are tinged with purple ; and ab. *sublunaria*, Stephens, from Derbyshire, has the coloration very similar to that of the spring form of *S. tetralunaria*.

The caterpillar is figured on Plate 113, Fig. 2. The ground colour is usually some shade of brown, ranging from greyish or greenish to reddish, variegated with darker or paler clouds, and with traces of pale lines on the back. It occurs in the open from July to September, but may be reared both earlier and later in confinement. It feeds on sloe, plum, oak, birch, etc. The moth, in May and June, is sometimes seen on hedges or on the plants growing below ; or it may be jarred from the branches of trees, when it is more apt to fall to the ground than to fly. Like others of this group it is fond of light, and is frequently attracted thereto at night. The species is rarely plentiful, and always more or less local, but it is widely distributed over the British Isles to the Orkneys.

Purple Thorn (*Selenia tetralunaria*).

On Plate 112, Fig. 5 represents a specimen of the spring brood, and Fig. 6 one of the summer brood (var. *æstiva*, Staudinger). The ground colour of the typical form is whitish, sometimes tinged with grey, and sometimes with pinkish ; the patch at the tip, and the basal two-thirds of the fore wings, also the basal half of the hind wings, are purplish brown, varying almost to blackish ; or they may be rich red brown. Var. *æstiva* is rarely whitish in ground colour, but this is frequently

1-3. Early Thorn.　　　4. Lunar Thorn.
5, 6. Purple Thorn.　　7, 8. Lilac Beauty.

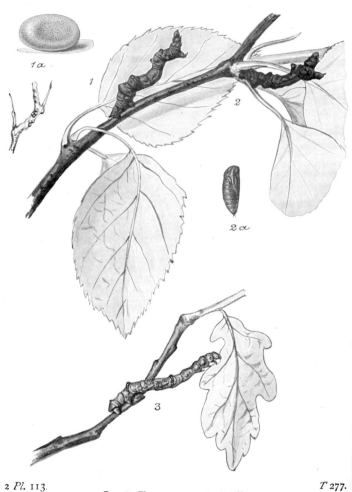

1. 1a. **Purple Thorn**: *eggs and caterpillar.*
2, 2a. **Lunar Thorn**: *caterpillar and chrysalis.*
3. **August Thorn**: *caterpillar.*

of a pinkish tinge, and the darker portions of the wings are brownish, inclining to olive ; sometimes the general colour is ochreous brown with dark brown cross lines, and a rust-coloured lunule at the tips of the fore wings. The hybrid resulting from a female of this species that had paired with a male *bilunaria* has been named *parvilunaria*, Bastel. At the time it is laid, the egg is pale olive green, but it changes to shining reddish, and just before hatching to purplish black. (Plate 113, Fig. 1*a*.)

The caterpillar is reddish brown, mottled with darker brown, and with pale greyish. It feeds on birch, alder, oak, sallow, cherry, etc. : June and July, and again in the autumn. (Plate 113, Fig. 1.)

The moth is out in April and May, and the second generation emerges in July and August. A few specimens of a third generation have been reared in October, but this is unusual.

The species is more or less local, and rarely common, at least in the moth state ; it occurs in all the southern counties of England, and a few specimens have been recorded from some of the midland and northern counties, and from South Wales. In Scotland, noted from Rannoch, Perthshire, and a specimen was reared on April 25, 1901, from a caterpillar found at Dunkeld, in the same county, the previous autumn.

Abroad, the range extends to Amurland and Japan.

Lilac Beauty (*Hygrochroa (Pericallia) syringaria*).

The sexes of this species are shown on Plate 112, and it will be noted that the male (Fig. 7) is rather smaller and decidedly more brightly coloured than the female (Fig. 8). An older English name is "Richmond Beauty," Wilkes. Figures of the curiously shaped caterpillar and chrysalis will be found on Plate

115, Figs. 2, 2a. The former is yellowish brown, variegated with reddish and violet; it feeds on honeysuckle, lilac, and privet, and may be beaten or searched for in May and early June, after hibernation. I have found it commonly on privet hedges in the Mill Hill district, Middlesex, but in woods, and especially in the New Forest, it is obtained from honeysuckle. In my experience, the privet-feeding caterpillars always produce larger moths than those reared from caterpillars fed on honeysuckle. The moth emerges in June and July, the former month chiefly in confinement, and from such early moths a second generation may be obtained in the autumn.

Although most frequent in the southern half of England and Wales, the range of the species extends to the northern counties; and single specimens have been recorded from Durham and Northumberland, but the species has not been noted in Scotland.

The distribution abroad extends to Amurland and Japan.

Scalloped Hazel (*Gonodontis bidentata*).

This species varies in ground colour, from pale whity brown through shades of grey brown, olive brown, ochreous, and dark brown to black; the blackish cross lines of the fore wings are generally edged with white, but the edging is sometimes absent, and occasionally it alone remains distinct; the central space enclosed by the cross lines is often darker than the general colour, and not infrequently it is faintly reddish. Figs. 1 and 2, Plate 114, represent two of the more usual forms of the species. Fig. 3 is the black ab. *nigra*, Prout, which occurs on the mosses of Lancashire, and in Yorkshire.

The yellowish and brown mottled, purplish caterpillar is figured on Plate 115, where also are shown the eggs (turquoise blue, changing to reddish brown), and the reddish brown chrysalis. The latter, which is twice the natural size, is from

1-3 Scalloped Hazel.   4. 5. Feathered Thorn.   6, 7. Scalloped Oak.

2 *Pl.* 115.

T 279.

1, 1a, 1b. **Scalloped Hazel :** *eggs, caterpillar and chrysalis.*
2, 2a, **Lilac Beauty :** *caterpillar and chrysalis.*

a photograph by Mr. H. Main. The caterpillar feeds on the foliage of oak, birch, sallow, hawthorn, sloe, plum, larch, etc.; it grows very slowly, and may be beaten out in most of the months from July to October. The moth is out in May and June, and sometimes earlier. Pretty generally distributed over the British Isles, but not noted in the Orkneys or Shetlands. The range abroad extends to Amurland and Japan.

Feathered Thorn (*Himera* (*Colotois*) *pennaria*).

A more or less typical but rather small male specimen is shown on Plate 114, Fig. 4, but the ground colour is frequently more tawny in tint, and sometimes it is much paler inclining to yellowish; the cross lines may be either wider apart, or closer together, and the inner one is often clouded with blackish; sometimes both lines become almost bandlike; the submarginal, usually interrupted, line is occasionally well defined. The female, often browner than the specimen depicted (Fig. 5) is frequently tinged with purple, and occasionally with pink.

The batch of eggs, as deposited, was photographed by Mr. Main. The egg is olive green with a ring of pale specks around the micropylar end. The caterpillar is slaty grey inclining to purplish, with a series of not clearly defined ochreous diamonds on the back and a row of ochreous dots on each side; the raised points on the last ring are tipped with reddish (Plate 116). It feeds on oak, birch, poplar, sallow, apple, hawthorn, sloe, etc. April to June. The moth is out in October and November, but is seldom noticed in the daytime; at night, the males are frequently seen at gas and electric light. The species is generally common in woodlands, especially as caterpillars, over the southern half of England and Wales, and occurs more or less frequently over the rest of the country, also in Scotland to Moray, and in Ireland.

Scalloped Oak (*Crocallis elinguaria*).

Fig. 6 on Plate 114 shows the usual form of this species, in which there are blackish dots on the outer margins of all the wings. Fig. 7 depicts a form with the ground colour paler, and the outer marginal dots absent (ab. *trapezaria*, Boisduval). The ground colour varies to almost whitish on the one hand and to reddish buff on the other ; the cross lines on the fore wings are distinct as a rule, but occasionally meet on inner margin (ab. *signatipennis*) ; the central space between the lines is most often brownish, sometimes tawny, but not infrequently this area is but little darker than the general colour. The blackish discal spot on the hind wings varies in size and some-what in shape, but this and also the line beyond, are sometimes absent. Porritt (*List of Yorkshire Lepidoptera*) mentions two gynandrous specimens. Eggs, pale grey, with darkish grey marking (Plate 116, Fig. 2*b*). The caterpillar, of which two figures from coloured drawings by Mr. A. Sich are given on Plate 116, Figs. 2, 2*a*, varies from ochreous grey to dark grey tinged with purple ; the front rings are often paler above, and the back has diamond-shaped marks upon it ; the elevation on the last ring is edged with black. It feeds on the leaves of most trees and bushes during the spring. The moth is out in July and August, sometimes earlier. A pretty generally distributed species throughout the British Isles, but so far it has not been noted from the Hebrides, Orkneys, or Shetland.

Abroad, the range extends to East Siberia.

Orange Moth (*Angerona prunaria*).

Typical males of this species are orange and the females pale ochreous, all the wings sprinkled or freckled with purplish grey. (Plate 117, Figs. 1 ♂, 7 ♀.) Ab. *corylaria*, Thunberg (Figs. 2 ♂,

8 ♀), is brownish on the basal and outer marginal areas of the fore wings, and nearly the whole of the hind wings. The typical ground colour appears on the fore wings as a central band, but as a rule this does not quite reach the inner margin. Ab. *pickettaria*, Prout, is a modification of the *corylaria* form, in which the typical ground appears on the front margin above the brownish basal patch, and also along the outer margin, thus narrowing the brownish border on that area ; in one male specimen the right pair of wings were *corylaria* and the left pair *pickettaria*. Another modification has the basal and outer marginal areas "a nondescript grey shade in the male and a golden brown in the female" (ab. *pallidaria*, Prout). Ab. *spangbergi*, Lampa, is of the typical form, but is without the dark freckles. Other aberrations have been named, and at least one gynandrous specimen is known. The eggs, which are laid in June, hatch in about twelve days. The caterpillars feed slowly until September or October, and then hibernate ; but it has been noted that when reared in confinement, and supplied with privet, they nibble the stems during the winter. Occasionally, a caterpillar will feed up and assume the moth state in the autumn, but the usual habit is to complete growth in the spring, enter the chrysalis state in May, and appear as moths about the end of that month, if in captivity, or in June and July in the open. Various food plants have been given, among which are hawthorn, sloe, plum, birch, lilac, privet, and honeysuckle. The caterpillar is figured on Plate 118, Fig. 2.

The male flies in the early evening, but the female not until later. The species frequents woods, and may be disturbed by day from among the bracken and other undergrowth. It is more or less common in many woods throughout the southern half of England, and its range extends northwards to York-shire. In Ireland, it has occurred locally in counties Waterford, Cork, Kerry, Limerick, Clare, and Galway. It has been recorded from the Isle of Arran, but not from the mainland of Scotland.

Abroad, the distribution spreads to Amurland, Corea, and Japan.

Swallow-tailed Moth (*Ourapteryx sambucaria*).

This conspicuous-looking insect (Plate 117, Fig. 6) is frequently seen in gardens, lanes, and the outskirts of woods, pretty well all over England, Wales, and Ireland. In Scotland, it seems to be rare and confined to the south, but has been noted up to Glasgow. Very rarely the cross lines of the fore wings are placed close together, but, except in the matter of size, there is, as a rule, little variation.

The caterpillar, of which a figure, from a coloured drawing by Mr. A. Sich, is given on Plate 118, Fig. 1, is brownish, variegated with reddish or purplish. It feeds, from August to June, on the foliage of hawthorn, sloe, elder, etc., but is especially partial to ivy.

The moth is out in July, and sometimes an odd specimen or two will appear in the autumn ; one was captured at Gravesend on October 22, 1904.

The species is represented in Amurland and Japan by the smaller and whiter var. *persica*, Ménetries.

Scorched Wing (*Eurymene dolabraria*).

The crumpled or shrivelled appearance of the wings, coupled with the brown coloration of the streaks and other markings on the wings, no doubt suggested the English name of this species (Plate 117, Fig. 3).

The twig-like caterpillar is brownish, tinged with greenish or reddish, and variegated with darker, especially along the back of the first three rings, the hump on ring 8, and a cross stripe

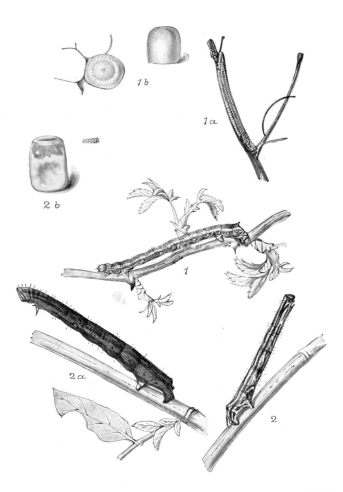

1, 1a, 1b. **Feathered Thorn:** *eggs, natural size and enlarged, and caterpillar.*
2, 2a, 2b. **Scalloped Oak:** *eggs, natural size and enlarged, and caterpillar.*

1, 2, 7, 8. **Orange Moth.** 3. **Scorched Wing.**
4, 5. **Brimstone.** 6. **Swallow-tailed.**

on the last ring. It feeds on oak, birch, and sallow, from July to September.

The moth, which inhabits woods, and is out in late May and in June, is sometimes attracted to sugar, but rather more frequently to light. It is, however, far more rarely seen than the caterpillar, which has been obtained in almost every English county up to Yorkshire. The moth has been recorded from Darlington, Durham, Northumberland, and Cumberland. It occurs in Wales and Ireland, and several larvæ were beaten from a beech hedge in Perthshire.

The range abroad extends to Amurland and Japan.

The Brimstone (*Opisthograptis luteolata*).

This generally distributed and often common yellow species (Plate 117, Figs. 4 and 5) has the front margin of the fore wings marked with reddish, and occasionally a stripe of this colour extends along the front margin from the base to the tip; the discal mark is whitish outlined in reddish brown; the wavy cross lines are often faint, and not infrequently quite absent. White specimens, ab. *lacticolor*, Harrison, have been recorded from Cheshire and Durham, and probably have occurred elsewhere, since I have a specimen said to have been taken in Staffordshire; an orange-yellow form has occurred in the last-named county. (Also known as *Rumia cratægata*.)

The twig-like caterpillar is brownish tinged with greenish or purplish; there is a double-pointed hump on the back of ring 6 and smaller projections on 8. It feeds on hawthorn chiefly, but sometimes on sloe, plum, etc. It may be found after hibernation in the spring, and a second generation occurs in the summer.

The moth seems to have been noted in each month from April to August, but it is most frequent in May and June.

Bordered Beauty (*Epione apiciaria*).

The orange-yellow moth whose portrait is shown on Plate 119 (Fig. 1) has the outer margins, beyond the second blackish line, more or less shaded with purplish grey, inclining to purple near the line ; on the fore wings, the first cross line is angled at the middle, and the second line runs to the tips of the wings. Gynandrous specimens of this and also the following species have been noted.

The early stages are figured on Plate 121, Figs. 2, 2a. The eggs, which are laid in July and August on the food plant, are pale yellow at first, then reddish, with white dots and patches. The caterpillars generally emerge in the following spring, but sometimes, at least in captivity, they hatch in about a fort-night, feed up quickly, and attain the moth state in September or October.

Caterpillar, brown, with a greenish or ochreous tinge ; along the back of rings 3 to 6 is an ochreous patch, and within this a black mark, and on the rings following 6 there are more or less distinct ochreous diamonds ; a dull yellowish line low down along the sides ; head, dull reddish brown. It feeds, in May and June, on willow, sallow, alder, etc. The moth is out in July and August, and is not uncommon in many parts of Southern and Eastern England. Its range extends through England, Wales, and Scotland to Sutherland. In Ireland, it is widely distributed, and not at all scarce in some northern localities.

Dark Bordered Beauty (*Epione parallelaria*).

As will be seen on referring to Plate 119 the sexes of this species are strikingly different. The male (Fig. 2) is very similar to the last species, except that the first cross line is curved and

1. Swallow-tailed : *caterpillar.*
2. Orange Moth : *caterpillar.*

1. Bordered Beauty.   2, 3. Dark Bordered Beauty.
4. Little Thorn.   5, 6. Speckled Yellow.
7. Peacock.   8. Sharp-angled Peacock.
9, 10. Tawny-barred Angle.

reddish brown in colour; the second line runs to the front margin before the tip, and the outer margin beyond is almost entirely purple. The female (Fig. 3) has the ground colour pale yellowish, and the outer borders narrowed, especially on the fore wings. Very occasionally, the ground colour in the male approaches that of the female. The eggs (Plate 121, Fig. 1) are pale yellow when deposited, but afterwards become honey yellow, freckled with reddish, and later they are red all over. The caterpillar is dingy brown, inclining to greyish on the back of the first four rings, a dark mark about the middle of the back, and on each side of this two slender whitish lines are fairly distinct; underside, whitish tinged with pale violet. It feeds, in May and June, sometimes later, on dwarf sallow and willow, birch, aspen, etc.

The moth is out in July and August, sometimes later. Although odd specimens have been recorded from Norfolk, St. Ives (Hunts), Newbury (Berks), and Arundel (Sussex), the species is a northern one, occurring chiefly near York (Sanburn Moss).

In 1863, two specimens were secured at Learmouth Bog, near Cornhill-on-Tweed, and in 1890, Bolam found it at Newham Bog, on the Northumberland border. Renton states that it is fairly common in good seasons at Adderstone-lea Moss, Roxburghshire; and Salvage found it widely distributed in Sutherlandshire.

Little Thorn (*Cepphis* (*Epione*) *advenaria*).

This species (Plate 119, Fig. 4) is usually whitish, freckled and clouded with grey brown; cross lines rather darker. The markings may be tinged with ochreous, or with red (Sheffield).

A uniform brown-coloured specimen with white fringes has been bred (Surrey).

The caterpillar is greyish brown, minutely freckled with blackish; two white spots on front of ring 5, and two smaller ones on 11 ; the rings between 5 and 11 with pale diamonds on the back, and whitish marks on the sides ; head, black, white dotted. It feeds, in July and August, or even later, on dogwood, bilberry, sallow, etc. Mr. A. J. Scollick, who kindly provided the caterpillar figured on Plate 121, Fig. 3, informs me that in rearing larvæ from the egg he finds that they prefer dogwood as a pabulum, and that in the locality where he takes the moth in June there is no bilberry, but plenty of *Cornus sanguinea*. This local species, which is out from late May well into June, is generally associated with bilberry, but by no means confined to localities where this plant flourishes. In some of its haunts it affects bramble, and in others rose. It occurs, in woodlands, in Essex, Kent, Surrey (Leith Hill, Horsley, Chilworth, etc.), Berkshire, and Oxfordshire (near Watlington), Sussex (Abbots Wood, St. Leonards Forest, etc.), Hampshire (New Forest), Devonshire (Haldon), in the West to Shropshire, and South Wales ; Derbyshire and South Yorks.

The range abroad extends to Amurland, Corea, and Japan ; thus it has a more eastern distribution than either of the species of *Epione*, which only reach Amurland.

Speckled Yellow (*Venilia maculata*).

This pretty blackish-spotted yellow species (Plate 119, Figs. 5 and 6) varies somewhat in the tint of ground colour, but more so in the number and size of the markings ; occasionally some of these are united, forming bands or blotches; or they may be reduced in number and size, leading up to ab. *quadrimaculata*, Hatchett (Pinion-spotted Yellow), a form that used to occur rarely in the Dartford district, Kent, and of which an example is depicted on Plate 61, Fig. 2.

The caterpillar is green, with white lines and stripes ; head, shining green. It feeds, in July and August, on wood sage (*Teucrium*), woundwort (*Stachys*), and dead nettle (*Lamium*).

The moth is a lover of the woodlands, and as it flies in the daytime, especially when sunny, will be almost certainly noted on the wing by any one rambling through the woods in June, or even late May. It is generally plentiful in the south and west of England, but although its range extends through the northern parts of the country, and widely over Scotland to Sutherland, it is more or less local and often rare in the northern area indicated. In North Wales and South-west Ireland, it is local, but not uncommon.

The Peacock Moth (*Semiothisa (Macaria) notata*).

Whitish, with an ochreous tinge, and clouded with ochreous grey ; three indistinct cross lines on the fore wings, commencing as brownish spots on the front margin ; a larger brownish spot, inclining to reddish, on the front margin beyond the angle of outer line, and a large blackish or brownish divided spot below it ; a shallow notch under the tips of the wings, edged with dark brown, and fringed with smoky brown. (Plate 119, Fig. 7.)

The caterpillar is green, with brown markings on the sides, or brownish with green markings ; head, black as a rule, but occasionally green. It feeds, in late June and in July, on birch and sallow ; there is a second brood in August and September. The moth may be beaten out from birch bushes in May and June, and again in July and August. Woods are its favourite haunts, especially those where heather and small birch abound, but it is very local in the south of England, although it occurs in most of the counties from Kent to Cornwall. Barrett states that it is rather common in heathy woods in Staffordshire and Cheshire, and Forsythe gives it as local and uncommon in the Lancaster district ; also recorded from Cambridgeshire, Suffolk, Herts (Bentley Wood, 1901), and Gloucestershire ; Glamorganshire, South Wales ; Inverness and Ross, in Scotland.

Sharp-angled Peacock (*Semiothisa alternata*).

Whitish clouded and suffused with greyish; fore wings crossed by three dark lines, commencing in blackish spots on the front margin; a greyish band follows the outer line, a reddish brown spot at the costal end, and a blackish spot about the middle, the spot broken up by the veins, which are here ochreous; a rather deep notch below the tip is edged with black and fringed with blackish. Hind wings with a black central dot, and a greyish band beyond. (Plate 119, Fig. 8.)

Mr. A. J. Scollick has recorded that some caterpillars, presumably about a week old on June 24, 1905, went into chrysalis July 7 to 12. One moth emerged July 18, but no other appeared until December 20. A third came up on January 5, 1906, and a fourth on February 5.

The caterpillar is pale green, with reddish brown blotches on the sides, and sometimes the back is also reddish brown. It feeds on alder, sallow, and sloe, in June, and as a second generation in the autumn. (Eggs and a caterpillar, the latter after Hofmann, are figured on Plate 123.) The moth flies in May and early June, and occasionally in July or August.

This species, which is always local, is perhaps most frequently met with in the New Forest, Hants, but it is not uncommon in some parts of the Isle of Wight, Dorset, Devon, and Kent. Also noted from a few other southern counties, and from Suffolk, Norfolk, and Westmoreland. In Wales, it has occurred at Neath, Glamorganshire.

The range of this species abroad, and also that of the last, extends to Amurland.

Tawny-barred Angle (*Semiothisa liturata*).

The more frequent forms of this species are shown on Plate 119, Figs. 9, 10. In some examples the cross lines

1, 3. **Early Moth.**   2, 4, 5, 6. **Spring Usher.**
7, 9. **Scarce Umber.**   8, 10, 11, 12. **Dotted Border.**

1. **Dark-bordered Beauty:** *eggs.*
2, 2a. **Bordered Beauty:** *eggs and caterpillar.*
3. **Little Thorn:** *caterpillar.*

are almost absent, but in others they are very distinct and blackish in colour; the orange yellow band in the outer marginal area varies in width and in strength, but it is usually present, even in the sooty brown form ab. *nigrofulvata*, Collins (Plate 61, Fig. 7), described from Delamere, Cheshire, also found in Shropshire, Warwick, N. Lancs., and Kendal.

The caterpillar (Plate 123, Fig. 2) is green, with white or creamy transverse lines and stripes; head, reddish. Another form is pale ochreous grey or brownish, with pale grey lines and stripes; head, almost black, with purple tinge. It feeds on the needles of Scots pine (*Pinus sylvestris*), in July and August, and occasionally in September and October. A photograph of the chrysalis by Mr. H. Main, enlarged to twice natural size, is shown on Plate 123.

The moth is to be found in fir woods, where it lurks among the branches or sits on the trunks, or on the fallen needles on the ground. The moths of the first generation appear in June and July and, where it occurs, the second flies in August and September. Widely distributed over the British Isles, but not noted north of Moray, in Scotland.

Early Moth (*Hybernia rupicapraria*).

Although generally common, and often abundant, over England, Wales, the south of Scotland, and Ireland, this species (Plate 120, Figs. 1 ♂, 3 ♀) hardly ever comes under notice unless hedgerows and hawthorn bushes are examined in January and February, by the aid of a lantern, after darkness has set in. Then the males, and almost wingless females, will be found in numbers, sitting at the ends of the twigs.

The caterpillar is whitish green, clouded with darker green, striped with white along the back, and marked with white on the sides. The general colour is sometimes very dark green, approaching black, and in this form the white markings are

Series II. U

more striking. It feeds, in April and May, on hawthorn, sloe, plum, and bilberry.

Spring Usher (*Hybernia leucophæaria*).

On Plate 120 are shown the typical and more usual forms of this variable species. Fig. 2 represents the male, and Fig. 4 the female. The form with blackish base and outer margin is ab. *marmorinaria*, Esper (Plate 120, Fig. 5). Ab. *merularia*, Weymer, is entirely black, and a modification of this form is shown in Fig. 6. Between each of these extremes and the type there are various gradations.

FIG. 9.
Spring Usher at rest.
(Photo by W. J. Lucas.)

The caterpillar is usually some shade of green, with yellowish lines on the back, and some have brownish marks on the sides; in others there are dark brown marks on the back of each ring. It feeds on the leaves of oak, in April and May.

The moth rests on tree-trunks, fences, etc., and the males may be thus found during the day in February, earlier or later in some seasons; the female is less often obtained on trees and fences, but may be beaten, together with the male, from the dead leaves which remain upon oak and other bushes.

The species appears to occur, more or less locally, in most of the English counties; it has also been recorded from Pembrokeshire and Flintshire, in Wales. In Scotland, it is obtained in the south, and northwards to Aberdeenshire. There are but two records from Ireland, and these are doubtful.

Abroad, the range extends to Amurland and Japan.

Scarce Umber (*Hybernia aurantiaria*).

One specimen of each sex of this orange yellow species will be found on Plate 120, where Fig. 7 represents the male, and Fig. 9 the female ; the cross lines, in the male, are usually distinct on all the wings, but those on the hind pair are sometimes very faint, and occasionally absent. The ground colour is paler in some specimens than in others, and there is variation in the amount of purplish speckling, in the purplish clouding following the second line, and in the submarginal series of purplish marks of the fore wings. The marginal dots are sometimes absent from the hind wings, most frequently in specimens with faint cross lines on these wings.

The eggs (Plate 125, Fig. 2), when I received them in February, were purplish, or violet brown.

The caterpillar is yellowish, inclining to ochreous, lined with brown on the back, and striped with purplish on the sides ; underside, dark purplish brown, inclining to blackish, and striped with yellowish. It feeds in the spring, sometimes to June, on oak, birch, blackthorn, etc., and may be found on the leaves during the day. The moth is out in the latter part of the year, from October, and is best obtained at night, when sitting on the twigs of trees and bushes, but a specimen or two may be found on tree-trunks, palings, etc., in the daytime.

The species is widely distributed over England, and in some parts it is common in woods ; also occurs in Wales. In Scotland it is very rare and local in Roxburghshire ; local and uncommon in the Clyde area, and has been recorded from other parts of the country up to Aberdeen. Rare in Ireland, but noted from

Tyrone (local among birches at Cookstown), Monaghan, Fermanagh (Enniskillen), and Galway.

Abroad, the range extends to Amurland and Japan.

Dotted Border (*Hybernia marginaria*).

On Plate 120 four specimens of this rather variable species are depicted. Figs. 8 ♂ and 10 ♀ show the more usual form; Fig. 12 represents the northern English, blackish var. *fuscata*, Harrison, and Fig. 11 an intermediate form resulting from a cross-pairing of *fuscata* ♀ with a southern ♂. Somewhat distinct on all the wings, but those on the hind pair are sometimes very faint, and occasionally absent. The ground colour is paler in some specimens than in others, and there is variation in the amount of purplish speckling, in the purplish clouding following the second line, and in the submarginal series of purplish marks of the fore wings. The marginal dots are sometimes absent on the hind wings, and frequently in specimens with faint cross lines on these wings.

year, and may be found on tree-trunks, palings, etc., in the daytime. Most frequently, however, it may be beaten from the twigs on which it rests, and in this way both sexes may be found on the twigs but a specimen or two parts it is common in woods; also occurs in Wales. In similar forms to the last have been captured in Wear Dale, Durham.

The caterpillar is figured on Plate 125, from a coloured drawing by Mr. A. Sich. It is described by Fenn as dull yellow, olive green, or greenish brown; a series of dark grey X-like marks

1-5. Mottled Umber.   6-8. March Moth.   9-11. Pale Brindled Beauty.

1a

1

2

2a

1. Sharp-angled Peacock : *eggs and caterpillar.*
2. Tawny-barred Angle : *caterpillar and chrysalids.*

on the back, most distinct on rings 5-11; the spiracles are white, each placed in a black cloud, and the spaces between them paler, sometimes yellowish; the last ring is often brown without marking, and the front rings have a purplish stripe above; under surface, paler throughout. It feeds, in April and May, as a rule, but has been found later, on hawthorn, sloe, oak, birch, alder, sallow, etc., and may be obtained in the daytime.

The moth is out in March and April, and after their short evening flight the males may be seen in numbers on hedgerows and the twigs of trees. It is not infrequent at sallow catkins, and sometimes is not scarce on palings and tree-trunks. The female may occasionally be detected in the crevices of bark on tree-trunks, but is more easily obtained on the twigs at night.

The species is common over the whole of England and Wales, also in Ireland. As regards Scotland, it is abundant in the south, but its range does not seem to extend beyond Aberdeen; the var. *fuscata* occurs in Renfrewshire.

Mottled Umber (*Hybernia defoliaria*).

A female (Fig. 3) and four examples of the male of this variable species are shown on Plate 122. The ground colour of the fore wings in the male varies from whitish, through ochreous brown to dull russet brown; the cross bands (when present) range in colour from reddish brown to dark purplish, almost blackish, brown; in all the paler specimens the ground colour is more or less sprinkled or suffused with brownish; the darker specimens are sprinkled with dark purplish or blackish. Ab. *obscurata*, Staud., is almost uniformly dull brownish, and an example approaching this form is represented by Fig. 4.

When deposited the eggs (Plate 125, Fig. 1*b*) were deep straw yellow.

The caterpillar (figured on Plate 125, Fig. 1, from a coloured drawing by Mr. A. Sich) has various shades of reddish brown on the back, and yellowish on the sides and beneath; the line above the red-marked white spiracles is black, and this has an interrupted edging of white. Fig. 1a shows a pale form. It feeds on the foliage of birch, oak, and other forest trees, also on fruit trees, rose, honeysuckle, etc. It often occurs in great abundance, and is largely responsible for the leafless condition of the trees, sometimes noticed in May.

The moth appears from October to December, and occasionally in January, February, or March.

Generally abundant throughout England and Wales; widely distributed, and often common in Ireland; not uncommon in the south of Scotland, but becoming less frequent northwards to Perthshire and Aberdeen.

March Moth (*Anisopteryx æscularia*).

Examples of each sex are shown on Plate 122, Figs. 7 and 8 ♂,

FIG. 12.
March Moth, male.

FIG. 14.
March Moth,
female ×2.
(Photos by H. Main.)

FIG. 13.
March Moth, female.

6 ♀. The male varies in the general colour from pale to dark

1-3. **Small Brindled Beauty.** 4-6. **Belted Beauty.** 7, 8. **Brindled Beauty.**

1. **Mottled Umber:** *egg, natural size and enlarged, and caterpillars*
2. **Scarce Umber:** *egg, natural size and enlarged.*
3. **Dotted Border:** *caterpillar.*
4. **March Moth:** *caterpillar.*

grey ; the central area being sometimes smoky tinged. In the
north of England, chiefly in Yorkshire, blackish specimens occur
in which the markings are more or less obscured.

The caterpillar is pale green with a rather darker line along
the back, and yellowish lines along the sides. It feeds on hawthorn, sloe, privet, lilac, currant, plum, cherry, rose, etc., also on
oak, hornbeam, and some other trees : April to June. The
figure of the caterpillar on Plate 125, Fig. 4, is from a coloured
drawing by Mr. A. Sich.

The moth is out in the spring, and may be found on palings,
tree-trunks, etc., in the daytime, and more freely flying about,
or sitting on hedges, at night, when the
spider-like wingless female is more frequently obtained. The male is attracted
by light, and sometimes is not uncommon
on gas lamps.

Except that it seems not to have been
noted north of Perthshire in Scotland, the
species is generally distributed over the
British Isles.

FIG. 15.
Pale Brindled
Beauty.
(Photo by H. Main.)

Pale Brindled Beauty
(*Phigalia pedaria*).

The fore wings of this species (Plate 122,
Figs. 9 ♀, 10, 11 ♂) are greyish, tinged
with greenish or brown, and sprinkled with
darker grey or brownish ; the irregular
cross lines are blackish. Occasional specimens in the north of England are more or
less sprinkled with yellow buff or orange
buff, and in these the cross-markings may be
present or absent. A more frequent form of
aberration in the north is a general darkening of the colour in

the direction of ab. *monacharia*, Staud., which is smoky black with the veins black, and occurs chiefly in South Yorkshire.

The caterpillar, figured on Plate 126, Fig. 1, from a coloured drawing by Mr. A. Sich, is dull reddish brown, relieved with rust red mottling ; the notched head is greyish brown. It feeds, in the spring, on birch, oak, elm, lime, poplar, sallow, hawthorn, sloe, plum and other fruit trees, rose, etc.

The moth is out as a rule during the first two or three months of the year, but it has been noted in November and December, and also in mid-June. It may be seen in the daytime on tree-trunks, palings, etc., but the female secretes herself in any convenient cranny, and is not easily detected. The male flies at night, and comes freely to light.

The species is pretty generally distributed throughout England and Wales, and Scotland up to Aberdeen. In Ireland, it has a wide distribution, but Kane states that, except in the Belfast district, it is decidedly scarce in the country.

Small Brindled Beauty (*Apocheima hispidaria*).

In the male (Plate 124, Figs. 1 and 2) the fore wings are ochreous grey inclining to brownish, usually much paler on the outer margin ; cross lines black. Hind wings, greyish white, with a blackish central band. Fringes of all the wings chequered with blackish. Often the central area of the fore wings, between the first and second lines, is more or less blackish ; less frequently the whole of these wings, up to or just beyond the submarginal line, is blackish ; and sometimes the pale outer marginal area is broken up by the blackish nervules. Very rarely, the ground colour is almost white, and the cross-markings on the fore wings dusky grey. The female (Plate 124, Fig. 3) varies from brown to blackish.

The caterpillar is brown, inclining to blackish or purplish, the raised spots are black, and occasionally the sides are freckled with orange (Plate 126, Fig. 2, from a coloured drawing by Mr. A. Sich). It feeds in May and early June on oak, and will also eat hawthorn, birch, and elm.

FIG. 16.
Small Brindled Beauty at rest.
(Photo by H. Main.)

The moth, which is out in February and March, appears to be local, but has a wide distribution through England from Durham to Hampshire, and even Devonshire. It has also been recorded from Denbighshire, North Wales. A well-known locality is Richmond Park, in Surrey, and here it is found resting on oak trunks or on the grass stems, etc., under or around the trees. The male is attracted by light.

Rannoch Brindled Beauty (*Nyssia lapponaria*).

The sexes of this species are shown on Plate 134, where Fig. 3 represents the male, and Fig. 5 the female. It was not known to occur in the British Isles until 1871, when a male specimen was captured in Perthshire, on April 20 of that year. Mr. William M. Christy, in 1895, bred some moths from larvæ obtained in the Highlands of Scotland, and he sent eggs to Mr. F. W. Frohawk, who worked out the life history, and described and figured all the stages from egg to perfect insect (*Entom.* xxviii. 237). In July, 1900 and 1901, Mr. E. A. Cockayne found caterpillars, in Perthshire (Rannoch district), on ling, heath, and bog-myrtle ; and in June, 1904, he published (*Entom.* xxxvii. 149) some interesting observations on the habits of the species in its native haunts.   The greenish yellow eggs are laid in batches of 10 to 150 in the dry corollas of the cross-leaved heath, and less frequently between the stem and sheath of reeds, or in cracks in dead bracken stems, etc.   The caterpillar (Plate 126, Fig. 3) is pale drab, inclining to a yellowish tint ; irregular yellow stripes along the back and sides, and lines of blackish streaks between the stripes.   It will eat birch, sallow, and hawthorn, in captivity ; but in the open it feeds on heather and bog-myrtle : May–July.   The chrysalis is reddish brown, rather paler on the wing covers (figured on Plate 126 from a photo, twice natural size, by Mr. H. Main).   The moth is out in April and May, and sits on the twigs of heather and the stems of bog-myrtle.   It has only been recorded from Perthshire, and is there very local, frequenting damp places near streams.

Mr. A. W. Mera has obtained hybrids from a crossing of this species with *N. zonaria*.

Belted Beauty (*Nyssia zonaria*).

Two males and a female of this species are depicted on Plate 124 (Figs. 4, 5 ♂, 6 ♀).   There is variation in the ground colour of the male, from white to greyish, and the markings are sometimes greyish brown and sometimes blackish.   Kane states that, in Ireland, a large number of Connemara specimens have the fore wings entirely white, broken by dark veins, front margin, and three streaks parallel to the outer margin.   The caterpillar is greenish, with dusky grey lines and freckles on the back, and a yellow stripe low down along the sides ; the latter is edged below with blackish ; the underside is black and striped with grey ; head, greyish, freckled with darker.   It feeds on sallow, dandelion, dock, plantain, clover, yarrow,

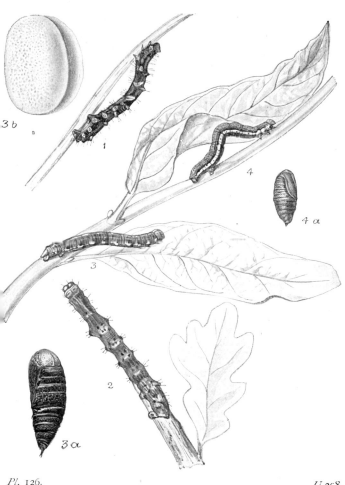

1. Pale Brindled Beauty: *caterpillar.*
2. Small Brindled Beauty: *caterpillar.*
3*a*, 3*b*. Rannoch Brindled Beauty: *egg, natural size and enlarged, caterpillar and chrysalis.*
4, 4*a*. Belted Beauty: *caterpillar and chrysalis.*

Pl. 127.

1-3. **Oak Beauty.**

grass, etc. : May to August. (Plate 126, Fig. 4 ; chrysalis, Fig. 4a ; eggs, Plate 133, Fig. 4.) The moth is out in March and April, and rests by day on or among herbage. The male has been known to fly in the sunshine, but its more usual time of flight is the early evening.

The species is locally common on sand hills, on the coast of Cheshire, Flintshire, and Carnarvon ; Wallasey is a noted locality, and the earliest British specimens were taken in that district about 1832 ; it also occurs on the Lancashire coast, in the Liverpool and Blackpool districts. In Ireland, it was first noted in Co. Antrim, where caterpillars were found at Bally-castle, and about twenty-two years ago moths were captured at the same place. Other Irish localities are Achill Island, off the coast of Mayo ; Slyne Head and Roundstone, Connemara coast. There are records of its occurrence in the Isles of Skye and Tiree ; also in South Uist, Outer Hebrides.

Brindled Beauty (*Lycia hirtaria*).

A male and a female are shown on Plate 124 (Figs. 7 ♂, 8 ♀), and these represent the more usual form of the sexes in the London district. Some specimens are paler, others are darker ; and not infrequently the wings are sprinkled with yellowish.

On Plate 1 (Figs. 4, 6, 8) will be found figures of a female and two male examples of a large race taken by Mr. H. McArthur this season (1908) at Aviemore, in Scotland. One of these males is of a remarkable ochreous coloration, whilst in the other the contrast of grey ground and black marking is equally striking. The female is blackish sprinkled with ochreous.

The caterpillar is purplish grey or reddish brown clouded and freckled with darker, and spotted with yellow on rings 5–8 ; the first ring is also marked with yellow in front, the head is freckled with black, and about the jaws with yellow. It feeds on lime, elm, willow, and fruit trees, especially plum and pear, in May, June, and July. For the example figured on Plate 128, Fig. 1, I am indebted to Mr. Norman Riley; an Aviemore example is shown in colour on Plate 1, Fig. 7. The chrysalis (Plate 128, Fig. 1a) is dark reddish brown inclining to blackish. The moth comes out in March and April and is often a common object on tree-trunks, etc., in the London parks, squares, and gardens. Its range extends over the south of England, and northwards to Yorkshire and Cumberland, but it is nowhere so plentiful in England as throughout the Metropolitan area. It occurs in Wales, in Ireland, and in Scotland up to Inverness.

Oak Beauty (*Pachys (Amphidasys) strataria*).

The fore wings of this species (Plate 127, Figs. 1–3) are white, sprinkled and cross lined with black; the first line is bordered inwardly, and the second line outwardly with brownish; frequently these two lines fall closely together on the inner margin, and sometimes they are united by a blackish blotch at this point; the brownish borders of the lines vary in width, and in some specimens the outer area beyond the second black line is almost entirely brownish; in other specimens the central and outer areas are almost free of black speckling, and in such examples the brownish borders of the lines stand out conspicuously. The caterpillar (Plate 128, Fig. 2) is usually some shade of brown—greyish, violet, or purplish—mottled and freckled with a darker hue. It feeds on oak, birch, and elm, will also eat sloe, plum, rose, etc., and is found from May to July. In confinement, larvæ hatched in early May have gone down to pupate during the second week in June.

The moth is out in March and April as a rule, but has been noted in late February, and also in early May. It may be seen resting during the day on trunks of trees, palings, etc., generally near the ground; when on the wing at night the male will come to light. Although not generally common it is widely

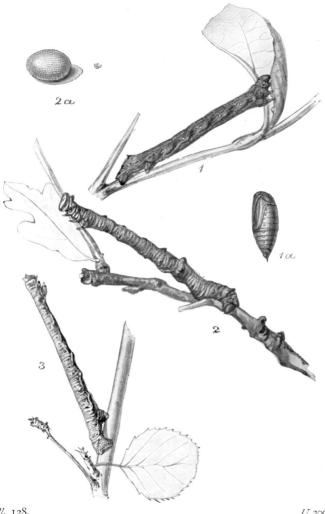

Pl. 128.   U 300.

1. **Brindled Beauty:** *caterpillar and chrysalis.*
2. **Oak Beauty:** *eggs, natural size and enlarged, and caterpillar.*
3. **Peppered Moth:** *caterpillar.*

1-3. **Peppered Moth**.

distributed over England and Wales. In Ireland it has occurred in Wicklow, Westmeath, and Cork, and has been reared from pupæ obtained at Glenmalure in the former county.

Hybrids resulting from a cross between *strataria* ♂ and *betularia* ♀ have been named *herefordi*, Tutt.

Peppered Moth (*Pachys betularia*).

Typically (Plate 129, Figs. 1 ♂, 3 ♀) the wings are white, "peppered" with black, and with more or less distinct cross lines, also black. The black speckling varies in amount, in some examples it is almost absent, whilst in others it is so dense that the wings appear to be black sprinkled with white. Specimens of the last form are intermediate between the type and the melanic ab. *doubledayaria*, Millière (Fig. 2). This black form, which seems to have been unknown about sixty years ago, is now much commoner than the type in the South-west Riding of Yorkshire, and has spread into Lancashire, Cheshire, and southwards to Lincolnshire. On the wolds of the latter county, and on Cannock Chase, Staffordshire, it is said to be the dominant form of the species. The aberration also occurs in the eastern and the southern counties of England to Hampshire. Northwards, the form has extended to Clydesdale in Scotland, where one was reared from a caterpillar obtained near Paisley. In Wales *doubledayaria* is in the ascendant at Newport, Monmouth, and in Ireland one example of this variety together with some intermediate and typical specimens were reared from caterpillars collected at Castle Bellingham, Co. Louth. Possibly the liberal distribution of the eggs of *doubledayaria* may have had something to do with the comparatively rapid extension of this form, at least to districts far away from its original locality.

What is known as the buff var. of this species dates back to the year 1874, when a buff female, paired with a black male, was captured at Heaton Park. From the eggs she deposited caterpillars hatched, and in due course pupated, but the moths reared from them were all either typical, or black. Some of the female moths were, however, given to other collectors to pair with black males with the result that buff specimens appeared among the moths reared by seven collectors. Subsequently, by breeding only from buff males and females 80 per cent. of this form were said to be obtained. By the year 1880, however, the race was extinct. In all the examples of the buff var. that I have seen, including a pair in my own collection, the ground colour is normal, but the usual black markings of the wings are brownish buff; I understand, however, that there are specimens in which the ground colour is ochreous. The vapour of chlorine will change an ordinary specimen to a buff var.; and it is said that caterpillars reared in an apartment where this vapour is present will produce these buff varieties. Mr. Mansbridge has recently described ab. *ochrearia*, and in this form the typical black markings are present on an ochreous ground. The specimen, a female, was captured at St. Annes, Lancashire, June, 1891.

Gynandrous examples have been obtained, and seven of these abnormal forms occurred in a single brood reared from eggs by Mr. A. Harrison.

The caterpillar (Plate 128, Fig. 3, from a photo by Mr. H. Main) is green, brownish green, or purplish brown; in the green form, which is minutely dotted with white, there is generally a faint purplish line along the back, two purplish knobs on ring 8, and a purplish patch enclosing two ochreous spots on ring 11; the deeply notched head is ochreous, shaded with purplish; the last ring of the body is tinged with purplish, as also are the two small points thereon. It feeds, from July to September, on oak, birch, elm, beech, sallow, plum and other fruit trees; also on rose, bramble, etc. The moth is out in May and June, sometimes in July. The species is generally distributed, and sometimes common in the caterpillar state, but seems to be absent from the Scottish Isles.

Waved Umber (*Hemerophila* (*Synopsia*) *abruptaria*).

A male and a female specimen are figured on Plate 130. The males are usually darker than the females, but they vary in the amount of darker clouding and suffusion. Three forms of the species have been named as follows—ab. *brunneata*, Tutt, a modification of the female rather more strongly coloured than the darkest typical male. Ab. *fuscata*, Tutt, sooty brown, tending to blackish ; both sexes somewhat paler in central area of fore wings. Ab. *unicolor*, Tutt, similar to ab. *fuscata*, but without pale marking ; the thorax is also darker. (Plate 134, Fig. 7, ab. *fuscata*.) The eggs, furnished by Mr. Norman Riley, were verdigris green when laid, but on the third day changed to greyish.

FIG. 17.
Waved Umber at rest.
(Photo by J. W. Lucas.)

In general colour the caterpillar is greyish brown sometimes tinged with green ; pinkish brown blotches along the back, often united on the front and hind rings. In some cases the caterpillar is almost black, with a lighter mark on front of the first ring. It feeds on privet and lilac, and is said to eat currant, broom, and jasmine : May to August. (Plate 133, Fig. 3.)

The moth is out in April and May, and is fond of resting on palings, trees, and even walls. It appears to be most plentiful in the London district, in the north and east of which the dark forms occur ; but it is found more or less frequently over the greater part of England, and in South Wales ; single specimens were taken at Hartlepool, Durham, in 1874 and 1875. One example has been recorded from Kincardineshire, Scotland ; and one from Enniskillen, Ireland.

Ringed Carpet (*Boarmia cinctaria*).

Two specimens are shown on Plate 130. Fig. 3 represents the more or less typical form, and Fig. 4 depicts an example in which the central area is almost free of dark speckling, so that the whitish ground colour comes out distinctly. There is a good range of variation in the direction of both darker and paler forms than those figured. In some specimens with a clear white central area, the basal and outer marginal areas of the fore wings, and the outer area of the hind wings, are black or blackish ; similar aberration is sometimes found in the more speckled specimens also. Occasionally, there is a projection from below the middle of the second black line to the basal band.

The caterpillar is green, with darker green and whitish lines along the back and sides. It feeds on birch, sallow, and heath (*Erica cinerea*), and may be reared on knot-grass. The moth is out in May, sometimes late April or early June. The New Forest in Hampshire is the district *par excellence* for this species, the most favoured locality being the heathy tract near Lyndhurst, where the moths are very common, in some years, on tree-trunks, especially birch, and on heather. Other localities in England are Poole Heath, Parley Heath, and Bloxworth in Dorset ; Tilgate Forest, etc., in Sussex ; Reading district in Berks, first noted in 1891. In Ireland, it is widely distributed, and is abundant at Killarney and some other parts of Kerry.

The range abroad extends to Amurland and Japan.

1, 2. **Waved Umber.**   3, 4. **Ringed Carpet.**   5, 6. **Willow Beauty.**

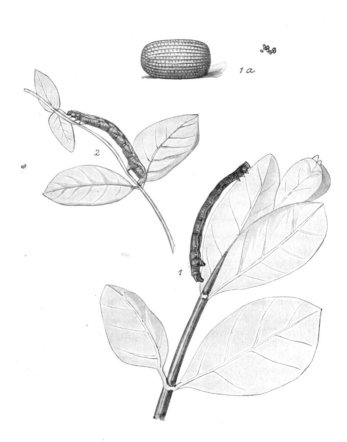

1. **Willow Beauty:** *eggs and caterpillar.*
2. **Mottled Beauty:** *caterpillar.*

Willow Beauty (*Boarmia gemmaria*).

The two portraits on Plate 130 represent the best known forms of this species. Stephens in 1831 referred the smoky or dark slaty grey form (Fig. 6), which is the ordinary one in the London district, now as then, to *rhomboidaria*. Newman subsequently named this form *perfumaria*, and he, and other entomologists of the time, considered it as a species distinct from *gemmaria* = *rhomboidaria*. We now know that the smoky grey specimens are not peculiar to the metropolitan area, but occur in other parts of England (Warwickshire, Yorkshire, Lancashire, etc.), and are found, with the type, at Howth and other localities in Ireland. The more general forms throughout England, Wales, Ireland, and Scotland up to Perthshire, are pale brown, or greyish brown (typical), sometimes ochreous tinged (Fig. 5); the latter is referable to ab. *consobrinaria*, Haworth. Black forms (ab. *rebeli*) have been recorded from Norwich, in Norfolk, and blackish specimens have been noted from Ashdown Forest, Sussex; from Cannock Chase, Staffordshire; and from the south of Scotland.

The eggs (Plate 131, Fig. 1a) are green at first, changing to pink mottled with green, and finally to dark grey; the latter change indicates early hatching of the caterpillar, which usually occurs about a fortnight after the eggs are deposited.

The caterpillar (Plate 131, Fig. 1, after a coloured drawing by Mr. A. Sich) is dull reddish brown, mottled more or less with ochreous; traces of diamond-shaped marks on the back, the latter sometimes well defined. It feeds on ivy (in London gardens especially), hawthorn, birch, privet, lilac, rose, clematis, broom, and many other shrubs, and also on yew and fir, in August, and after hibernation in the spring. The moth is out in July and August; sometimes a second brood occurs in September.

Series II.

X

This species is the *gemmaria* of Brahm (1791), but *rhomboidaria*, Schiffermüller (1776), although only a catalogue name until figured by Hübner, about 1797, is adopted by some authors.

Satin Carpet (*Boarmia abietaria*).

As an inhabitant of Britain this species was first noted from Hampshire, and in 1825 was figured and described by Curtis as *Alcis sericearia*. Two specimens of this form, from the New Forest, are depicted on Plate 132, Figs. 1, 2 ; but paler, and also darker, examples are found in this locality ; and, occasionally, melanic specimens occur as well. The latter form, some examples of which might be described as sooty black with black veins, is more prevalent among the yews and firs of Surrey.

The caterpillar, for the example of which (and also the egg), figured on Plate 138, Figs. 1, 1a, I am obliged to Mr. Arthur J. Scollick, is, in one form, ochreous brown with paler cream-coloured patches on the back ; and in another dark grey-brown with paler patches, sometimes of a light cinnamon brown ; a pale, thin line along the middle of the back runs through a series of brownish diamonds ; there are other pale lines on the back and sides, and these are edged with brownish, and partly with blackish ; spiracles outlined in black. (Adapted from Buckler.) It feeds on spruce, pine, yew, oak, birch, sallow, etc., from August to June. A larva has been found on bilberry in Devon

The moth is out from late June to early August, but captured specimens are not often suitable for the cabinet, they are generally more or less frayed or scarred.

Beside Surrey and Hants, previously mentioned, the species occurs in Sussex (Tilgate Forest), Buckinghamshire (Halton), and has been recorded from Berkshire ; Egg Buckland, Oxton,

1, 2. Satin Carpet.   3-6. Mottled Beauty.

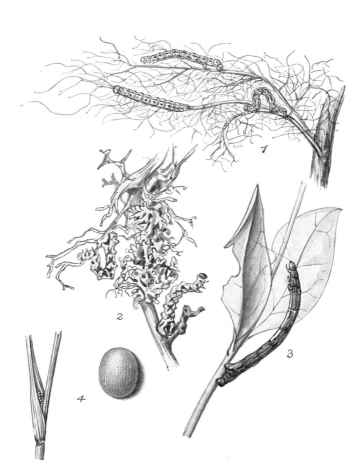

1. **Dotted Carpet:** *cat... pillars*
2. **Brussels Lace:** *caterpillars*
3. **Waved Umber:** *caterpillar*
4. **Belted Beauty:** *eggs.*

Bickleigh Vale, and other Devonshire localities ; also from Cornwall, Somersetshire, Gloucestershire (the Cotswolds), and Monmouthshire.

Staudinger and other recent authors have adopted *ribeata*, Clerck, for this species.

Mottled Beauty (*Boarmia repandata*).

Two examples of the more ordinary mottled form of this species are shown on Plate 132, Figs. 3 ♂, and 4 ♀. Fig. 6 represents ab. *destrigaria*, Haworth (*muraria*, Curtis) ; and Fig. 5 depicts a specimen near var. *sodorensium*, Weir, from the Isle of Lewis. Dark-brown forms, inclining to blackish, are not uncommon in the London district, but in South Yorkshire coal-black specimens with whitish submarginal lines occur ; a sooty black example from the Sheffield district is figured on Plate 134, Fig. 4, and, it may be added, these melanic forms are referable to ab. *nigricata*, Fuchs.

Two forms of ab. *conversaria*, Hübner, will be found on Plate 134, where Fig. 1 depicts a specimen from the New Forest, and Fig. 8 represents an extreme example from North Devon. The *conversaria* form occurs chiefly in the south and west of England, and is perhaps most plentiful along the North Devon coast ; also in South Wales ; Durham (rarely, on the coast). Broad dark banded specimens are recorded from Arran and Argyll.

The caterpillar (figured on Plate 131, Fig. 2, after Sich) is brownish inclining to ochreous ; a dark brownish line along the middle of the back, and a series of brownish diamond-shaped marks most distinct on the back of the middle rings ; a line of blackish marks along the sides shows up in the paler examples. Sometimes the general colour is dark reddish brown, freckled with dark brown ; but in all cases the underside is paler than the upper, and is striped and lined with dark and pale brown.

It feeds on hawthorn, birch, elm, hazel, bilberry, heather, etc., from July to May.

The moth is out in June and July, and specimens of a second generation have been reared in September. Generally common throughout the British Isles.

Great Oak Beauty (*Boarmia roboraria*).

The fine Boarmid moth shown on Plate 135, Fig. 2, has all the typical markings well defined. Occasionally the black cross lines are more distinct, but sometimes they are more or less absent, or obscured. An almost black specimen is mentioned by Barrett as taken in the Reading district, Berkshire ; and the same author states that a black example was captured in the Midlands about the year 1887, but no other specimen was observed until 1893, when a female was obtained, and from eggs deposited smoky black moths were reared.

The caterpillar is very like an oak twig in shape, especially when in repose. (See Fig. 18.) In colour it is reddish brown, inclining to ochreous brown ; brownish grey on the humps on rings 5 and 11, and on the skin folds. It feeds on oak during the autumn, and, after hibernation, in the spring. The moth is out in June and July, and may be

FIG. 18.
Caterpillar of Great
Oak Beauty.
(Photo by " A. Forester ".)

1, 4, 7, 8. Mottled Beauty, vars.   2. Speckled Beauty.
3, 5. Rannoch Brindled Beauty.   6. September Thorn.
9. Large Thorn, var

2. Great Oak Beauty. 1, 3. **Pale Oak Beauty.**

found on oak trees rather high up the trunks. When on the wing at night it will visit the sugar patch.

The species occurs most frequently in the New Forest, Hampshire, where, in some years, it is very common. Other English counties in which it has been found, or still exists, are—Devon (Cann Woods), Dorset (Cranborne and Bloxworth), Wilts. (Savernake Forest), Sussex (Abbots Wood, Charlton Forest, Holme Bank, etc.), Surrey (Addington, June, 1902), Kent, Essex (Epping Forest), Berks., Bucks., Warwick (Prince-thorpe Wood), Worcester (Wyre Forest), Stafford (Cannock Chase), Cheshire (Dunham Park), York (wood near Selby), Lancashire (Corporation and Quernmore Woods).

Pale Oak Beauty (*Boarmia consortaria*).

Some specimens are rather greyer, and the cross markings are occasionally less distinct than in Figs. 1 ♂, and 3 ♀ on Plate 135, which represent the typical forms of this species in England. Examples of a blackish form have been noted from a wood in West Kent, and these are apparently referable to the melanic ab. *humperti*, Humpert, but the Kentish specimens I have seen had the second line of fore wings edged with white, and a white submarginal line.

The caterpillar, which in shape is somewhat like that of the last species, varies in colour. One form is greenish grey, with three lines, the central one darker than those on each side. In another the colour is pale brown mottled with reddish and a darker brown. It feeds on oak, birch, and sometimes sallow, in July and August.

The moth is out in June and July, and specimens have been recorded as captured in September. It may be found on the trunks of oak and fir trees, and will come to sugar and light at night. Although local it is not uncommon in the New Forest and other woods in Hampshire; also in Sussex, Surrey, Kent, and Berkshire. It has been recorded from Buckinghamshire, Wiltshire, and Dorsetshire ; and as local and scarce in the Lancaster district.

The range abroad extends to Amurland and Japan, and in both countries it is represented by var. *conferenda*, Butler.

Speckled Beauty (*Cleora angularia*).

Stephens, who in 1831 figured this insect as *Cleora viduaria*, Wien. Verz., remarks, "All the examples I have seen of this beautiful species were captured in the New Forest : the first about June, 1822, the remainder in 1825 and 1826 : I believe in the vicinity of Lyndhurst." Barrett states that the late Mr. Samuel Stevens obtained a number of specimens "by sweeping the upper branches of oak trees in the New Forest with a long pole." This was in 1849 ; and between that year and 1872, about which time it seems to have disappeared, the moth was found, by those who knew where to look for it, in the Forest between Brockenhurst and Lyndhurst. Specimens have also been taken, in the past, in Tilgate Forest, Sussex, by the late William Tester, and by Mr. Merrifield, at Holm Bank, near Henfield, in the same county. There have been recent rumours of its reappearance in the New Forest, but I have been unable to ascertain anything definite about this. The specimen depicted in Plate 134, Fig. 2, has been kindly lent by Mr. R. Adkin.

The caterpillar, stated by Hofmann to feed on lichen growing upon oak and birch, is brownish variegated with paler shades.

Brussels Lace (*Cleora lichenaria*).

The greenish grey species shown on Plate 136, Figs. 1 ♂, 2 ♀, varies in tint ; the fore wings are often clouded with olive, and occasionally with blackish ; there is frequently a tinge of ochreous between the black cross lines, but sometimes this area is flushed with orange.

Two figures of the caterpillar will be found on Plate 133, Fig. 2. In colour and marking it so closely resembles the greenish-grey lichen upon which it feeds, that its detection thereon is not always easy. May and June are the best months in which to collect the caterpillars (although they may be found during the autumn and early spring), and they may then be jarred from the lichen (*Usnea barbata*), etc., growing on branches of trees and bushes, or searched for among the lichen on the tree trunks, or on wooden pales and fences.

The species is widely spread over the southern half of England, but is more or less rare from the Midlands northwards. It has occurred in South Wales and the Isle of Anglesea ; and Kane states that it is widely distributed and locally common in Ireland. In some parts of South Scotland it is not uncommon, and its range extends to Aberdeen and Ross.

The Dotted Carpet (*Cleora jubata*).

This species (Plate 136, Figs. 3, 4) has long been known as *glabraria*, Hübner, but as authorities are agreed that *jubata*, Thunberg, is an earlier name, it must be adopted. The general colour is whitish, powdered with dark grey and black ; there are four black spots on the front margin and from these blackish markings cross the wings, but only the first line is generally distinct, although a second line, beyond the large black discal spot, is sometimes clearly defined and entire ; occasionally a central shade and a submarginal line are both in evidence. The hind wings have a black central spot and a blackish line beyond, but the latter is often absent. Exceptional aberration takes the form of leaden black blotches, clouds, and streaks on the fore wings, and dusky clouding on the hind wings, chiefly on the basal area.

The caterpillar is of a faint bluish green, inclining to greenish white on the back ; a row of black spots along the back, and a broken black narrow stripe along each side. It feeds on tree lichens (*Usnea barbata*), etc., from September to June or July. Three figures of this caterpillar are given on Plate 133, Fig. 3.

The moth is out in July and August, and may be found at rest on tree trunks now and then, but is more frequently obtained by jarring the lichen-clad branches of oak. Although it is known to occur very locally and somewhat rarely in the counties of Wilts., Dorset, and Devon, the New Forest in Hampshire is the English district where one is most likely to meet with this species. It has been recorded from Cornwall (Falmouth district, 1904), Hereford, Pembrokeshire, Carnarvonshire (Beddgelert), and Cumberland. Charlton Forest, Sussex, has also been mentioned. In Scotland, Renton states that it is generally common in Roxburghshire ; it occurs in several of the woods in Clydesdale, and has been noted from Argyllshire.

The Engrailed (*Tephrosia bistortata*).

In the following brief remarks on *T. bistortata*, Goeze (= *biundularia*, Borkhausen), I have included reference to *crepuscularia*, Hübner (= *biundularia*, Esper). The former (which is also named *abietaria*, Haworth, and *laricaria*, Double-day) appears on the wing in March and April, and there is a second flight in July and August. Moths of the second genera-tion are few in number and small in size, and are referable to abs. *consonaria* and *strigularia*, Stephens. A third generation of still smaller moths has been reared. *Crepuscularia* is out in May and June, rarely in April ; its caterpillar feeds in June and July or later ; according to Barrett, a second generation of the moth has occurred in August. One or two moths have been captured in September or October, but whether these were referable to *bistortata* or *crepuscularia* is not quite clear.

By some authorities the double-brooded *bistortata* is

considered specifically distinct from the, normally, single-brooded *crepuscularia;* others hold the opposite view. The March and April moths are generally rather browner in colour than those

appearing in May and June, but I have some specimens taken in Wiltshire at the end of March, which are quite as pale as any example in the May — June series. Probably, we should be right in regarding *crepuscularia* as the older stock from which the double-brooded race, *bistortata*, has sprung. The former has a more extensive range, as it inhabits Northern Europe (Sutherland-shire in British Isles), whilst *bistortata* seems to be confined to Central Europe. A Perth-shire form of the May —June race is shown on Plate 136, Fig. 7; and an example of ab.

FIG. 19.
Small Engrailed, at rest.
(Photo by W. J. Lucas.)

delamerensis, White, from Delamere Forest, Cheshire, is represented by Fig. 8. Figs. 6 ♂, 7 ♀, represent examples of the March and April race. Black or blackish forms, with the sub-marginal line more or less distinctly white, occur in both races, chiefly in Glamorganshire, South Wales.

A photograph, by Mr. H. Main, of the caterpillar, is reproduced on Plate 138, Fig. 3. The general colour is grey,
inclining to yellowish or brownish; sometimes it is reddish
brown; two broken dark-grey lines on the back, and some pale
blotches on the sides. The caterpillars of the first race
(*bistortata*) feed in May and June, and again in August and
September. Those of the second race in June and July, or
later. They seem to eat the foliage of trees, including those in
orchards.

NOTE.—Cross-pairings between *bistortata* ♂ and *crepuscularia* ♀ resulted in the ab. *ridingi*, Tutt, whilst the offspring of
a crossing of *crepuscularia* ♂ and *bistortata* ♀ have been named
bacoti, Tutt. Pairings of *bistortata* ♂ and *delamerensis* ♀
produce ab. *ridingi-suffusa*, Tutt; and those of *delamerensis* ♂
and *bistortata* ♀ = *bacoti-suffusa*, Tutt. Further, *bacoti-suffusa*
will pair with *ridingi-suffusa*, or the last named with *crepuscularia*; the progeny being in the first case *mixta*, Tutt, and
in the latter, *reversa*, Tutt.

Brindled White-spot (*Tephrosia luridata*).

Two examples of this species (also known as *extersaria*,
Hübner) are depicted on Plate 137, Figs. 1 ♂, 2 ♀. There is
variation in the amount of black speckling and in the strength
of the cross lines.

The caterpillar is dull hazel or chocolate brown, often tinged
with green; a row of whitish dots on each side of a series of
pale spots along the middle of the back; rings 4 and 8 barred
with black-brown or dusky rust colour. Sometimes the general
colour is green. (Adapted from Fenn.) It feeds in July and
August, or even later, on oak and birch, sometimes on alder
and sallow. The moth is out in May and June, earlier or
later in some seasons. In Britain apparently confined to England, where it occurs locally, in woods, from Worcestershire

southwards to Kent and Cornwall, and eastward to Norfolk and Suffolk. In the New Forest, Hampshire, where it is often plentiful, it may be seen on the boles of trees, but is more easily obtained after dark when it comes to the sugar patch.

Square Spot (*Tephrosia consonaria*).

Two examples of this species will be found on Plate 137, Figs. 3 ♂, 4 ♀. There is variation in the greyish or brownish speckling of the wings, and this in some typical examples is so sparse that the wings appear to be almost white with brownish basal band and brownish markings on the outer area; the most conspicuous of the latter being the middle square spot between the second and submarginal lines, more or less distinct in all forms, to which the English name refers. In other specimens the wings are, especially the front pair, densely covered with the dark speckling. Some Surrey specimens, chiefly from the Leith Hill district, have an ochreous tinge; and quite recently a black form of the species has occurred in a wood near Maidstone, in West Kent. The last phase of aberration seems to be unknown in any other part of Britain, and also, I believe, elsewhere.

The egg (Plate 138, Fig. 2) is yellowish green when laid; later it becomes yellow, and orange red markings appear, chiefly at one end.

The somewhat wrinkled caterpillar is ochreous brown above, inclining to greyish between the rings; an ochreous line along the middle of the back is only clearly defined on the front rings; the under side is greenish ochreous, and sometimes this colour extends to the upper side also; the head, which is notched on the crown, is pale ochreous, more or less marked with brown. It feeds at night, in June and July, on birch, beech, oak, pine, etc.

The moth is out in May and June, earlier in some districts. In the daytime it may be seen on the trunks or boughs of trees, most frequently at too great a height to be easily secured ; but still a few sit low enough for capture, especially on the trunks of fir trees. The species is a decidedly local one, and seems to be largely confined, in Britain, to the southern parts of England, Wales, and Ireland. It occurs in some of the woods of Kent, Surrey, Sussex, Hampshire, Dorsetshire, Devonshire, Cornwall, Gloucestershire, Oxfordshire, Buckinghamshire, Bedfordshire, Essex, and Suffolk. Edwards notes the species as rare at Malvern, Worcestershire. Forsythe, in " A List of the Macro-Lepidoptera of Lancaster and District " (*Entom.* 1905, p. 182), states that the moth may be found sitting on the fir-tree trunks at the end of May, at Witherslack and Quernmore ; and a single specimen has been recorded from Upton, near Birkenhead, Cheshire. The occurrence of *T. consonaria* in the north of England seems open to question. The only county in Wales appears to be Glamorganshire, as mentioned by Barrett. Kane (*Catalogue of the Lepidoptera of Ireland*) noted the species from Derrycunihy, and Mucross, Killarney, where he has taken it in moderate abundance ; he also gives Clonbullogue, in King's County.

The range abroad extends to Amurland and Japan.

Grey Birch (*Tephrosia punctularia*).

Three examples of this greyish species are shown on Plate 137. The wings are usually whitish grey in the ground colour, and sprinkled or dusted with darker grey ; there are three blackish, or black dotted, cross lines on the fore wings, often indistinct, but rarely entirely absent, and even then represented by black marks on the front margin. Sometimes the first and third lines may be well in evidence and the central one absent ; occasionally the second line is placed quite close to the first ; the

1,2. **Brussels Lace.**   3, 4. **Dotted Carpet.**   5, 6. **Small Engrailed.**

7, 8. **The Engrailed.**

1, 2. Brindled White-spot.   3, 4. Square Spot.
5-7. Grey Birch.   8, 9. Horse Chestnut.

sub-marginal line is whitish, inwardly shaded with dark greyish, especially at the middle and towards the front margin. The hind wings have two cross lines corresponding with the first and third on the fore wings. There is a good deal of variation in the amount of dark speckling, and this is occasionally so heavy that the insect becomes dark grey in colour; I have taken such specimens at Oxshott in Surrey. Dark aberrations are perhaps more frequent in the north of England, but the species is more local and less plentiful in that part of the country.

The caterpillar, which may be beaten from birch, and sometimes alder, in July, is bright apple green with yellowish lines on the sides and back; the ring divisions are yellow, and the head is tinged with that colour. (Adapted from Porritt.) Sometimes the caterpillars are brownish, or greenish grey in general colour. The moth, which is out in May and June, will be found in woods, or on heaths, where birches grow. It rests on the trunks of the trees and may be boxed, as a rule, with ease. On some occasions, however, it is very lively, and the net will have to be brought into action for its capture.

The distribution of this species extends through England, but it is far more plentiful in the south than in the north, although it has been recorded from several places in Yorkshire, and from Coal Law Wood in Northumberland. It is found also in Wales, and in Scotland up to Moray. In Ireland it is not frequent, but has been noted from Mucross, and the Upper Lake of Killarney, in Kerry, and from Tinahely in Wicklow; Kane also gives Clonbrock in Galway, and adds that "some specimens from this locality have the spots very large on a clear whitish ground, so that they have a superficial resemblance to *Cleora glabraria.*"

The range abroad spreads to East Siberia, Amurland, and Japan.

NOTE.—Staudinger places the last four species in *Boarmia*, Treitschke; but Prout and others refer them to the genus *Ectropis*, Hübner. The latter will probably have to be adopted.

Horse Chestnut (*Pachycnema hippocastanaria*).

The rather long and somewhat oval fore wings of this species (Plate 137, Figs. 8, 9) are brownish grey, inclining to purplish grey ; the two cross lines are blackish, edged with whitish, but generally indistinct ; when the lines are well defined, the enclosed central area is sometimes darker than the other parts of the wings ; there is a black central dot, and occasionally there is a well-marked dusky central shade. Hind wings, whitish, more or less tinged with smoky grey ; frequently there is a dusky. curved line beyond the middle, and this is sometimes outwardly edged with whitish.

The caterpillar is greyish brown, dotted with black, and marked on the back and sides with reddish brown. When at rest on the twigs of its food plant, heather or ling (*Calluna vulgaris*), this caterpillar agrees so well with its surroundings that it is not at all easy to see ; at least, we may see it. but fail to distinguish it from the twigs of the plant. It may be obtained in June and July, and again in the autumn. (Figured on Plate 140, after Hofmann.)

The first flight of the moth occurs in April and May ; the second in August, but specimens of the later generation are usually small in size and in number, as compared with those of the early brood.

In Britain, this species has so far only been found on the heaths of Kent, Surrey, Sussex, Hampshire, Dorsetshire, Somersetshire, Berkshire, and Suffolk ; in all these counties it is more or less local, but it abounds in some of its haunts. It has been recorded from Hereford, and Edwards states that it occurs rarely in the Malvern district of Worcestershire.

1 a

1

3

2.

3 a

1. **Satin Carpet :** *egg and caterpillar.*
2. **Square Spot :** *eggs.*
3. **The Engrailed :** *caterpillar and chrysalis.*

1-3. **Annulet.**   4, 5. **Scotch Annulet.**   6, 7. **Black Mountain Moth.**

The Annulet (*Gnophos* (*Sciadion*) *obscurata*).

In a general way, all the grey specimens of this species are referable to the type form *obscurata*, Schiffermüller; the true type, however, appears to be rare in Britain, even if it occurs at all. It is, perhaps, best represented by well-marked dark specimens from limestone districts, or the lighter ones from peaty ground. At Folkestone and in other chalky localities on the Kentish coast, the bulk of the specimens are pale grey inclining to whitish, usually with the black cross lines showing more or less clearly. Sometimes the lines are obscured by heavy freckling (ab. *woodiata*, Prout); not infrequently, at Folkestone chiefly, the inner and outer areas are pale, more or less free of freckling, but the central area, defined by black lines, is densely freckled ; this is the banded form (ab. *fasciata*, Prout). A form occurs on the chalk hills at Lewes in Sussex, in which the wings are almost white, without freckling, but with distinct black lines and rings (ab. *calceata*, Staudinger) ; a modification of this whitish form from Lewes has been described by Prout as ab. *mundata*, "Almost pure whitish, with virtually no markings, excepting the annulets." On heaths in Surrey and Hampshire, and on the mountains of Aberdeen and Perthshire, a blackish form occurs (ab. *obscuriorata*, Prout = *obscuraria*, Hübner, 146) ; and sometimes specimens are found in which the wings are of "an intense and almost uniform black " (ab. *saturata*, Prout). In Devonshire and Cornwall, the species is darkish grey inclining to brownish (ab. *anthracinaria*, Esper) ; whilst on the coasts of North Devon and Wales it is of a slaty grey, more or less tinged with brown, and almost without markings ; the Welsh specimens are large, and the wings are rather shining (ab. *uniformata*, Prout). A form, which I have not seen, of "a sandy or reddish colour " is referred by Prout (*Trans. City of Lond. Ent. Soc.*, 1903, p. 39) to ab. *argillacearia*, Staudinger ; it occurs in sandstone localities. (Plate 84, Figs. 1, Folkestone ; 2, New Forest ; 3, Lewes.)

The rather rough and dumpy caterpillar is dark greyish brown above, inclining to purplish brown beneath ; the raised dots are capped with white, and there is a pair of white-capped warts on the last ring (adapted from Barrett). It feeds on rock rose (*Helianthemum*), cinquefoil (*Potentilla*), salad burnet (*Poterium*), etc. ; or the larvæ may be reared on groundsel, chick-weed, and strawberry, both wild and cultivated : September to May. (Plate 140, Fig. 2.)

Mr. A. J. Scollick kindly gave me some eggs, laid by a female taken in Surrey ; they were yellowish green at first, but changed to pale brownish. The caterpillars hatched and seemed to thrive on groundsel, but they died during the winter.

The moth is out in July and August, and is widely distributed in England, but except that it occurs in Surrey, Berkshire, Herefordshire, and Worcestershire, it seems to prefer the sea-board counties, and in them chiefly affects localities near the sea. It is found in Wales, and in Scotland up to Moray ; but in both these countries and also in Ireland it is most frequent on the coast.

Scotch Annulet (*Gnophos myrtillata*).

This species (Plate 139, Figs. 4 ♂, 5 ♀) was introduced, as a species new to Britain, by Curtis, who described and figured it as *Charissa operaria* in 1826, from specimens captured in Scotland. Subsequently, it was found to be the *obfuscaria*, of Hübner, and also the *obfuscata* of the Vienna Catalogue (1776). The latter, however, being only a bare name without description, was not generally accepted, although, if valid, it would be prior to Hübner. Still later the species was ascertained to be the *myrtillata* of Thunberg (1792), and as this name is much earlier than *obfuscaria* it is here adopted. As a matter of fact,

1 **Horse Chestnut:** *caterpillar.*
2. **Annulet:** *caterpillar.*
3. **Bordered White:** *caterpillar, and chrysalis (enlarged).*

1, 2. **Netted Mountain Moth.**   3. **Frosted Yellow.**
4-7. **Common Heath.**   8-10. **Bordered White.**

both names are in use, as that of Hübner applies to our ashy
grey form of the species, whilst that given by Thunberg belongs
to the typical fuscous grey form.

The rather stout caterpillar is grey with darker lines and
V-shaped marks along the middle of the back, and dark-edged
pale lines on the sides ; two erect whitish points on ring 12.   It
feeds on heather (*Calluna*), broom (*Sarothamnus scoparius*),
and needle furze or petty-whin (*Genista anglica*), but it may be
reared on knot grass.   September to June, sometimes later.

The moth is out in July and August, and frequents heaths,
moor, and mountain, in Scotland from Clydesdale (including
Bute and Arran) to Aberdeen and Ross, and the Isle of Lewis.
A male specimen has been recorded from Ireland (Dowros
Head, co. Donegal, 1898).   It may be found resting upon
rocks, stone walls, etc.; where these have suitable holes,
crannies, or projections they are selected as hiding places.
Sometimes the moth has been noted on the wing during the
day, but at night it flies freely, and will then visit light.

Black Mountain Moth (*Psodos coracina*).

The smoky-grey species represented on Plate 139, Figs. 6 ♂,
7 ♀, has two black lines on the fore wings ; these are often edged
with whitish, and the space between them blackish ; the submarginal line is whitish, and the discal spot is black ; the
hind wings have a black central spot and two pale lines or
bands.   The female is rather smaller and much paler.   In
both sexes the central band of the fore wings is generally
narrowed below the middle, and sometimes it is completely
divided at this point.

As regards the British Isles, this species is known only to
occur in the Highlands of Scotland.   It is a day flyer, and
very fond of sunshine, but its favourite haunts are situated at
elevations of from 2000 to 4000 feet.

Series II.

NOTE.—Newman (*British Moths*, p. 68) figures this species as The Dusky Carpet (*Mniophila cineraria*), and the insect, then known by the latter name, is figured as *Psodos trepidaria*, a synonym of the present species. In referring to this transposition of names, it may be well to add that *M. cineraria*, catalogued as British by Doubleday, and stated by Stainton (*Manual* ii., p. 31) to have once occurred at Tenby, South Wales, can only be regarded as an "accidental." The specimen, which is in the Natural History Museum, at South Kensington, appears to be *Tephronia sepiaria*, Hufnagel, which is the *cineraria* of Hübner.

A moth, supposed to be a specimen of *Dasydia tenebraria*, Esper = *torvaria*, Hübner, was reported as taken in Ireland "many years" before 1843, but at the present time that specimen, apparently, does not exist, and there is no exact description of it extant.

Netted Mountain Moth (*Fidonia carbonaria*).

The white wings of this species (Plate 141, Figs. 1 ♂, 2 ♀) are freckled with blackish and crossed by black stripes; sometimes the freckling is so heavy that the white ground colour is much obscured and only distinctly seen as edging to the cross stripes.

The caterpillar is dingy ochreous or whity brown marked with wavy darker stripes. It feeds at night on birch and sallow; *Vaccinium, Erica*, bearberry (*Arctostaphylos uva-ursi*) have also been mentioned as food plants.

In April and May, the moth, which is to be found locally, high up on the mountains of Scotland from Perthshire to Ross, is on the wing, and flies in the sunshine. Writing of this species at Rannoch in May (about 17th), 1905, Mr. E. A. Cockayne remarks that the moths began to fly about noon, when they appeared on all sides and were fairly active on the wing.

The distribution abroad is northern and Alpine, and the range extends to North-east Siberia.

Frosted Yellow (*Fidonia limbaria*).

This black-bordered orange-yellow species (Plate 141, Fig. 3) is not likely to be confused with any other occurring in Britain. The wings are more or less sprinkled with black, but this is usually most noticeable on the hind wings which are some-times thickly sprinkled, or, more rarely, the yellow ground colour is entirely obscured. The form with a black discal spot on all the wings has been named ab. *quadripunctaria*, Fuchs. In ab. *fumata*, Mathew, the orange yellow is replaced by smoky umber brown, tinged with orange, and dusted with black atoms (bred July, 1899).

The caterpillar is greenish with grey-edged yellowish lines along the back, and a black-edged yellow one along the sides. The ground colour is sometimes purplish brown. It feeds on broom chiefly, but will eat other Genisteæ. There appears to be two broods, one in June, and the other in September, or earlier sometimes. The moth is out in May and early June, and again in July and August, but it has been known to remain in the chrysalis for four years. It flies in the sunshine, and when resting, it sits like a butterfly, with its wings brought together over its back.

Stephens (1831) states that the species was "not uncommon among high broom in the vicinity of Birch-wood in Kent." Later authors give Stowmarket (common), Needham, Barham, and Ipswich, in Suffolk. There are no recent records from the county of Kent; and not much has been heard of the species from Suffolk, although it may still exist, in greatly reduced numbers, in some of its old haunts therein.

Common Heath (*Ematurga atomaria*).

Four specimens of this variable species are shown on Plate 141 (Figs. 4, 5 ♂, 6, 7 ♀). The general colour of all the wings in the male is ochreous, inclining to whitish or to brownish. Usually the wings are speckled with brown, and the cross lines, or bands, are dark brown. Occasionally the cross markings are absent; but more frequently the three lines on the fore wings are much broadened and more or less united, sometimes forming a central band in which are a few ochreous scales towards the front margin: ab. *obsoletaria*, Zetterstedt. Dark brown or blackish specimens (ab. *unicolorata*, Staudinger) are captured now and then in the southern counties of England, but such uniform dark varieties are more frequent in the north (Staffordshire and Yorkshire). The female is white in colour, and usually only lightly speckled with blackish; the cross lines are more conspicuous, as a rule, than in the male, but they are subject to pretty much the same kind of aberration. Sometimes examples of this sex greatly resemble *Fidonia carbonaria*, and have been confused with that species by Haworth and other entomologists in the past. An abnormal specimen with six wings has been recorded, and Barrett mentions a gynandrous example—the right side like a small dark female, and the left an ordinary male; both antennæ shortly pectinated.

The caterpillar, according to Fenn, is variable in colour and markings, all shades of brown, greenish brown, ochreous, purple, and grey; in some examples there are pale diamonds, and in others whitish spots, along the back. It feeds on ling and heath, and will eat clover, trefoils, broom, etc.: July and August, and occasionally September. The moth is out in May and June, and sometimes there are specimens on the wing in August. Abundant on almost every heath throughout the British Isles, except in the Shetlands.

1. **V-moth:** *caterpillar.*   2. **Yellow Belle:** *caterpillars.*
3. **Bordered Grey:** *caterpillar.*   4. **Grey Scalloped Bar:** *caterpillar.*

1, 2. Bordered Grey.   3. V-moth.   4, 5. Rannoch Looper.
6. Brown Silver-line.   7-9. Latticed Heath.

Bordered White (*Bupalus piniaria*).

Two forms of the male of this species are represented on Plate 141. Fig. 9 shows the yellow English form (ab. *flavescens*, White), and Fig. 10 the white North English and Scotch forms. In southern localities, however, specimens occur which are almost as white as the northern or even Scotch examples; I have two such specimens from Surrey. There is considerable variation in the size of area occupied by the pale colour, both in white and yellow forms. In one of the former, from Forres, in Scotland, the white is represented by a small oval spot and dappled streak on the fore wings; an entirely black specimen (ab. *nigricarius*, Backhaus) has been noted from Berkshire. In other specimens there is an unusually large proportion of pale colour. The females are usually orange, or orange yellow, in the south (Fig. 8); and yellowish brown, or dingy orange brown, in the north. The brownish-coloured females occasionally occur in the south, and the brighter form of this sex is sometimes taken in the Midlands, where the two forms of the species seem to overlap.

The long, greenish caterpillar is marked with whitish or yellow lines; those along the back are edged with black, and along the sides with dark green. It feeds from August to October on the needles of the pine, and also on other firs. (Plate 140, Fig. 3; Fig. 3*a* shows a photo of the chrysalis, twice natural size, by Mr. H. Main.) The moth is out in May and June, later in the north; it is generally common in pine woods throughout England, Wales, and Scotland.

Bordered Grey (*Selidosema ericetaria*).

Portraits of the male and female of this species (known also as *plumaria*) will be found on Plate 143, Figs. 1 ♂, 2 ♀. The cross markings are more distinct in some specimens than in others, and the central one of the fore wings varies in width.

The caterpillar (Plate 142, Fig. 3, from a photograph by Mr. H. Main) is grey, with a dark-brown or blackish irregular double line along the back, and pale lines along the sides, the lower one edged above with reddish brown; spiracles, black, as also are the dots on the back; the last ring ends in a point. (Adapted from Porritt.) It feeds on ling (*Calluna*), from September well on into the following spring.

The moth occurs on heaths and mosses in July and August, but it is local. On warm days the males are very active, but about dusk they are not difficult to capture. In southern England, the New Forest, Hants, appears to be its special home, but it is also found in other parts of that county, including the Isle of Wight, in Dorsetshire, and in Surrey; also noted from Berkshire. It is scarce in Cheshire, fairly common on the Witherslack mosses in North Lancashire, and at Ullswater in Cumberland. It has been recorded from the Isle of Arran (1882), Mallaig, Invernesshire (1909), and Loch Shiel, Argylls. (1913). In Ireland it is widely distributed, and is abundant at Kinsale, co. Cork.

The V-moth (*Thamnonoma* (*Itame*) *wauaria*).

The popular name of this species (Plate 143, Fig. 3) refers to the black discal mark on the more or less violet-tinged pale, greyish fore wings; but there is a good deal of variation in this character. Occasionally the wings are suffused with smoky (ab. *vau-nigraria*, Hatchett), or more rarely with blackish brown (ab. *fuscaria*, Thunberg).

On Plate 142 is a figure of the caterpillar, from a coloured drawing by Mr. A. Sich. The general colour is greenish, or some shade of brown; the lines on the back are white, and that low down along the sides is broad, and yellow; the raised dots are black with short bristles. It feeds in April, May, and June on the foliage of gooseberry and currant, and is especially fond of the tender shoots.

The moth, which is out in July and August, is often common in gardens and orchards where bush fruit is grown, pretty well throughout the United Kingdom. It appears to occur only rarely in Ireland.

Abroad, the range extends to Amurland, and a form is found in Labrador.

Rannoch Looper (*Thamnonoma brunneata*).

All the wings are of a rusty ochreous colour, sometimes, chiefly in the male, inclining to a purplish tint on the fore wings ; the brownish cross lines are usually most distinct in the female, which sex Hübner figured as *pinetaria*. (Plate 143, Figs. 4 ♂, 5 ♀.)

The caterpillar is reddish brown, with a black-edged dark-green irregular line along the middle of the back ; a white line on each side of the central one, and following this are a dark-brown shade-like stripe and some brownish-green lines ; the line along the spiracles is whitish, inclining to yellow. In general appearance it closely resembles a twig of bilberry (*Vaccinium*), upon the foliage of which plant the caterpillar feeds in the spring.

The moth is out in June and July, but in the British Isles it is only to be obtained in Perthshire and northwards in Scotland. Black-wood, Loch Rannoch, is the original, and a now well-known, locality for this species, which Curtis in 1828 figured as *Speranza sylvaria*.

The range abroad extends to Amurland and Japan, and to North America.

Brown Silver-line (*Lozogramma* (*Phasiane*) *petraria*).

The two cross lines on the pale-brown, sometimes pinkish, fore wings, are edged with whitish, but this is most distinct on the outer one. In some specimens there is a distinct sub-marginal line, but this character is only faintly in evidence as a rule, and occasionally it is entirely absent. (Plate 143, Fig. 6.)

The caterpillar feeds in June, sometimes earlier, on bracken or brake-fern (*Pteris aquilina*). It is olive green marked with reddish brown lines, and there is a whitish line under the black spiracles.

In most English and Welsh localities where bracken is plentiful, this moth should be found in May and June; also in the south of Scotland, but its occurrence in that country north of Clydesdale appears to be only casual. It is common in several parts of Ireland.

The distribution abroad includes Amurland and Japan.

Latticed Heath (*Chiasmia (Strenia) clathrata*).

In its ground colour this species (Plate 143, Figs. 7, 8 ♂, 9 ♀) varies from ochreous of some shade to white. The dark-brown or blackish cross lines and veins give a latticed appearance to the wings, hence both the Latin and popular names for this insect. There is much variation in the width of the cross markings; sometimes two or more unite and so form bands; more rarely, perhaps, the outer lines are absent, and the others broken up into dashes; or the blackish cross lines may be slender and the veins remain of the ochreous ground colour (ab. *radiata*, Haworth). A less frequent aberration has the wings dark brown or blackish all over, except a row of whitish or ochreous spots on the outer margins (ab. *nocturnata*, Fuchs = *nigricans*, Oberthür).

The caterpillar, which feeds on clovers and trefoils, is green, with white lines along the back and sides; the slightly notched head is rather glossy, and the mouth is brownish: June to September, in two broods.

The first generation of the moth is out in April and May, and

the second in July and August. It may be found in clover
fields and on chalk slopes, etc., where the food plants flourish;
although it is an active day flyer, it is not difficult to capture
with the net. It is most plentiful in southern and eastern
England, but its range extends throughout the United Kingdom
to Clydesdale, and the species is widely distributed in Ireland.

The distribution abroad extends to East Siberia, Amurland,
and Japan.

Grey Scalloped Bar (*Scodiona fagaria*).

In its typical form this species (also known as *belgiaria*,
Hübner) is grey, more or less tinged with ochreous, speckled
with brownish grey, and crossed by black-marked brownish-
grey lines. The bulk of British specimens, especially those
from southern localities, are whitish grey, thinly sprinkled with
darker grey scales in the male, and sometimes heavily powdered
in the female; a pair are figured on Plate 144, 1 ♂, 2 ♀. The
whiter form of the male, occurring in Britain chiefly in the New
Forest, Hampshire, has been named *albidaria*, Staudinger.

The roughened caterpillar is figured on Plate 142 (photo by
H. Main). In general colour it is dingy brown, with a whitish
stripe along the back and some greyish marking on the sides.
It feeds on ling and heath; growing slowly in the late summer,
but more quickly in the spring, after hibernation, when it may
be obtained at night from the tips of the heather twigs, either
by searching or by means of the sweeping net. The moth is
out in June and July in the south, and later in the north. It is
found on moist heaths, moors, and mosses; when resting on
the dark-coloured earth it so closely resembles a stone that it is
probably frequently passed unnoticed.

The species is apparently more plentiful in the New Forest
than in its other known southern localities (Kent, Surrey, Berkshire, Sussex, and Dorset). Its range northwards in England

extends from Worcestershire (Malvern, rare) to Cumberland and Northumberland. It seems to be distributed over the greater part of Scotland, including the Hebrides and the Orkneys. In Wales it has been recorded from Flint, Denbigh, and Carnarvon; and it is widely spread over Ireland, occurring chiefly on the bogs.

Black-veined Moth (*Scoria lineata*).

This slightly ochreous tinged silky white moth has the veins of the wings blackish, and this is especially noticeable on the underside of the fore wings. A male specimen is shown on Plate 144, Fig. 3; the wings of the female are slightly smaller, and the body is stouter and shorter. This species is the *dealbata* of Linnæus, but *lineata*, Scopoli, is older by four years. The long caterpillar is greyish inclining to ochreous or brownish; several irregular darker lines on the back and sides. It feeds, in confinement, on knot-grass, dock, bird's-foot trefoil, etc., but in the open is said to eat wood grasses, such as *Brachypodium*, upon the blades of which the female moth has been seen to deposit eggs: July to May. The moth is out from late May through June; it flies in the sunshine, or rests among long grass, etc., from which it is readily disturbed. Its chief British haunts are in Kent (Higham, Wye, etc.); but it has been recorded from Sussex, Dorset, Somerset, Gloucester, and Herefordshire, chiefly in single specimens.

Abroad, the range extends to Amurland.

Straw Belle *(Aspilates gilvaria).

This straw-coloured species (Plate 144, Fig. 4 ♂, 6 ♀) will be easily recognised by the brownish stripe on the fore wings, which extends from the front margin, near the tip, almost to the inner

* On Plate 144, Figs. 4, 6, Straw Belle; Fig. 5, Yellow Belle.

margin; this is sometimes faint, but rarely quite absent. The hind wings are paler and have a dusky central dot and incomplete band. The caterpillar, which in shape is somewhat similar to that of the next species, is ochreous grey inclining to pinkish on the sides; a dark almost blackish line along the middle of the back is edged on each side with pale ochreous, and there are other pale and dark lines along the sides. It feeds on thyme, cinquefoil, yarrow, and other low-growing plants; it may be reared on knot grass: September to June. The moth is out in July and August, and, although very local, is not uncommon on downs and hilly fields on the chalk in Kent and Surrey— Dover, Folkestone, and Rochester in the former county, and Leatherhead, Box Hill, and Reigate in the latter, are the best-known localities. It has also been reported from Sussex (Brighton, Horsham, near Polgate, Shoreham). In Devonshire it is said to occur at Braunton and Ilfracombe, but is scarce. In his catalogue of the Lepidoptera of Suffolk (1890) the Rev. E. N. Bloomfield notes the species as very plentiful in clover fields about Tuddenham. Also recorded from Somerset, Gloucestershire, Cheshire (West Kirby and Hale), and from near Harrow in Middlesex.

Very local and scarce in Ireland (Kane).

The range abroad extends to East Siberia and Amurland.

Yellow Belle (*Aspilates ochrearia*).

As will be seen from Fig. 5 ♂ on Plate 144, this species differs from the last in its yellower colour and rather smaller size; the fore wings have two cross bands, generally well defined, but in the male they are sometimes very faint and slender, and specimens have been recorded in which the bands were missing.

The roughened caterpillar, figured on Plate 142, from a coloured drawing by Mr. A. Sich, is pale ochreous brown, lined and striped with darker brown. It feeds on wild carrot, plantain, hawks'-beard, etc., and will thrive on knot-grass. There are two broods, one feeding in the spring, after hibernation ; and the other in June and July, sometimes later. The first generation of moths flies in May and June, and the second in August and early September. The species occurs in all the southern sea-board counties of England from Kent to Cornwall, frequenting the downs and rough fields near the coast ; also in the Sand-breck district of the eastern counties. It occurs in South Wales ; and odd specimens have been reported from Cheshire (Delamere), and from Cumberland.

The range abroad extends to North-west Africa and Asia Minor.

Grass Wave (*Perconia (Aspilates) strigillaria*).

A male and a female of this species are depicted on Plate 144, Figs. 7 ♂ and 8 ♀. There is variation in the amount of dark speckling on the wings, and in the number and width of the cross markings ; sometimes the first and second on the fore wings are united throughout their length, or towards the inner margin ; coupled with this there is sometimes considerable increase in the width of the first cross marking of the hind wings. A rare variety in Britain is ab. *grisearia*, Staudinger, which is of an almost uniform greyish or greyish-brown colour, with the markings obscured.

The caterpillar is purplish grey, marked with paler and darker ; two warts on the back of rings 7–10, the middle pair the largest and most prominent. It feeds on ling, heath, broom, and the flowers of gorse or furze, and is best obtained in the spring after hibernation.

The moth, which is out in June and July, occurs on most of the heaths and moors throughout England ; apparently commoner and more generally distributed in the south than in the north ; but it seems to be rare on the eastern side of the

1, 2. **Grey Scalloped Bar.**   3. **Black-veined.**   4, 5. **Yellow Belle.**
6. **Straw Belle.**   7, 8. **Grass Wave.**

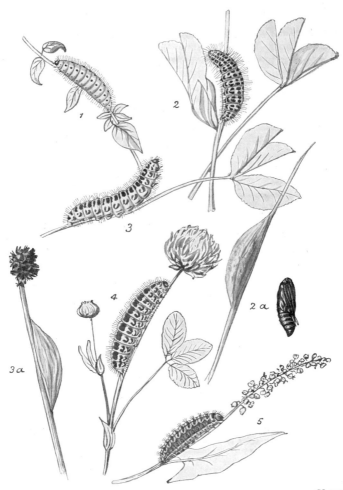

1. **Transparent Burnet:** *caterpillar.*
2, 2a. **Narrow-bordered Five-spot Burnet:** *caterpillar, chrysalis and cocoon.*
3, 3a. **Five-spot Burnet:** *caterpillar and cocoon.*
4. **Six-spot Burnet:** *caterpillar.*   5. **Forester:** *caterpillar.*

country altogether. From Cheshire it spreads into Flint and Denbigh, North Wales. In Scotland, it is found in Roxburgh (Bellion Moor), Clydesdale (local, but common), and northwards to Ross. It is found on the boggy heaths of Ireland, and Kane states that it is abundant where it occurs.

The range abroad extends to Scandinavia and eastward to Asia Minor.

ZYGÆNIDÆ.

The moths belonging to this family are popularly known in Britain as Burnets and Foresters. Of the former seven kinds occur in the British Isles, and of the latter there are only three species.

All the species live in colonies, so that when a specimen is seen or captured others may be expected to occur on, or somewhere around, the same spot. The caterpillars bear a close resemblance to each other, and are not always easily distinguished.

Over thirty species of *Zygæna* are found in Europe, and about thirty-six more have been described from other parts of the Palæarctic Region. There are at least twenty-five Palæarctic species referred to the genus *Ino*, and about ten of these are European.

By most authors *filipendulæ* is regarded as the type of the genus *Zygæna*, Fabricius ; but others refer this species, and its allies, to the genus *Anthrocera*, Scopoli, using the Fabrician genus for *phegea*, Linnæus. The latter species and its allies are perhaps more frequently referred to *Syntomis*, Ochsenheimer, the typical genus of the family Syntomidæ, the systematic position of which is near the Arctiidæ. It may be added that *S. phegea*, and also *Naclia ancilla*, have been reported as British. There does not seem, however, to be any reason to suppose that the occurrence of either species in Britain could be other than accidental.

The Transparent Burnet (*Zygæna purpuralis*).

Two Welsh specimens are depicted on Plate 146, Figs. 1 and 2 ; these are of the typical form. A rare aberration has the spots and the hind wings more or less suffused with blackish (ab. *obscura*, Tutt), but a still rarer variety has the crimson of spots and hind wings replaced by yellow (ab. *lutescens*, Tutt).

Newman in 1861 referred an Irish specimen to *achilleæ*, but a little later, after seeing other examples, in the same year he changed the name to *nubiginea*. Birchall (*Ent. Mo. Mag.*, iii. pt. i.) figured four forms of the species from Ireland ; his *minos* (Figs. 5*a* and 5*b*) seems to represent two modifications of ab. *interrupta*, Staudinger, in which form the red blotches are widely separated or interrupted by the ground colour ; and his *nubigena* is made up of more or less typical *purpuralis* (Fig. 6*a*), and a variety (Fig. 6*b*), with red marks between the lower and central blotches.

The caterpillar (Plate 145, Fig. 1) is dark green inclining to olive above and paler below ; the spots are black (outer row) and yellow (inner row) ; the line along the back is obscure whitish ; hairs, whitish. It feeds on thyme and burnet saxifrage (*Pimpinella*). *Trifolium* and *Lotus* have also been given among other food plants. In late summer, and after hibernation, in the spring. The moth flies in June, and is locally common in Ireland (Clare and Galway), Wales (Abersoch), and Scotland (Oban, Loch Etive). It has been reported from Tintagel, Cornwall, and possibly, as suggested by Tutt, these Cornish specimens may turn out to be *Z. achilleæ*, the latest addition to our small band of Burnets. Perhaps the Scottish specimens recorded as *purpuralis*, or at least some of them, may prove to be *achilleæ*.

This species was figured by Brünnich, in 1763, as *purpuralis*, and authorities are now agreed that this name must be adopted in place of *pilosellæ*, Esper (1781), or *minos*, Fuessly (1782).

Scotch or Mountain Burnet (*Zygæna exulans*).

This semi-transparent and rather greyish moth has five reddish spots on the fore wings. (Plate 146, Fig. 3.) So far as concerns the British Isles it is only known to occur in Aberdeenshire, where it was discovered on the mountains at Braemar in July, 1871, and where it may be still found by those who are acquainted with the situation of its lofty haunts. The late Dr. Buchanan White named the Scottish form *subochracea*, but others consider that it is not readily separable from *vanadis*, Dalman, which in turn is said by Tutt to be pretty much the same form of the species as that described as the type *exulans*, Hochenwarth.

The caterpillar is dark green above, and paler below; two velvety black stripes on the back, each stripe interrupted by yellow spots; warts with black hairs; head, black. It feeds on *Silene acaulis*, cyphel (*Arenaria cherleria = Cherleria sedoides*), clover, trefoils, *Azalea procumbens*, etc.; has been known to eat dock and knot-grass: August to June. The cocoon has been found on a stem of crowberry (*Empetrum*), and on heath and grass stems. The moth is out in July, and, like the rest of its kindred, delights in the sunshine.

Zygæna achilleæ.

A specimen of this species, quite recently introduced as British, has been kindly lent by Mr. B. Adkin. It was taken, with others, in the vicinity of Oban, Argyllshire. Mr. Sheldon informs me that he believes that a worn Zygænid he captured in 1898, in the Glencoe district, was this species.

On Plate 1, with the Scottish example (Fig. 2) referred to, is also shown a specimen from the continent (Fig. 3), and it will be noted that the former is very like the latter. In some respects this species is not unlike some confluent-spot forms of *filipendulæ*, but it is a more slender-looking insect, and the body is more hairy. Further, the upper basal spot of the fore wings is lengthened almost to the upper spot of the middle pair, and the fifth and sixth spots together form an almost oval mark. Both specimens depicted seem to be referable to var. *viciæ*, Hübner. In the typical forms the spots are larger. A yellow form ab. *flava*, Oberthür, is known on the continent.

The caterpillar, after Hofmann, is figured on Plate 1, Fig. 5. It is said to feed on *Astragalus* and *Coronilla*.

New Forest Burnet (*Zygæna meliloti*).

Two examples of this, normally, five-spotted little species are shown on Plate 146, Figs. 4 ♂, 5 ♀; a variety, referable to ab. *confusa*, Staudinger (spots run together forming streaks somewhat as in *purpuralis*), is depicted in Plate 148, Fig. 1. Occasionally a sixth spot is in evidence (ab. *sexpunctata*, Tutt). A form in which the body has a red belt is known abroad as ab. *stentzii*, Freyer, and examples having traces of this belt have been recorded from the New Forest, which, it may be added, is the only locality in Britain producing this species.

The caterpillar is of a dull pale greenish colour, with numerous black speckles; three whitish lines on the back, the central one greenish tinged and broader than the others, which are interrupted on each ring by a yellow spot; between the lines is a series of black dots, one on the outer edge of each ring; hairs, from greenish warts, white and short; head, black, dotted with white. It feeds on bird's-foot trefoil (*Lotus corniculatus*), and other trefoils and clovers : August to May. Sometimes the caterpillars do not complete growth until they have passed two winters in hibernation. The cocoon, which is yellow or yellowish white, has been found on a grass stem, but it is generally placed so low down among herbage that it seems to be rarely detected.

The moth is out in June and early July.

As previously stated the only part of Britain that the species inhabits is the New Forest, Hampshire. Here it was first met with in Stubby Copse, about 1869, but was apparently not distinguished from *Z. trifolii* until 1872. It is now less frequent in its old haunt than formerly, although it still occurs there; in other spots around, I believe, it is not uncommon in some years.

Some authorities refer this species to *viciæ*, Schranck.

Five-spot Burnet (*Zygæna trifolii*).

Four specimens of this species are portrayed on Plate 146. In the typical form (Figs. 7 ♂, 8 ♀) the central pair of crimson spots are united and often form a large blotch ; ab. *orobi*, Hübner (Figs. 6 ♂, 9 ♀), has the spots placed well apart. Other more or less frequent aberrations are depicted by Mr. Horace Knight on Plate 148 where Fig. 2 represents ab. *glycirrhizæ*, Hübner (spots 3, 4, and 5 united) ; Fig. 3, ab. *basalis*, Selys (spots 3 and 4 united with the basal pair) ; and Fig. 4, ab. *minoides*, Selys (all the spots united, forming an irregular patch). An extreme development of the last-mentioned form has been named ab. *extrema*, Tutt (see *Entom.* xxix., p. 341, Fig. 2). Specimens with a sixth spot as in *Z. filipendulæ* have been occasionally recorded, and an example with the lower spot of the central pair absent has been taken in West Sussex by Mr. W. M. Christy, who has also obtained a number of specimens of a yellow form (ab. *lutescens*, Cockerell) in the same locality. The yellow form is shown on Plate 148, Fig. 5. Some of the yellow aberrations also exhibit variation in the spots pretty much as in the ordinary form. In some localities, especially marshy ones, the spots on the fore wings and the hind wings are occasionally dull orange ; and I have noted specimens in the Weybridge district, Surrey, with the spots on the fore wings of a pinky ochreous colour, whilst the hind wings were of the usual crimson. Such "aberrations" as those last mentioned probably result from weather exposure. In 1899, Mr. G. B. Corbin recorded the capture, near Ringwood, Hants, of a specimen which had the spots on the fore wings and the red of the hind wings darkened over with dull smoky black, so that the insect when seen at a distance seemed to be wholly black. Dr. Hodgson has recently obtained several of these melanic specimens in Sussex. A form with the spots and hind wings suffused with brownish has been named ab. *obscura*, Oberthür.

With regard to six-spot examples referred to this species, I am inclined to suppose that they may be the offspring of a chance pairing of *trifolii* and *filipendulæ*. That such crossing does occur in nature I have evidence, as on one occasion I found four mixed pairs, the male being *trifolii* in each case, and the female typical *filipendulæ*. This was in the Weybridge district, where I had come across a colony of the latter species and was closely examining the specimens for aberrations.

The caterpillar (Plate 145, Fig. 3) is green inclining to yellowish and to bluish, with black marks on the back ; a series of black streaks low down along the sides. It feeds on *Lotus corniculatus*, and on other trefoils and clover : July to May. Sometimes taking two years to complete its changes.

In damp meadows the moth is out in May and June, but in marshes it does not appear, as a rule, until July, and may be found in early August. The marsh specimens, which are sometimes rather large in size, have been referred to *palustris*, Oberthür, and are treated by Tutt (*Nat. Hist. Brit. Lep.*, vol. i.) as a sub-species.

In the British Isles, the species is apparently confined to England and North Wales. In the former country it is locally

1, 2. **Transparent Burnet.**   3. **Scotch Burnet.**
4, 5. **New Forest Burnet.**   6-9. **Five-spot Burnet.**

1, 2. **Narrow-bordered Five-spot Burnet.**   3-5. **Six-spot Burnet.**
6. 7. **Scarce Forester.**   8, 9. **The Forester.**
10, 11. **Cistus Forester.**

common in most of the southern counties ; still more local in
the eastern counties, and northwards to Lancashire and Yorkshire. There are records from Armagh and Fermanagh, but
Kane appears to doubt the occurrence of the species in Ireland.
There is no doubt that the next species has frequently been
mistaken for the present one, therefore the actual range of
trifolii in the British Isles has probably not been fully
ascertained.

Narrow-bordered Five-spot Burnet (*Zygæna loniceræ*).

As will be seen from the two specimens represented by
Figs. 1 ♂ and 2 ♀ on Plate 147, this species bears considerable
resemblance to ab. *orobi* of *Z. trifolii*. The chief differences
are in the rather longer fore wings and the more pointed tips
of the hind pair ; the borders of the hind wings are often
narrower. In a broad way, it may be stated that the general
tone of colour in the male of *loniceræ* is bluer than that of
trifolii. The union of any two or more spots is rarely seen in
this species in Britain, but specimens with all the spots joined
together have certainly been noted. A yellow form, ab. *citrina*,
Speyer (= *flava*, Oberthür), is known on the continent, and
Barrett states that it has occurred in England. In ab. *lutescens*,
Hewett, the hind wings are orange. Ab. *eboraceæ*, Prest, is
semi-transparent, steel blue ; the spots and the hind wings are
pink, the border of the hind wings brown, and the fringes of all
the wings are whitish.

The caterpillar (Plate 145, Fig. 2) is very similar to that of
the last species, but the black marks on the sides are heavier,
and the hairs of the body are longer. It feeds on trefoils and
clover, and sometimes passes two winters before becoming full
grown. The cocoon, which is attached to stems of grass, etc.,
is generally placed well up above the ground, so that it is
readily seen.

The moth, which is out in late June and in July, occurs in woods and plantations ; also said to be found in meadows, and on rough waste ground, as well as in marshes and salterns. The distribution is much as in the last species, but it is plentiful in East Yorkshire, and the range extends to Cumberland and Northumberland.

Six-spot Burnet (*Zygæna filipendulæ*).

This species (Plate 147, Figs. 3–5) is the most generally common of our Burnets. Perhaps the most frequent form of variation in the spots of the fore wings is that in which the outer pair run together, and so form a blotch ; but union of the middle pair is not an uncommon occurrence. In ab. *cytisi*, Hübner, the three pairs of spots are each united, so that the fore wings have three separate blotches, and when these are of a dull scarlet instead of the usual crimson, ab. *ramburi*, Lederer, is represented. Occasionally, the spots are united, as in ab. *cytisi*, and the blotches thus formed are connected by reddish streaks in various modifications leading up to ab. *conjuncta*, Tutt, which has all the spots merged into a large blotch, extending over the disc of the fore wings. From the normal crimson, the spots and the hind wings vary now and then to orange (*aurantia*, Tutt), or to yellow (ab. *flava*, Robson = *cerinus*, Robson and Gardner) ; intermediate shades between these two extremes, and the typical coloration, are rather more frequent. I am indebted to Mr. R. Adkin for the loan of the example of the yellow form shown on Plate 148, Fig. 6. Pink, and orange, forms have been noted from various parts of England, but they seem to occur, or have been found, more especially in Cambridge and the north-east corner of Essex. Fig. 7, Plate 148, represents an example of ab. *chrysanthemi*, Hübner, and is copied from Oberthür's *Etudes d'Entom.*, xx., Plate 8, Fig. 134. A few specimens referable to this form,

1. New Forest Burnet, ab. ***confusa.***   2, 3, 4, 5. Five-spot Burnet, vars.
6, 7. Six-spot Burnet, vars.

1. **Festoon Moth:** *caterpillars and cocoons.*
2. **Triangle Moth:** *caterpillars.*

probably not exceeding half a dozen altogether, have been recorded as taken in England. In typical *filipendulæ* the dark blue border of the hind wings is narrow, but in ab. *hippo-crepidis*, Stephens (*tutti*, Rebel), the borders are rather broad. Another character of this form is that the nervule upon which the sixth spot is placed is here of the ground colour, and therefore divides the spot. (Plate 147, Fig. 3.) At Northwood, Middlesex, I have found this form in May and June, and also in the Weybridge district, Surrey, in late July ; and, it may be added, there was a flourishing colony of *Z. trifolii* hard by in each locality. For this reason, *plus* the fact that *trifolii* ♂ is known to pair with *filipendulæ* ♀, I hold the opinion that *hippocrepidis* is a hybrid. It may be noted here that hybrids have been raised from the crossing of *filipendulæ* and *lonicerœ;* the sexes of *lonicerœ* and *trifolii* pair somewhat readily, and the hybrid offspring of such pairings are fertile.

It seems, then, that *trifolii*, *lonicerœ*, and *filipendulæ* have not, so far, lost the power of fertile cross-pairing. Wherever colonies of two of the kind exist within visiting distance of each other, there, it appears, we may reasonably expect to find hybrids.

From a number of cocoons collected in a Yorkshire locality for *lonicerœ*, I reared, in 1907, a good many examples of that species, and also about a dozen six-spot specimens, which agree in colour with *filipendulæ*, but they have the vein-interrupted sixth spot and broad border to hind wings, as in *hippocrepidis*.

The caterpillar (Plate 145, Fig. 4) is greenish, with black markings and some yellow spots, the latter chiefly on the hind edges of the rings. It feeds in the autumn and after hibernation, on trefoils, clover, bird's-foot (*Ornithopus*), and kidney-vetch (*Anthyllis*), completing growth in the spring.

The moth flies on sunny days in July and August, on chalk downs, etc., inland, and on cliffs and sand hills on the coast, also in marshes ; but, as previously stated, it also occurs locally in meadows in May and June.

Scarce Forester (*Ino (Rhagades) globulariæ*).

Of the three species occurring in Britain this is slightly the
larger, at least in the male. The fore wings are green, sometimes with a slightly golden sheen ; fringes, greyish. The male
is best distinguished from *statices* by its more slender body, and
by the pectinated and rather pointed antennæ. The female is
a good deal smaller than the male; the antennæ are simple,
and somewhat thread-like, compared with those of the females
of *statices* and *geryon*. (Plate 147, Figs. 6 ♂, 7 ♀.)

The caterpillar is green, with the raised spots inclining to
bluish; two yellowish-white lines along the back, and a dark green
stripe along the sides; head and plate on first ring of the body,
black. It lives on knapweeds (*Centaurea nigra* and *C. scabiosa*),
feeding on the leaves much in the same manner as the caterpillar of the next two species.

The moth is out in June and July; it is partial to blossoms of
salad burnet (*Poterium sanguisorba*), and only flies in the sunshine. The late Mr. J. Jenner Weir, who found the species
commonly on the downs near Lewes, Sussex, was the first
entomologist to record it as British. The best known localities
in Sussex are Hollingbury Vale and Cliffe Hill, but it also
occurs at the Devil's Dyke near Brighton. In Kent it is found
on the downs behind Folkestone and Shorncliffe Camp.

The Forester (*Ino (Adscita) statices*).

In its most frequent form in Britain, this species is bronzy
green (ab. *viridis*, Tutt) ; the typical bluish green type is much
less frequent. The female is smaller than the male, but the
difference in size is hardly ever so marked as in the sexes of
globulariæ. The antennæ of the male are pectinated, but the
tips are thickened. (Plate 147, Figs. 8 ♂, 9 ♀.)

The caterpillar (Plate 145, Fig. 5) is whitish, inclining to green, yellow, or pinkish, on the back, and the sides are pinkish brown ; the hairy warts are brown or pinkish brown, and the small head is glossy black. It feeds on sorrel (*Rumex acetosa*), and it attains full growth, after hibernation, about the end of April. On leaving the egg-shell in the summer, the young caterpillar bores into a leaf, and eats the tissue between the upper and lower skins ; later on it attacks the foliage from the underside, but leaves the upper skin intact ; or the process may be reversed, and the under skin left.

The moth is on the wing in June, sometimes late May. It occurs, locally, in meadows, frequently damp ones, where there is plenty of ragged-robin (*Lychnis flos-cuculi*), the blossoms of which plant it seems to prefer to all others.

Widely distributed over England, but in Wales only recorded from Capel Curig and Barmouth, in the north of that country (1900). In Scotland its range extends to Moray ; and in Ireland it is found in counties Wicklow, Cork, Clare, Westmeath, Monaghan, Sligo, and Galway.

Cistus Forester (*Ino (Adscita) geryon*).

This species is much smaller than the last ; the fore wings, the outer margins of which are somewhat rounded, are bronze green, but, in the male, rather dull in tint, sometimes tinged with golden towards the base. The antennæ are more stumpy than those of *statices*, but in other respects they are similar in appearance. The female is not much smaller than the male. (Plate 147, Figs. 10 ♂, 11 ♀.)

The caterpillar is yellowish white, with bristle-bearing warts of pretty much the same colour ; three lines on the back, the central one whitish, edged on each side with purplish, the others waved and of a claret colour ; a reddish-brown stripe low down along the sides ; head and plate on first ring of the body black, the latter edged in front with yellowish. It feeds on rock rose (*Helianthemum chamæcistus*). At first it attacks the leaf from the upper side, and partly burrows therein ; when older it clears away patches from the under surface, leaving the upper skin of the leaf more or less transparent; as it approaches full growth it likes to take its meals in the sunshine, and then eats the top skin as well as other parts of the leaf, and also tender shoots : July to May. The moth is out in June and July, as a rule, but is sometimes observed in May. Its haunts are on warm slopes of chalk downs and limestone hills, where it flies in the sunshine.

This species was first noted as British in March, 1860, when specimens from Worcestershire were recorded as *Procris tenuicornis*. It seems, however, to have been considered doubtfully distinct from *statices* until 1863, when the caterpillar was found, and the occurrence of the species in several other English counties recorded. At the present time *I. geryon* is known to inhabit Sussex (Brighton and Lewes districts), Kent (Canterbury and Shorncliffe), Bucks (Aylesbury and Tring), Oxfordshire (Chinor), Gloucestershire (Cotswolds), Worcestershire (Malvern Hills), Derbyshire and North Staffordshire (Bakewell and Dovedale), Yorkshire (Richmond, Barnsley, Sheffield, etc.), and Durham (banks on the coast). In Wales, it is sometimes common on Great Orme's Head, Carnarvonshire.

COCHLIDIDÆ.

This family of moths mainly comprises tropical species, and is but poorly represented in the Palæarctic Region. Only two species are European, and both occur in Britain.

As *Cochlidion*, Hübner, supersedes *Limacodes*, Latrielle, the name of the family so long known as Limacodidæ, will have to be changed to that here adopted. Meyrick, who sinks *Limacodes* in favour of *Apoda*, Haworth, uses Heterogeneidæ as the family name.

The Festoon (*Cochlidion* (*Heterogenea*) *limacodes*).

The fore wings of the male are orange brown, more or less smudged or clouded with blackish; two oblique black lines, the first inclined inwards, and the second outwards and apparently terminating on the outer margin just above the inner angle, but there is a slender dusky curve from this point enclosing a clear, orange-brown spot. Hind wings blackish, except on the inner margin, which is broadly orange brown. Female, ochreous brown, with lines on the fore wings as in the male; hind wings suffused with dark grey or blackish, except on the inner area; generally rather larger than the male. (Plate 153, Figs. 1 ♂, 2 ♀.) Not infrequently, the fore wings of the male are so much clouded with blackish that the cross lines are obscured, and the spot on the inner margin alone remains clear.

The caterpillar (Plate 149, Fig. 1, from a coloured drawing by Mr. A. Sich) is green, with two reddish-edged yellow lines on the back; between these lines are yellowish spots; a yellow line along the sides extends along the front edge of the second ring, where it is marked with red. It feeds on oak, and may be beaten from the boughs in the autumn. The brownish cocoon is depicted on Plate 149; Fig. 1a shows the hinged lid which covered the opening through which the chrysalis protruded previous to the moth's escape; Fig. 1b represents one from which the moth has not emerged, and in nature this would be attached to a leaf and covered with a delicate film of silk. The moth is out in June and July, and both sexes may be beaten from the branches of trees, or seen flying around their tops in the sunshine.

This species, often referred to as *Limacodes testudo*, and said to be the *avellana* of Linnæus, is an inhabitant of oak woods, and occurs in Hampshire, Sussex, Kent, Essex, Suffolk, Oxfordshire, Bucks, Gloucestershire, and Worcestershire. A male and two females have been reported from Clonbrock, Co. Galway, Ireland.

The Triangle (*Heterogena asella*).

The fore wings of this little species (Plate 153, Figs. 4 ♂ and 5 ♀) are of triangular shape ; in the male, which sex is smaller than the female, they are dark brown, sometimes almost blackish (ab. *nigra*, Tutt), and those of the female yellowish brown varying to ochreous yellow (ab. *flavescens*, Tutt). The hind wings of the male are blackish, and of the female clouded with blackish.

The curious woodlouse-shaped caterpillar is green, sometimes inclining to yellowish ; the broad reddish band on the back broadens out before the middle, thus giving the idea of a rough cross, or, as sometimes described, a blunt spear head. It is found, by searching, in August and until October, on the foliage of beech and oak. Birch has also been mentioned as a food plant, and on the continent it is said to feed on poplar, lime, hazel, and hornbeam. Fig. 2 on Plate 149 is from a photo by Mr. H. Main.

Although the caterpillar constructs its gall-like cocoon on a leaf or in the fork of a twig in the autumn, it does not change to a chrysalis until late in spring, sometimes not until June. The moth is out in June and July and flies in the sunshine, chiefly in the afternoon, and might easily be confused with the Lechean Tortrix (*Ptycholoma lecheana*).

The species appears to be very local in England and confined to the south. Its chief haunts seem to be in Bucks, where it is not uncommon in beech woods at Marlow, and in Hampshire.

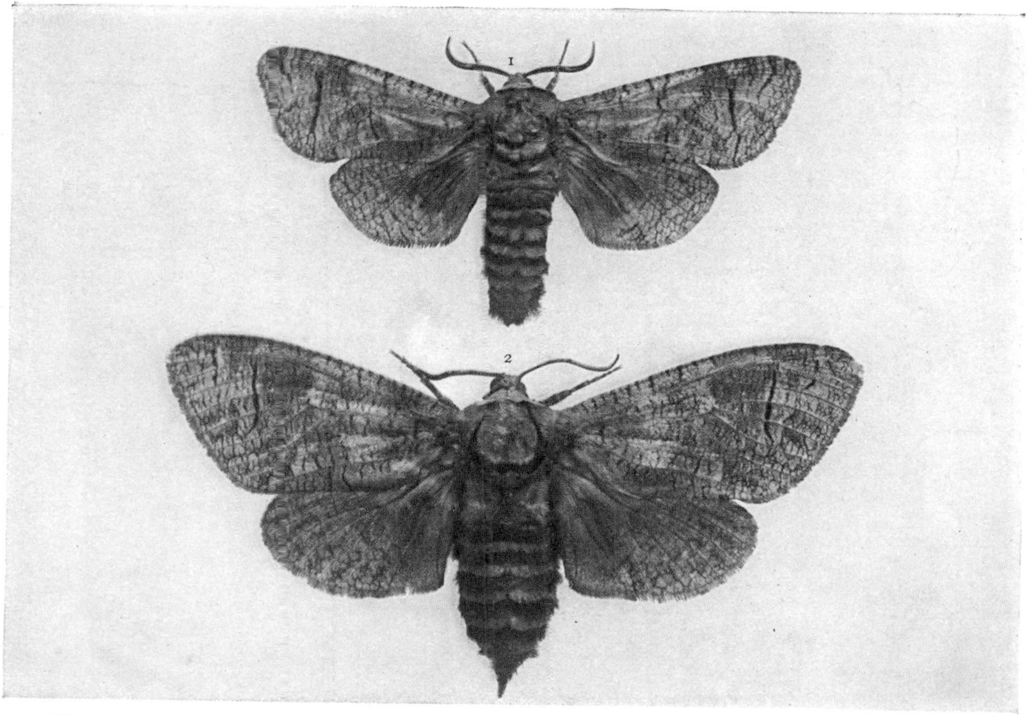

2 *Pl.* 150

1. 2. Goat Moth.

Z 346.

Goat Moth : *caterpillar, chrysalis and cocoon.*

especially parts of the New Forest. It has been found in
Epping Forest, Essex; rarely in Abbot's Wood and Rewell
Wood, Sussex; also recorded from Bickleigh Vale and the
Plym Valley, Devonshire.

The range abroad extends to Amurland.

COSSIDÆ.

Of the eighty-six Palæarctic species referred to this family,
by far the larger number are eastern, only about eight appear
to be found in Europe, and
but three of these occur in
Britain.

Meyrick separates *Cossus
cossus* (*ligniperda*) from
our other two species,
adopts *Trypanus*, Rambur,
as the generic name, and
removes it to the Tortricina
as a family of that group
under the name Trypanidæ.

FIG. 20.
Goat Moth at rest.
(Photo by Hugh Main.)

The Goat Moth (*Cossus cossus* (*ligniperda*)).

The English name of
this species (Plate 150, Figs.
1 ♂, 2 ♀) applies more
especially to the caterpillar,
as this creature gives off
an odour which has been
compared to that of ·the
he-goat. In general colour the caterpillar is pinkish ochreous,

inclining to dark reddish on the back ; the small head is black and glossy, and the mark on the first ring of the body is black. It feeds in the solid wood of various trees, especially elm, ash, and willow, but is three or four years in completing growth. When mature, it often leaves its burrow and wanders in search of a suitable place for pupation.   When met with at such times it should be, if taken, placed in a roomy tin box with a good supply of sawdust or decayed wood, when it will make its cocoon, and appear as a moth in due course.   The early stages are shown on Plate 151.

Caterpillars are more likely to come under the notice of the country rambler than are the moths , examples of the latter, however, may be seen occasionally, in June or July, resting on a tree-trunk, a fence, or a gate post ; sometimes, although practically tongueless, the moth visits the sugar patch and either settles on the tree or flutters around.

The species seems to occur in all parts of the British Isles, except perhaps the extreme north of Scotland and the Hebrides.

Abroad, the range extends to Amurland and to North-west Africa.

The Leopard Moth (*Zeuzera pyrina*).

As will be seen from the portraits of this blue-black spotted white species on Plate 153, the male (Fig. 6) is smaller than the female (Fig. 7) ; it will be further noted that the antennæ of the male are bi-pectinated on the basal half, and thread-like on the outer half ; the antennæ of the female are thread-like throughout.

The caterpillar (Plate 152, Fig. 1, from a coloured drawing by Mr. A. Sich) is dull whitish, more or less tinged with yellow ; the spots are black, and the head and plates on the first and last rings of the body are blackish brown.   It feeds in branches

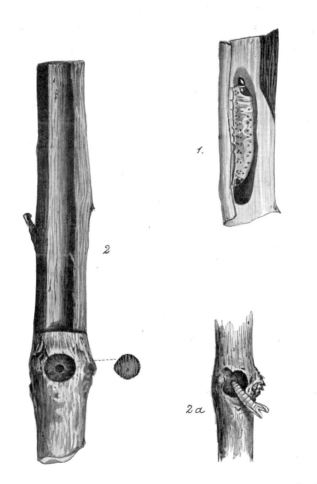

1. **Leopard Moth:** *caterpillar.*
2. **Orange-tailed Clearwing:** *caterpillar's burrow and exit hole; chrysalis skin*

1. 2. **Festoon.**   3. **Reed Leopard.**   4, 5. **Triangle.**   6, 7. **Leopard Moth.**

and stems of trees and shrubs. Hatching from the egg, say in the late summer of 1908, the caterpillar will not be full grown until May or June of 1910, or possibly 1911; forming a cocoon of silk and wood particles, it turns to a reddish brown chrysalis in the burrow, and near the bark of the stem or branch. The moth comes out in the summer, and is most often seen in the London district, where the female especially is not infrequently found on tree-trunks or on grass, etc., under trees. It visits light, and the electric arc lamps are very attractive to it.

The species occurs in the south and east of England, and through the north-west counties to Cheshire. It has been recorded from Cardiff, South Wales, and doubtfully from Ireland.

Abroad, the range extends to Corea and Japan. In America it seems to be established in parts of the State of New York.

The Reed Leopard (*Phragmatœcia castaneœ*).

A male of this species (*Macrogaster arundinis* of some authors) is shown on Plate 153, Fig. 3. The female is rather larger, with longer body, and the antennæ are without pectinations.

The wrinkled and rather shining caterpillar is ochreous white with reddish-brown stripes along the back. It feeds low down on the stems of reed (*Phragmites communis*) and is full grown in the spring of the second year following that in which it left the egg in late summer. Thus, a caterpillar hatching in August, 1908, would be mature about May, 1910, pupate in that month, or the next, and the perfect insect would appear in June or July.

The moth flies at night, and may be attracted by a brilliant light. The earliest known British locality for the species was Holme Fen in Huntingdonshire (1841–1848). In 1850 it was found abundantly at Whittlesea Mere. Its haunts in the

present day are Wicken and Chippenham fens in Cambridge
shire, but specimens from these localities are somewhat smaller
than the old Hunts examples. Barrett states that he put down
some eggs of the species in Ranworth Fen, Norfolk, and that five
years later two males were captured within a short distance of
the spot where the eggs had been placed.

The range abroad extends to China and Japan.

SESIIDÆ.

This family—the Ægeriadæ of some authors—has over one
hundred Palæarctic species assigned to it ; these are distributed
among five genera, two of which are not represented in Britain.
Fourteen species are found in the British Isles, but to obtain
fine specimens of most of them the mature caterpillars or the
chrysalids will have to be collected and the moths reared. All
species emerge from the chrysalis early in the forenoon, and then
only under the influence of sunshine.

The caterpillars are somewhat maggot-like, and live in
stems, branches, and roots of trees and shrubs ; or in the
crowns and roots of low-growing plants. The majority,
possibly all, are nearly two years in arriving at full growth.

Hornet Moth (*Trochilium apiformis*).

As indicated by the English name this moth, and also that
next to be mentioned, are very like the hornet (*Vespa crabro*).
On turning to Plate 154, Fig. 1, it will be seen that this species
has a yellow head and patches of yellow on the shoulders ;
these characters at once separate it from *T. crabroniformis*.

The caterpillar is yellowish white, with a red brown head,
and a yellow plate on the first ring of the body. It feeds on
the roots and lower portion of the trunks of poplar. The

1. Hornet Moth.   2. Welsh Clearwing.   3. White-barred Clearwing.
4. Clear Underwing.   5, 6. Currant Clearwing.   7. Lunar Hornet Moth.

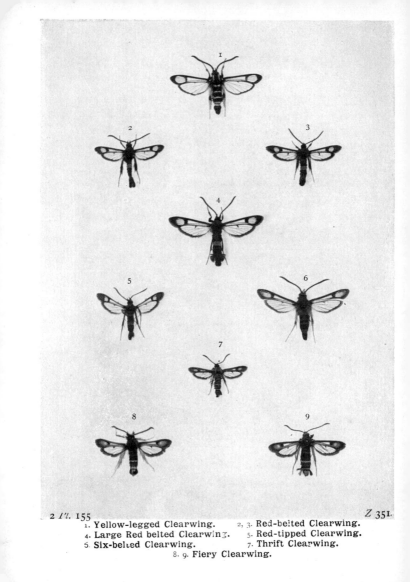

1. Yellow-legged Clearwing. 2, 3. Red-belted Clearwing.
4. Large Red belted Clearwing. 5. Red-tipped Clearwing.
5. Six-belted Clearwing. 7. Thrift Clearwing.
8. 9. Fiery Clearwing.

brown shining chrysalis is enclosed in a cocoon of wood scrapings woven together with silk. The moth is out in May and June ; and has been found, newly emerged, sitting on stems of poplar in the morning.

The eastern counties of England appear to be most favoured by this species, but it also occurs northwards to Yorkshire, southwards to Devonshire, and a specimen has been recorded from Rhyl, North Wales. In Scotland, it has been reported from some localities in the south ; Kane states that he has reason to believe that the species occurs in the northern half of Ireland, and that he found caterpillars plentiful in young poplars growing in a marsh near the city of Waterford.

Lunar Hornet (*Trochilium crabroniformis*).

Another hornet-like moth, best distinguished from that just mentioned by the yellow collar behind the black head (Plate 154, Fig. 7 ♀). The male is rather smaller, but otherwise similar.

The caterpillar is yellowish white, with dark brownish head, and a blackish edged yellow plate on the first ring of the body. It feeds in stems of sallow, willow, and poplar. In late June and through July the moth is on the wing, and may occasionally be seen at rest on leaves or stems of sallow, etc.

The species, known also as *bembeciformis*, Hübner, is generally distributed throughout England, Wales, and Ireland ; in Scotland its range extends into Perthshire.

Abroad it seems pretty much confined to Holland, Northern and Central Germany, Austria, and Bohemia.

Clear Underwing (*Sciapteron tabaniformis*).

This species is the *Trochelium vespiforme* of some British authors, and the *Ægeria asiliformis* of Stephens and others.

Another English name for it is the Dusky Clearwing, and this refers to the cloudy fore wings.

Stephens, writing of it in 1828, remarks: "Occasionally taken on poplars, near London, in June. I have obtained it from the neighbourhood of Bexley, and from Birchwood; but it is doubtless a rare species, and exists in few collections: of the male, I have hitherto seen but two specimens, one of which I possess." Both places mentioned by Stephens are in Kent, and one or two specimens of the species have since been reported from Ashford in the same county. The late Henry Doubleday took specimens at Epping, Essex. Colney Hatch Wood in Middlesex has also been given as a locality in the past; two specimens have been recorded from Chiswick, and one was captured on a poplar trunk close to Portsmouth in July, 1909. (Plate 154, Fig. 4).

The caterpillar lives under the bark of poplar trunks, and the moth flies in June and July.

Welsh Clearwing (*Sesia scoliæformis*).

As a British species this insect was first noted from Llangollen, in North Wales, somewhere about fifty years ago. In 1867 it was found to inhabit birch woods in the Rannoch district of Scotland, and later on its presence was detected in Sutherlandshire. It has been recorded from Hereford; one example was reported from Wiltshire in 1857; and two from Delamere Forest, Cheshire (1901 and 1905). A pupa obtained June, and a moth captured in July, 1913, Cannock Chase, Staffs. Kane states that moths have been taken at Killarney, and caterpillars obtained in the same district, and also at Kenmare.

The caterpillar (Plate 156, Fig. 3; after Hofmann) feeds on the inner layer of bark of large birch trees, and is full grown about May. It turns to a dark brownish chrysalis, in a cocoon formed close up to the bark, which thinly covers the outer end of the burrow. The moth flies in June or sometimes July. It is of comparatively large size, and may be distinguished from the next species by the yellow belts on its body, and the chestnut coloured tuft at the tail. (Plate 154, Fig. 2.)

White-barred Clearwing (*Sesia spheciformis*).

Although generally smaller, some specimens run very close to the last species in size. It may be distinguished by the single belt on the body and the black tail (Plate 154, Fig. 3). One of the best known localities for the species in England is Tilgate Forest, in Sussex; but it also occurs in Hampshire (Basingstoke), Hereford (Tarrington), Worcestershire (Wyre Forest), Staffordshire (Burnt Wood), Cheshire (one, Delamere Forest, 1901), Denbighshire (Llangollen), Lancashire (Chat Moss), and Yorkshire (Bishop's Wood, 1894).

The caterpillar feeds in stems of alder, and is full grown in May of the third year after hatching from the egg. It is said that the chrysalis may sometimes be found by bending and twisting the stems of alder, so as to cause the thin skin of bark over the exit hole of the burrow to crack, and so disclose its whereabouts. The burrow is generally low down the stem. The moth is out in June and early July, and is sometimes to be seen on sunny mornings at rest on alder leaves, or flying over and around the bushes.

Orange-tailed Clearwing (*Sesia andrenæformis*).

Although known to be a British species since 1829, when a specimen was taken in a wood near Greenhithe, Kent, this insect continued to be very rare until quite recently. For a long time the caterpillar was supposed to feed in the stems of dogwood, but it is now known to live in the stems of the wayfaring tree (*Viburnum lantana*), and several specimens of the moth

Series II.

have been reared during the past year or two. Unfortunately the caterpillar is much infested by parasites, and comparatively few escape attack. Notes on the life history of this moth, by the Hon. N. Charles Rothschild, Mr. Eustace Bankes, and Dr. Chapman, are published in the *Transactions of the Entomological Society of London* for 1906 (Part IV., pp. 471-482).

Most of the known localities for the species are in Kent, but it has also been found in Surrey, Dorset, Gloucester, Hertfordshire (Tring district), and Northamptonshire (Oundle). Possibly it will be discovered in other parts of the country. I am indebted to Mr. L. W. Newman, of Bexley, for the specimen figured on Plate 1, Fig. 1. For the caterpillar mine in stem of *Viburnum* (Plate 152, Figs. 2, 2*a*) my thanks are due to Mr. Rayward, who kindly sent me a living pupa, from which the moth duly emerged, but, I regret to add, escaped from the box in which the stick containing the chrysalis was kept.

Newman, in 1833, described this species as *Trochilium allantiformis*, and in 1842 it was figured by Westwood and Humphreys as *T. andreniforme*. It is distinguished from *Sesia tipuliformis* by the two yellow belts of the body (the first sometimes indistinct) and the orange-yellow tuft in the blue-black tail ; on the underside of the body there is a broad yellow band on the fourth ring, sometimes extending to the fifth and sixth.

Currant Clearwing (*Sesia tipuliformis*).

In this species the body is narrowly belted with yellow, usually four belts in the male and three in the female ; the tail tuft is black in both sexes. The outer marginal border of the fore wings has a bronzy tinge, due to orange patches between the veins. (Plate 154, Figs. 5 ♂, 6 ♀.)

The caterpillar lives in the stems and shoots of black and red currant bushes ; it feeds on the pith, and works its way downwards. When full grown about May, it gnaws an outlet to the side of the stem, but does not penetrate the outer skin, although it reduces this to a very thin layer, through which the reddish brown chrysalis is able to force itself when the moth is ready to emerge. A figure of the caterpillar will be found on Plate 156, Fig. 1 ; the chrysalis protruding from currant stem (Fig. 1a) is from a photo by Mr. H. Main. In June or July, the moths are not infrequently seen on leaves of shrubs in gardens where there are currant bushes in or around such gardens, but the foliage of the food plant is a favourite resting place.

Generally distributed throughout England, the range extending into Wales, and South Scotland, but is apparently rare in these countries and also in some of the northern counties of England. Kane states that the species is common near Dublin, and is probably widely distributed in Ireland.

This species seems to have been introduced into North America, where its caterpillar is known as the "currant borer," and, as in England, is regarded with little favour by bush-fruit growers.

Yellow-legged Clearwing (*Sesia vespiformis*).

This species (Plate 155, Fig. 1), known also as *asiliformis*, Rottemburg (1775), and *cynipiformis*, Esper (1782), is now held to be correctly referred to *vespiformis*, Linnæus (1761). The crossbar of the fore wings is orange red in both sexes ; the body of the male has two more or less united yellow spots at the junction with the thorax, four yellow belts, and the tail tuft is black above, mixed with yellow below ; in the female the body belts are usually one less than in the male, the yellow spots at the junction are generally run together, and the tail tuft is almost wholly yellow. As indicated by the English name, the legs are largely yellow in both sexes.

The caterpillar feeds on the inner bark of oak trees, is full grown in May or June, and turns to a brownish chrysalis in a cell formed in the bark. A well-known locality for this moth, which is out in July and early August. is Hyde Park, London. It is also found in woods or oak-timbered parks in Kent (Tunbridge Wells), Surrey, Sussex (Abbot's Wood, Tilgate, etc.), Dorset (Glanvilles Wootton, etc.), Devon (Devonport, Plymouth, Topsham, etc.), Essex (Epping), Suffolk, Oxfordshire, Gloucestershire, Leicestershire, Staffordshire, and Yorkshire (Doncaster).

Red-belted Clearwing (*Sesia myopæformis*).

One example of each sex is shown on Plate 155, where Fig. 2 represents the male and Fig. 3 the female ; both have a single belt on the body ; as a rule, the belt is red, but occasionally it inclines to orange or yellow.

The caterpillar feeds on the inner bark of the trunks or boughs of apple, and sometimes pear, trees. It is nearly two years in maturing, but is full grown about June. The moth is out during the summer months, and is to be seen early on sunny mornings, newly emerged from the chrysalis on the trunks of the trees in which the caterpillar lives ; the chrysalis skins will also be noted at the same time, sticking out from holes in the bark. Later in the day it sits on leaves, etc., after its flights, and I have even found it occasionally on a gravel path, and once on the pavement of a road in North-west London.

The species seems to be most frequent in gardens and orchards around London, but it has been recorded from as far north as Lancashire and Yorkshire ; it is probably widely distributed over England. The Irish localities, mentioned by Kane, are Dublin, Cork, Killarney, and Clonbrock.

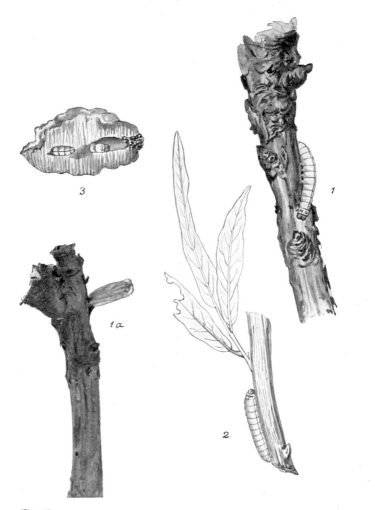

1. **Currant Clearwing**: *caterpillar and chrysalis skin.*
2. **Red-tipped Clearwing**: *caterpillar.*
3. **Welsh Clearwing**: *caterpillar.*

Large Red-belted Clearwing (*Sesia culiciformis*).

This species (Plate 155, Fig. 4) is very similar to the last, but it is larger, and the fore wings are dusted with reddish scales towards the base, sometimes also along the inner margin. The belt on the body is generally red, not infrequently with an orange tinge, but it is sometimes yellow or far more rarely white.

The caterpillar, which is full grown in May, feeds on the inner bark of birch trees and bushes, apparently preferring the stumps left in the ground where stems have been cut down. It is not difficult to find, but as it is about two years in this stage it should not be taken until nearly or quite full grown, and it is safer to leave it until it has entered the chrysalis state. The moth is out in June, or sometimes at the end of May; it flies over birch and rests on leaves, and has been known to visit flowers of the wood spurge and the rhododendron.

Kent and Sussex appear to be the counties most favoured by this species, but it occurs in most of the other English counties in which there are birch woods, certainly up to Yorkshire, and probably further north, as it is found in Scotland (Clydesdale, Perthshire, and Aberdeen). The Irish localities are Killarney, Ballinasloe, and Derry.

Red-tipped Clearwing (*Sesia formicæformis*).

This is another red-belted species, but it differs from either of the two immediately preceding in having the fore wings tipped with red. (Plate 155, Fig. 5.)

The caterpillar feeds in the twigs and stumps of osier (*Salix viminalis*), sometimes called "withe"; it is full grown about June. (Plate 156, Fig. 2; after Hofmann.) The moth is out in July and August; it is partial to marshes and other wet spots,

and is fond of a leaf as a resting place.   Like the rest of its
kind, it is very alert, and skips off quickly on one's approach.
Probably the species is more widely distributed in England,
but from the records, it only appears to have been noted from
Kent, Hampshire, Somersetshire, Gloucestershire, Herefordshire, Derbyshire, Yorkshire, Norfolk, Suffolk, Cambridgeshire,
and Essex.

Six-belted Clearwing (*Sesia ichneumoniformis*).

The inner and outer margins of the fore wings are tinged with
orange, and there is an orange mark on the outer edge of the
cross bar ; the body of the male has seven yellow belts, and
that of the female one less.   (Plate 155, Fig. 6.)

The caterpillar feeds in the roots of bird's-foot trefoil (*Lotus
corniculatus*), and kidney vetch (*Anthyllis vulneraria*) ; it is full
grown about June.   July and August are the months for the
moth, and its haunts are on chalk downs, and on banks by the
sea ; it seems partial to the edges of chalk pits, sloping banks,
and broken ground of undercliffs, etc.   In such places it is to
be seen on the wing in the early evening, and, I believe, in
the early morning also.   It has frequently been obtained by
sweeping the net over herbage in the vicinity of the food plants.

Mr. W. H. Flint records (1902) the species from the Forest
of Dean district, where, he states, he could easily have captured
two dozen a day, as they flew over trefoils, etc.

The species occurs in most of the southern seaboard counties
of England, from Kent to Cornwall and including the Isle
of Wight; Surrey, Bucks., Essex, and other eastern counties,
including Cambridge ; and it has been recorded from Yorkshire.   On the western side of the country it is found in
Somerset, Gloucester, Hereford, Worcester, Staffordshire, and
in South Wales.

Thrift Clearwing (*Sesia muscæformis*).

This is our smallest species of the genus, and it is further distinguished by narrow clear spaces on the blackish, or bronzy, fore wings, three whitish bands on the body, and traces of a whitish line along the middle of the back. (Plate 155, Fig. 7.)

The caterpillar feeds on the roots of thrift or sea-pink (*Armeria vulgaris*), and is full grown about June. The moth is out in June and July, and seems to have a liking for the flowers of thyme.

This species (also known as *philanthiformis*, Laspeyres) frequents rocky places on the coasts of Devon (Torquay, Lynmouth, etc.), Cornwall, Wales ; Isle of Man ; Scotland (Aberdeenshire) ; and Ireland (Saltee Islands, Wexford, and Seven Heads, Cork. Gregson recorded it from Howth).

Fiery Clearwing (*Sesia chrysidiformis*).

The orange red colour on the fore wings, and of the tail tuft, at once distinguish this species (Plate 155, Figs. 8 ♂, 9 ♀) from either of its British allies. The blackish body has two pale-yellow belts, but in the male the lower one is often double. As a rule, the body of the female is stouter than that of the male, but the bodies of some males appear quite as thick as those of the females, and the true sex is only disclosed by the ciliated antennæ, which is a character of the male alone.

The caterpillar feeds on the roots of dock and sorrel, and it is full grown about May. In June and July the moth is on the wing and flies in the sunshine, about noon, over the food plants.

The species occurs not uncommonly in the Warren at Folkestone, Kent. This locality, well known to entomologists, is a long stretch of rough broken ground lying between the railway and the sea ; and is probably the only spot in the British Isles where the Fiery Clearwing is almost certain to be found, either in its early or its perfect stage, at the proper season. The moth has been recorded from Eastbourne, Sussex (1874), and from the Forest of Dean, Gloucestershire (1902).

HEPIALIDÆ.

Of the twenty-two Palæarctic species belonging to this family, nine appear to occur in Europe, and the range of five of these extends to the British Isles.

In some of the more recent systems of classification, this family is relegated to almost the bottom of the scheme, and therefore occupies a much lower place than do the bulk of the families comprised in the old style "Micro-Lepidoptera." As, however, these insects, commonly called "Swifts," have long received the attention of collectors, and in collections usually occupy a position among the so-called "Bombyces," they have been included in the present volume.

Ghost Moth (*Hepialus humuli*).

On Plate 157 are portraits of a male and a female of the typical form of this species (Figs. 1 ♂ and 3 ♀) ; and two male examples (Figs. 2 and 4) of the Shetland race var. *thulensis*, Newman, better known perhaps as *hethlandica*, Staudinger, but the former is the older name. It will be noted that in the ordinary form the male has white wings, and that the female has yellowish fore wings marked with orange, and smoky hind wings. The Shetland male, represented by Fig. 2, has the fore wings whitish buff in colour with brownish markings similar in pattern to those of an ordinary female ; the hind wings are blackish. The second example of *thulensis* (Fig. 4)

1-3. **Map-winged Swift.**   4-6. **Common Swift.**   7, 8. **Gold Swift.**

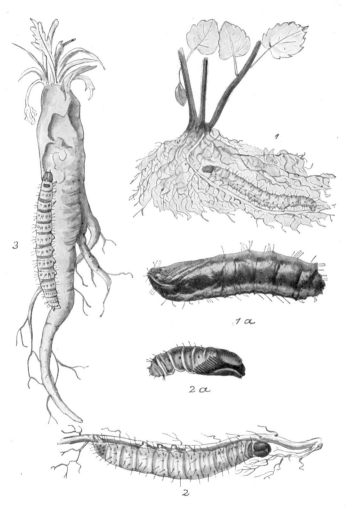

1, 1a. **Common Swift:** *caterpillar and chrysalis.*
2, 2a. **Ghost Moth:** *caterpillar and chrysalis (enlarged).*
3. **Orange Swift:** *caterpillar.*

is somewhat similar in appearance to a typical female. In other male specimens of this insular race the wings are pretty much of the typical colour, but the markings on the front pair are reduced both in number and size. Mr. H. McArthur, who has collected a good deal in the Shetland Isles, states that in Unst, the most northern island of the group, more or less typical *humuli* were found on the cliffs facing south-east, whilst the majority of the specimens obtained in boggy meadows, etc., were of the *thulensis* form.

The caterpillar feeds on the roots of plants, such as burdock, dandelion, dead-nettle, etc. It is full grown in May, and the moth is out in June and July. (Plate 159, Fig. 2; after Hofmann.) The males may be seen in the evening, sometimes in numbers in grassy places, swaying themselves to and fro without making progress, and appearing as though they dangled from the end of an invisible thread; the female flies straight, and, as a rule, in the direction of one or other of the pendulous males.

The species is generally distributed over the British Isles.

Orange Swift (*Hepialus sylvina*).

The male of this species (Plate 157, Figs. 5 ♂, 6 ♀) is usually some shade of orange brown, with greyish-edged white markings on the fore wings. Sometimes the female is orange brown, but more often it is some shade of grey brown.

The caterpillar (Plate 159, Fig. 3; after Hofmann) feeds on the roots of dock, bracken, viper's bugloss, etc., and is full grown about July. In late July and in August the moth may be seen in the early evening flying among bracken, and not infrequently around trees fairly high up. Occasionally, specimens are seen in the daytime on tree-trunks, fences, etc. At one time this species was known in the vernacular as "The Tawny and Brown Swift"; it is also "The Orange or Evening Swift" of Harris (1778) and the "Wood Swift" of Newman. It is common in many southern and eastern parts, but widely distributed over England, Wales, and Scotland to Moray. Only doubtfully recorded from Ireland.

Map-winged Swift (*Hepialus fusconebulosa*).

At one time this species (the *velleda* of Hübner) was known as the "Northern Swift," but as it is plentiful in North Devonshire and Somersetshire, and occurs less commonly in other southern English counties, that name is hardly suitable. Haworth's English name for it—"The Beautiful Swift"—does not quite meet the case, because, although the insect is prettily marked, it is scarcely beautiful. We have then to fall back on Donovan's Map-winged Swift as a popular name, and this seems a fairly apt one, as the markings on the fore wings are somewhat map-like in pattern, especially in the more typical specimens.

There is much variation in colour and in marking; some examples, chiefly those from Shetland, are prettily variegated. A uniform reddish-brown variety, ab. *gallicus*, Lederer, is depicted on Plate 158, Fig. 3; and a more or less typical specimen of each sex is shown on the same plate (Figs. 1 ♂, 2 ♀).

The caterpillar is ochreous white, with orange-brown plates, and rather paler raised dots; head, reddish brown, and spiracles black. It feeds on the roots of the bracken, and is full grown about May. The moth is out in June and July, and flies, in the gloaming, on hill slopes, heaths, and the edges of mosses and woods; it seems to be more active than either of the other British "Swifts"; at all events, I have always found it less easy to capture with the net.

The species is pretty generally distributed throughout the British Isles.

Common Swift (*Hepialus lupulina*).

Three examples of this species are shown on Plate 158. Fig. 4 is a typical male, Fig. 5 a whitish suffused variety, and Fig. 6 is a female. The latter sex is generally devoid of marking, and in the male the stripes and dashes are far more conspicuous in some specimens than in others.

The glossy whitish caterpillar has a brown head; the plate on the first ring of the body is brownish, and the raised dots are pretty much of the same colour. It feeds on the roots of grass and other plants, and is full grown about April. A figure of the caterpillar, from a drawing in colour by Mr. A. Sich, and a photo of the pupa by Mr. H. Main, are shown on Plate 159, Figs. 1 and 1*a*; the latter is twice natural size.

The moth is out in June, or sometimes late May, and occasional specimens have been noted in September. It is more frequently seen at rest, on fences, etc., than either of the other species of the genus ; but towards dusk it is on the wing, and may then be observed in large numbers careering over grass meadows or along stretches of green turf by the wayside.

Generally distributed, and often abundant, throughout the United Kingdom ; and it occurs in Monaghan, Mayo, Galway, and Kerry, in Ireland.

Gold Swift (*Hepialus hecta*).

Both sexes of this species are shown on Plate 158, where Fig. 7 represents the golden-marked male, and Fig. 8 the more dingy, dull, purplish-grey striped female. There is variation in number and in size of the markings on the fore wings of the male, and occasionally the hind wings in this sex are adorned with golden spangles on the outer area.

The pale greyish brown caterpillar has glossy darker brown

plates on rings 1-3, and the raised dots and the spiracles are black. It feeds on the roots of bracken, and is full grown about May. Buckler states that at first it burrows in the root, hibernates when small, resumes feeding in April, attains full growth before winter, and hibernates in the earth for a second time; in the spring of the second year it gnaws cavities in the young shoots of the bracken, and apparently drinks the flowing sap.

The moth is out in June. The males fly at dusk, something in the manner of *humuli*, over and among the bracken; but the females fly in a more or less direct line. An odour given off by the males of this species has been likened to that of the pine apple; whilst the " scent " of the Ghost Moth is said to be more of the billy-goat character.

In most woody localities, where the bracken flourishes. this species will be found throughout England, Wales, Scotland to Aberdeen and the Hebrides, and Ireland.

APPENDIX.

———◆———

P. 22. **Melinia ocellaris.**—On September 13, 1911, thirty-eight specimens were captured in one of the Thames Valley localities. Over two dozen specimens were taken among wych elm at Shelford, Cambs., in the autumn of 1914. (See *Entomologist* for 1915, pp. 43, 63, 86.)

P. 112. **Acidalia virgularia.**—From eggs deposited by a melanic female captured in south-east London, Mr. Bauman reared some twenty-three specimens, many of which agreed with the parent female in tint, others were grey, but none were of the typical colouration of *virgularia*. The blackish specimens are probably referable to *bischoffaria*.

P. 163. **Eustroma reticulata.**—In an interesting article on the variation of this species (*Entom.* xlv., 1–3, Pl. 1), Mr. Prout gives figures of fourteen forms, two of which are named *costimaculata* (type Fig. 5), and *ovulata* (Fig. 4). The early stages of *E. reticulata* are described by Mr. F. Littlewood (*Entom.* xlv., pp. 85–89), and photographs of the larva are given.

P. 175. **Thera variata.**—To the late Major Robertson Mr. Prout was indebted for the material which enabled him to confirm a doubt he had long held concerning the specific identity of *variata* and *obeliscata*. In December, 1911, the Major submitted six specimens of a *Thera* that he had bred from larvæ taken from a small ornamental spruce growing in the Chandlersford district. These Mr. Prout subsequently identified as the true *variata*, Schiff. Apart from a general greyer colouration, not always to be relied upon, the chief points of difference are as follows : "true *variata* can nearly always be differentiated at a glance by its better marked and strongly dentate subterminal line (often very clear and pale) and better marked hind wing, nearly always with a distinct central spot, and not rarely with a fairly definite postmedian line" (*Entom.* xlv., pp. 241–246). The larva, which is almost identical with that of *obeliscata*, feeds on spruce and not on Scotch fir.

P. 178. **Lampropteryx otregiata,** Metcalfe.—In bringing this forward as an addition to our Geometridæ, the Rev. J. W. Metcalfe (*Entom.,* 1917, p. 73) states, "I first captured the insect some ten years ago, flying in considerable numbers, in a remote locality in North Devon. The striking difference in the shape of the wings from those of *suffumata*, the small size, and the shining, silvery ground colour, at once attracted my attention. A subsequent visit led to further captures, and on coming to live in East Devon I was delighted to discover it again in a similar locality in this part of the county. In addition to this, Mr. Newman has now found a series in a collection made in Cornwall, where he reports that it was taken under similar conditions.

"The species seems to be absolutely constant in form, and in all specimens I have taken, well over a hundred, there has not been the slightest variation nor any approach to any of the known forms of *suffumata*. The general pattern and position of the wing markings correspond closely to those of *suffumata*, but the dark markings are much reduced, especially on the outer third of the wing, and are very delicately outlined with silvery white. The small size, the shining, silvery, ground-colour, and the shape of the fore wings, which are full and well-rounded (very unlike those of *suffumata*), serve to separate it at a glance. The hind wings are devoid of markings, shining whitish-grey. Seen in a series the general appearance is most striking, and somewhat suggests a cross between *suffumata* and *silaceata*."

P. 335. **Zygaena Achilleæ**—Further records.—Mr. Percy C. Reid, in a note to the *Entomologist* for 1919, p. 188, writes in the course of his account of a hunt for this species, "Eventually we fixed on a spot some twenty miles from Oban, which we thought might prove likely, and there we arrived on the afternoon of June 26. Though unsuccessful at first we were not prepared to own ourselves beaten, and it was not long before we were out again in a fresh direction, when suddenly E—— spotted a pair of 'Burnets' *in cop.*, which needed only a cursory examination to cause both of us to exclaim, '*Achilleae!*' Guided by this find, we soon came across others, and eventually found that the insect occurred nearly everywhere in suitable spots and was certainly the common 'Burnet' of this district. We found it to frequent dry and sheltered banks covered with an abundance of mixed vegetation—heath, birds-foot trefoil, wild thyme, vetch, *Potentilla*, etc., and I am inclined to think its chief food-plant is probably *Lotus corniculatus*. It occurred at all elevations up to 300 feet, and I have no doubt higher."

Mr. Esson, in the same number (675), p. 189, states that he met with this species after a tramp of over twenty miles in a locality ten miles from the place where Renton found it some ten years earlier.

INDEX.

ABRAXAS grossulariata, 260, Plates 103, 104; *sylvata*, 259, Plates 103, 104

Abrostola tripartita, 74, *Plate* 22; *triplasia*, 73, *Plates* 22, 27

Acidalia aversata, 120, *Plates* 46, 47; *bisetata*, 121, *Plate* 46; *contiguaria*, 109, *Plate* 45; *degeneraria*, 118, *Plate* 46; *dimidiata*, 121, *Plates* 46, 47; *emutaria*, 128, *Plate* 49; *fumata*, 131, *Plate* 50; *herbariata*, 111, *Plate* 45; *holosericata*, 116, *Plate* 45; *humiliata*, 115, *Plate* 45; *imitaria*, 129, *Plates* 48, 49; *immorata*, 126, *Plate* 49; *immutata*, 124, *Plate* 49; *inornata*, 119, *Plates* 46, 47; *interjectaria*, 114, *Plate* 45; *marginepunctata*, 125, *Plate* 49; *ochrata*, 132, *Plate* 50; *ornata*, 123, *Plate* 46; *perochraria*, 133, *Plate* 53; *remutaria*, 124, *Plate* 49; *rubiginata*, 130, *Plate* 50; *rusticata*, 110, *Plates* 45, 48; *straminata*, 113, *Plates* 45, 61; *strigilaria*, 127, *Plate* 49; *subsericeata*, 117, *Plate* 45; *trigeminata*, 122, *Plate* 46; *virgularia*, 112, *Plate* 45

Acidaliinæ, 109

Acontia lucida, var. *albicollis*, 53, *Plate* 19; *luctuosa*, 54, *Plates* 19, 23

Adscita geryon, 343, *Plate* 147; *statices*, 342, *Plates* 145, 147 Series II.

Alchymist, 78. *Plate* 29

Aleucis pictaria, 264. *Plate* 107

Amathes circellaris, 14, *Plates* 5, 7; *helvola*, 15, *Plate* 9; *litura*, 16, *Plate* 9; *lóta*, 12, *Plates* 5, 7; *lychnidis*, 16, *Plates* 5, 9; *macilenta*, 13, *Plate* 7

Amœbe olivata, 184, *Plates* 73, 75; *viridaria*, 185, *Plate* 75

Amphidasys. See *Pachys.*

Anaitis plagiata, 149. *Plate* 55

Anarta cordigera, 44, *Plate* 17; *melanopa*, 45, *Plate* 17; *myrtilli*, 44, *Plates* 17, 20

Anchocelis lunosa, 11. *Plate* 7

Angerona prunaria, 280. *Plates* 117, 118

Angle-barred Pug, 246. *Plate* 98

Angle-striped Sallow, 5. *Plate* 4

Ania emarginata, 133. *Plate* 50

Anisopteryx æscularia, 294. *Plates* 122, 125

Annulet, 319. *Plates* 139, 140

Anticlea badiata, 217, *Plates* 88, 89; *berberata*, 218, *Plate* 88; *cucullata*, 216, *Plate* 88; *nigrofasciaria*, 219, *Plates* 88, 89; *rubidata*, 218, *Plate* 88

Aplasta ononaria, 101. *Plate* 38

Apocheima hispidaria, 296. *Plates* 124, 126

Argent and Sable, 201. *Plates* 79, 82

Ash Pug, 247. *Plate* 98

Aspilates gilvaria, 330, *Plate* 144;

ochrearia, 331, *Plates* 142, 144;
strigillaria, 332, *Plate* 144
Asthena blomeri, 222, *Plates* 90, 91;
candidata, 220, *Plates* 90, 91;
luteata, 220, *Plate* 91; testaceata,
221, *Plate* 91
Atethmia xerampelina, 10, *Plate* 4
August Thorn, 271. *Plates* 109, 111,
113
Autumnal Moth, 189. *Plate* 78
Autumn Green Carpet, 174. *Plate* 68

BANKIA argentula, 57. *Plate* 21
Bapta bimaculata, 265, *Plate* 107;
pictaria, 264, *Plate* 107; temerata,
266, *Plate* 107
Barberry Carpet, 218. *Plate* 88
Barred Carpet, 211. *Plate* 85
Barred Red, 269. *Plates* 106, 108
Barred Rivulet, 208. *Plate* 83
Barred Sallow, 18. *Plate* 10
Barred Straw, 168. *Plate* 65
Barred Tooth-striped, 152. *Plates*
57, 59
Barred Umber, 268. *Plates* 106, 108
Barred Yellow, 169. *Plates* 65, 69
Beaded Chestnut, 16. *Plates* 5, 9
Beautiful Carpet, 202. *Plates* 76, 82
Beautiful Golden Y, 70. *Plate* 24
Beautiful Hook-tip, 85. *Plate* 36
Beautiful Snout, 92. *Plates* 35, 37
Beautiful Yellow Underwing, 44.
Plates 17, 20
Beech-green Carpet, 184. *Plates* 73,
75
Belted Beauty, 298. *Plates* 124, 126
Bilberry Pug, 253. *Plate* 100
Birch Mocha, 139. *Plates* 51, 53
Black Mountain Moth, 321. *Plate*
139
Blackneck, 83. *Plate* 32
Black-veined Moth, 330. *Plate* 144
Bleached Pug, 230. *Plate* 95
Blomer's Rivulet, 222. *Plates* 90, 91
Blood-vein, 134. *Plate* 50
Blotched Emerald, 104. *Plates* 41, 43

Bloxworth Snout, 93. *Plate* 36
Blue-bordered Carpet, 204. *Plate* 82
Boarmia abietaria, 306, *Plates* 132,
138; cinctaria, 304, *Plate* 130;
consortaria, 309, *Plate* 135; gem-
maria, 305, *Plates* 130, 131; repan-
data, 307, *Plates* 131, 132, 134;
roboraria, 308, *Plate* 135
Boarmiinæ, 259
Bomolocha fontis, 92. *Plates* 35, 37
Bordered Beauty, 284. *Plates* 119,
121
Bordered Grey, 325. *Plates* 142, 143
Bordered Pug, 240. *Plates* 92, 97
Bordered Sallow, 47. *Plates* 17, 20
Bordered Straw, 50. *Plates* 19, 20
Bordered White, 325. *Plates* 140,
141
Brephidæ, 97
Brephos notha, 98, *Plates* 38, 39;
parthenias, 97, *Plates* 38, 39
Brick, 14. *Plates* 5, 7
Bright Wave, 132. *Plate* 50
Brimstone, 283. *Plate* 117
Brindled Beauty, 299. *Plates* 1, 124,
128
Brindled Pug, 248. *Plate* 99
Brindled White-spot, 314. *Plate* 137
Broad-bordered White Underwing,
45. *Plate* 17
Broken-barred Carpet, 169. *Plates*
61, 65
Broom-tip, 151. *Plates* 56, 57
Brown Scallop, 161. *Plate* 60
Brown Silver-line, 327. *Plate* 143
Brown-spot Pinion, 16. *Plate* 9
Brussels Lace, 310. *Plates* 133, 136
Bupalus piniaria, 325. *Plates* 140,
141
Burnet Companion, 76. *Plate* 26
Burnets, 333
Burnished Brass, 65. *Plate* 22
Buttoned Snout, 94. *Plates* 35, 37

CABERA exanthemata, 267, *Plate*
107; pusaria, 266, *Plates* 105, 107

Calocampa exoleta, 34, *Plate* 14; *vetusta*, 35, *Plates* 8, 14

Calymnia affinis, 3, *Plate* 2; *diffinis*, 4, *Plates* 2, 3; *pyralina*, 2, *Plates* 2, 3; *trapezina*, 4, *Plate* 2

Campanula Pug, 232. *Plate* 95

Camptogramma bilineata, 212. *Plates* 61, 84, 85

Canary - shouldered Thorn, 272. *Plates* 110, 111

Carsia paludata, 150. *Plate* 55

Catephia alchymista, 78. *Plate* 29

Catocala electa, 79, *Plate* 31; *fraxini*, 78, *Plate* 29; *nupta*, 80, *Plates* 31, 33; *promissa*, 82, *Plate* 32; *sponsa*, 82, *Plates* 32, 33

Centre-barred Sallow, 10. *Plate* 4

Chalk Carpet, 145. *Plates* 52, 54

Chamomile Shark, 40. *Plates* 16, 18

Cheimatobia boreata, 157, *Plates* 58, 59; *brumata*, 156, *Plate* 58

Chesias rufata, 151, *Plates* 56, 57; *spartiata*, 150, *Plates* 56, 57

Chestnut-coloured Carpet, 176. *Plate* 70

Chestnut Moth, 24. *Plate* 11

Chevron, 165. *Plates* 63, 67

Chiasmia clathrata, 328. *Plate* 143

Chimney-sweeper, 147. *Plate* 55

Chloroclystis coronata, 251, *Plate* 100; *debiliata*, 253, *Plate* 100; *rectangulata*, 251, *Plate* 100

Cidaria corylata, 169, *Plates* 61, 65; *fulvata*, 169, *Plates* 65, 69; *immanata*, *Plates* 66, 69; *miata*, 174, *Plate* 68; *pyraliata*, 168, *Plate* 65; *sagittata*, 172, *Plate* 68; *siterata*, 173, *Plate* 68; *truncata*, 170, *Plates* 66, 69

Cirrhia citrago, 17. *Plate* 10

Cirrhœdia xerampelina, 10. *Plate* 4

Cistus Forester, 343. *Plate* 147

Clay Fan-foot, 90. *Plates* 34, 35

Clay Triple-lines, 137. *Plate* 53

Clear Underwing, 351. *Plate* 154

Clearwings, 350

Cleora angularia, 310, *Plate* 134; *jubata*, 311, *Plates* 133, 136; *lichenaria*, 310, *Plates* 133, 136

Clifden Nonpareil, 78. *Plate* 29

Cloaked Carpet, 200. *Plate* 82

Cloaked Pug, 251. *Plate* 99

Clouded Border, 262. *Plates* 105, 107

Clouded Magpie, 259. *Plates* 101, 103, 104

Clouded Silver, 266. *Plate* 107

Cochlididæ, 344

Cochlidion limacodes, 345. *Plates* 149, 153

Cœnocalpe tersata, 257, *Plate* 102; *vitalbata*, 256, *Plate* 102; *vittata*, 257, *Plate* 102

Collix sparsata, 254. *Plate* 102

Common Carpet, 197. *Plates* 79, 81

Common Emerald, 107. *Plates* 41, 43

Common Fan-foot, 91. *Plate* 34

Common Heath, 324. *Plate* 141

Common Marbled Carpet, 170. *Plates* 66, 69

Common Pug, 334. *Plates* 92, 97

Common Swift, 363. *Plates* 158, 159

Common Wave, 267. *Plate* 107

Common White Wave, 266. *Plates* 105, 107

Conformist, 29. *Plates* 8, 13

Conistra. See *Orrhodia*

Coremia designata, 183, *Plates* 74, 75; *ferrugata*, 182, *Plate* 72; *munitata*, 180, *Plate* 72; *quadrifasciaria*, 179, *Plate* 72; *unidentaria*, 181, *Plate* 75

Cosmia paleacea, 5. *Plate* 4

Cossidæ, 347

Cossus cossus (*ligniperda*), 347. *Plates* 150, 151

Craspedia. See *Acidalia*.

Cream Wave, 124. *Plate* 49

Crocallis elinguaria, 280. *Plates* 114, 116

Cucullia abrotani, 43, *Plate* 16; *absinthii*, 42, *Plate* 16; *artemisiæ*,

43, *Plate* 16 ; *asteris*, 30, *Plates* 15, 18 ; *chamomillæ*, 40, *Plates* 16, 18 ; *gnaphalii*, 41, *Plate* 13 ; *lychnitis*, 38, *Plates* 15, 18 ; *scrophulariæ*, 37, *Plate* 15 ; *umbratica*, 40, *Flate* 16 ; *verbasci*, 36, *Plates* 15, 18

Cudweed Shark, 41. *Plate* 13

Currant Clearwing, 354. *Plates* 154, 156

Currant Pug, 230. *Plates* 92, 95

DARK-BARRED Twin-spot Carpet, 181. *Plates* 74, 75

Dark Bordered Beauty, 284. *Plates* 119, 121

Dark Chestnut, 25. *Plate* 11

Dark Crimson Underwing, 82. *Plates* 32, 33

Dark Marbled Carpet, 171. *Plates* 66, 69

Dark Spectacle, 73. *Plates* 22, 27

Dark Spinach, 254. *Plate* 102

Dark Umber, 162. *Plate* 60

Dasycampa rubiginea, 26. *Plates* 6, 11

Dentated Pug, 254. *Plate* 102

Dicycla oo, 1. *Plate* 2

Dingy Mocha, 139. *Plate* 51, 53

Dingy Shears, 8. *Plates* 3, 4

Dingy Shell, 219. *Plate* 91

Dotted Border, 292. *Plates* 120, 125

Dotted Border Wave, 113. *Plates* 45, 61

Dotted Carpet, 311. *Plates* 133, 136

Dotted Chestnut, 26. *Plates* 6, 11

Dotted Fan-foot, 90. *Plate* 35

Double Kidney, 9. *Plate* 4

Double-striped Pug, 250. *Plate* 99

Drab Looper, 146. *Plate* 55

Dun-bar, 4. *Plate* 2

Dusky-lemon Sallow, 21. *Plate* 10

Dusky Thorn, 273. *Plates* 110, 111

Dwarf Cream Wave, 114. *Plate* 45

Dwarf Pug, 225. *Plate* 93

Dyschorista fissipuncta, 8, *Plates* 3, 4 ; *suspecta*, 7, *Plate* 4

EARLY Grey, 33. *Plates* 8, 12

Early Moth, 289. *Plate* 120

Early Thorn, 274. *Plate* 112

Early Tooth-striped, 153. *Plates* 57, 59

Edinburgh Pug, 239. *Plate* 96

Ellopia prosapiaria, 269. *Plates* 106, 108

Ematurga atomaria, 324. *Plate* 141

Emmelia trabealis, 62. *Plate* 21

Engrailed, 312. *Plates* 136, 138

Ennomos alniaria, 272, *Plates* 110, 111 ; *autumnaria*, 270, *Plates* 109, 110, 134 ; *erosaria*, 273, *Plate* 134 ; *fuscantaria*, 273, *Plates* 110, 111 ; *quercinaria*, 271, *Plates* 109, 111, 113

Entephria cæsiata, 191 ; *flavicinctata*, 192, *Plate* 80

Ephyra annulata, 138, *Plates* 51, 53 ; *linearia*, 137, *Plate* 53 ; *orbicularia*, 139, *Plates* 51, 53 ; *pendularia*, 139, *Plates* 51, 53 ; *porata*, 135, *Plate* 53 ; *punctaria*, 136, *Plate* 53

Epione advenaria, 285, *Plates* 119, 121 ; *apiciaria*, 284, *Plates* 119, 121 ; *parallelaria*, 284, *Plates* 119, 121

Epirrhoë. See *Xanthorhoë*

Epirrita. See *Oporabia*

Erastria argentula, 57, *Plate* 21 ; *fasciana*, 57, *Plate* 21 ; *uncula*, 58, *Plate* 21 ; *venustula*, 59, *Plates* 21, 25

Essex Emerald, 105. *Plates* 42, 43

Euchloris pustulata, 104, *Plates* 41, 43 ; *smaragdaria*, 105, *Plates* 42, 43

Euchœca obliterata, 219. *Plate* 91

Euclidia glyphica, 76, *Plate* 26 ; *mi*, 75, *Plates* 26, 30

Eucosmia certata, 159, *Plates* 60, 62 ; *undulata*, 160, *Plates* 60, 62

Eucymatoge togata, 251. *Plate* 99

Eudalimia margaritaria, 270. *Plates* 106, 108

Eulype hastata, 201. *Plates* 79, 82

Euphyia picata, 200, *Plate* 82 ; *unangulata*, 199, *Pla'e* 82

Eupithecia abbreviata, 248, *Plate* 99 ; *absinthiata*, 231, *Plate* 95 ; *albipunctata*, 234, *Plates* 92, 97 ; *assimilata*, 230, *Plates* 92, 95 ; *castigata*, 237, *Plates* 92, 97 ; *denotata*, 232, *Plate* 95 ; *distinctaria*, 229, *Plate* 95 ; *dodoneata*, 248, *Plate* 99 ; *exiguata*, 248, *Plate* 99 ; *expallidata*, 230, *Plate* 95 ; *extensaria*, 238, *Plate* 97 ; *fraxinata*, 247, *Plate* 98 ; *goossensiata*, 231, *Plate* 95 ; *haworthiata*, 242, *Plates* 90, 98 ; *helveticaria*, 239, *Plate* 96 ; *indigata*, 226, *Plate* 96 ; *innotata*, 246, *Plate* 98 ; *insigniata*, 226, *Plate* 96 ; *inturbata*, 246, *Plate* 98 ; *irriguata*, 225, *Plate* 93 ; *jasioneata*, 233, *Plate* 95 ; *lariciata*, 236, 97 ; *linariata*, 224, *Plate* 93 ; *nanata*, 247, *Plate* 99 ; *oblongata*, 222, *Plates* 92, 93 ; *pimpinellata*, 228, *Plate* 95 ; *plumbeolata*, 244, *Plate* 98 ; *pulchellata*, 223, *Plate* 93 ; *pumilata*, 250, *Plate* 99 ; *pusillata*, 225, *Plate* 93 ; *pygmæata*, 244, *Plate* 98 ; *satyrata*, 239, *Plate* 96 ; *scabiosata*, 242, *Plate* 97 ; *sobrinata*, 249, *Plate* 99 ; *subfulvata*, 241, *Plate* 97 ; *subnotata*, 237, *Plates* 94, 97 ; *succenturiata*, 240, *Plates* 92, 97 ; *tenuiata*, 245, *Plate* 98 ; *trisignaria*, 236, *Plate* 97 ; *valerianata*, 243, *Plate* 98 ; *v.nosata*, 227, *Plates* 92, 93 ; *virgaureata*, 235, *Plate* 97 ; *vulgata*, 234, *Plates* 92, 97

Eupsilia satellitia, 27. *Plate* 12

Eurymene dolabraria, 282. *Plate* 117

Eustroma silaceata, 162. *Plate* 93

FALSE Mocha, 135. *Plate* 53

Fan-foot, 87. *Plates* 34, 35

Feathered Thorn, 279. *Plates* 114, 116

Fern-Moth, 257. *Plate* 102

Series II.

Festoon, 345. *Plates* 149, 153

Fidonia limbaria, 323. *Plate* 141 ; *carbonaria*, 322. *Plate* 141

Fiery Clearwing, 359. *Plate* 155

Five-spot Burnet, 339. *Plates* 145, 146, 148

Flame Carpet, 183. *Plates* 74, 75

Flame Moth, 218. *Plate* 88

Flounced Chestnut, 15. *Plate* 9

Forester, 342. *Plates* 145, 147

Four-spotted, 54. *Plates* 19, 23

Foxglove Pug, 223. *Plate* 93

Frosted Yellow, 323. *Plate* 141

GALIUM Carpet, 195. *Plates* 79, 81

Garden Carpet, 194. *Plates* 61, 80

Gem, 258. *Plate* 102

Geometra papilionaria, 102, *Plates* 40, 42 ; *vernaria*, 103, *Plates* 40, 44

Geometridœ, 99

Geometrinæ, 101

Ghost Moth, 360. *Plates* 157, 159

Gnophos obscurata, 319, *Plates* 139, 140 ; *myrtillata*, 320. *Plate* 139

Goat Moth, 347. *Plates* 150, 151

Golden Plusia, 64. *Plates* 22, 27

Golden Rod Brindle, 32. *Plate* 12

Golden-rod Pug, 235. *Plate* 97

Gold Spangle, 67. *Plate* 24

Gold Spot, 68. *Plate* 24

Gold Swift, 363. *Plate* 158

Gonodontis bidentata, 278. *Plates* 114, 115

Graptolitha furcifera, 29, *Plates* 8, 13 ; *lamda*, 30, *Plate* 13 ; *ornithopus*, 31, *Plate* 12

Grass Emerald, 101. *Plates* 38, 41

Grass Rivulet, 209. *Plates* 83, 84

Grass Wave, 332. *Plate* 144

Great Oak Beauty, 308. *Plate* 135

Green Carpet, 185. *Plate* 75

Green Pug, 252. *Plate* 61

Grey Birch, 316. *Plate* 137

Grey Carpet, 148. *Plate* 55

Grey Mountain Carpet, 191. *Plate* 80

Grey Pine Carpet, 175. *Plates* 70, 71

Grey Pug, 237. *Plates* 92, 97

Grey Scalloped Bar, 329. *Plates* 142, 144

Grey Shoulder-knot, 31. *Plate* 12

Gymnoscelis pumilata, 250. *Plate* 99

HAPALOTIS fasciana, 57. *Plate* 21

Haworth's Pug, 242. *Plates* 90, 98

Heart Moth, 1. *Plate* 2

Heath Rivulet, 209. *Plate* 83

Heliaca tenebrata, 46. *Plate* 17

Heliothis armigera, 52, *Plates* 19, 20 ; *dipsacea*, 48, *Plate* 19 ; *peltigera*, 50, *Plates* 19, 20 ; *scutosa*, 49, *Plate* 19

Hemerophila abruptaria, 303. *Plates* 130, 133, 134

Hemithea strigata, 107. *Plates* 41, 43

Hepialidæ, 360

Hepialus fusconebulosa, 362, *Plate* 158 ; *hecta*, 363, *Plate* 158 ; *humuli*, 360, *Plates* 157, 159 ; *lupulina*, 363, *Plates* 158, 159 ; *sylvina*, 361 ; *Plates* 157, 159 ; *velleda*, 362

Herald, 63. *Plates* 22, 25

Herminia cribralis, 90, *Plate* 35 ; *cribrumalis*, 90, *Plate* 35 ; *derivalis*, 90, *Plates* 34, 35

Heterogena asella, 346, *Plates* 149, 153 ; *limacodes*, 345, *Plates* 149, 153

Himera pennaria, 279. *Plates* 114, 116

Hoporina croceago, 22. *Plates* 6, 10

Hornet Moth, 350. *Plate* 154

Horse Chestnut, 318. *Plates* 137, 140

Hybernia aurantiaria, 291, *Plates* 120, 125 ; *defoliaria*, 293, *Plates* 122, 125 ; *leucophæaria*, 290, *Plate* 120 ; *marginaria*, 292, *Plates* 120, 125 ; *rupicapraria*, 289, *Plate* 120

Hydrelia uncula, 58. *Plate* 21

Hydriomena elutata, 213 ; *furcata*, 213, *Plates* 86,87 ; *impluviata*, 214, *Plates* 86, 87 ; *ruberata*, 215, *Plate* 86

Hydriomeninæ, 141

Hygrochroa syringaria, 277. *Plates* 112, 115

Hylaea prosapiaria, 269. *Plates*, 106, 108

Hypena obsitalis, 93, *Plate* 36 ; *proboscidalis*, 93, *Plates* 35, 37 ; *rostralis*, 94, *Plates* 35, 37

Hypeninæ, 85

Hypenodes albistrigalis, 94, *Plate* 36 ; *costæstrigalis*, 25, *Plate* 36 ; *tænialis*, 94, *Plate* 36

Hyria muricata, 109. *Plate* 45

INO geryon, 343, *Plate* 147 ; *globulariæ*, 342, *Plate* 147 ; *statices*, 342, *Plates* 145, 147

Iodis lactearia, 107. *Plates* 43, 44

Isle of Wight Wave, 115. *Plate* 45

Itame wauaria, 326. *Plates* 142, 143

JASIONE Pug, 233. *Plate* 95

July Highflyer, 213. *Plates* 86, 87

Juniper Carpet, 177. *Plate* 70

Juniper Pug, 249. *Plate* 99

LACE Border, 123. *Plate* 46

Lampropteryx suffumata, 178. *Plates* 72, 74

Larch Pug, 236. *Plate* 97

Large Emerald, 102. *Plates* 40, 42

Large Red-belted Clearwing, 357. *Plate* 155

Large Thorn, 270. *Plates* 109, 110, 134

Large Twin-spot Carpet, 179. *Plate* 72

Laspeyria flexula, 85. *Plate* 36

Latticed Heath, 328. *Plate* 143

Lead Belle, 143. *Plate* 54

Lead-coloured Pug, 244. *Plate* 98

Least Carpet, 110. *Plates* 45, 48

INDEX. 375

Leopard Moth, 348. *Plates* 152, 153
Leptomeris. See *Acidalia*
Lesser Belle, 89. *Plates* 35, 39
Lesser Cream Wave, 124. *Plate* 49
Lesser-spotted Pinion, 3. *Plate* 2
Leucanitis stolida, 77
Lewes Wave, 126. *Plate* 49
Ligdia adustata, 263. *Plates* 105, 107
Light Crimson Underwing, 82. *Plate* 32
Light Emerald, 270. *Plates* 106, 108
Light Orange Underwing, 89. *Plates* 38, 39
Lilac Beauty, 277. *Plates* 112, 115
Lime-speck Pug, 222. *Plates* 92, 93
Ling Pug, 231. *Plate* 95
Lithomoia solidaginis, 32. *Plate* 12
Lithophane semibrunnea, 28, *Plate* 12 ; *socia,* 29, *Plate* 12
Lithostege griseata, 148. *Plate* 55
Little Emerald, 107. *Plates* 43, 44
Little Thorn, 285. *Plates* 119, 121
Lobophora carpinata, 153, *Plates* 57, 59 ; *halterata,* 155, *Plate* 57 ; *polycommata,* 152, *Plates* 57, 59 ; *sexalisata,* 156, *Plate* 58 ; *viretata,* 153, *Plate* 58
Lomaspilis marginata, 262. *Plates* 105, 107
Lozogramma petraria, 327. *Plate* 143
Lunar Double-stripe, 77. *Plate* 29
Lunar Hornet, *Plate* 154
Lunar-spotted Pinion, 2. *Plate* 2
Lunar Thorn, 276. *Plates* 112, 113
Lunar Underwing, 11. *Plate* 7
Lycia hirtaria, 299. *Plates* 124, 128
Lygris associata, 167, *Plates* 65, 67 ; *populata,* 166, *Plate* 63 ; *prunata,* 164, *Plates* 63, 67 ; *reticulata,* 163, *Plates* 61, 64 ; *testata,* 165, *Plates* 63, 67.
Lythria purpuraria, 142

MADOPA salicalis, 89. *Plates,* 35, 39

Magpie, 260. *Plates* 103, 104
Maiden's Blush, 136. *Plate* 53
Malenydris didymata, 187, *Plate* 77 ; *multistrigaria,* 186, *Plates* 73, 77 ; *salicata,* 186, *Plates* 73, 75
Mallow, 143. *Plates* 52, 54
Manchester Treble-bar, 150. *Plate* 55
Many-lined Moth, 256. *Plate* 102
Maple Pug, 246. *Plate* 98
Map-winged Swift.
Marbled Clover, 48. *Plate* 19
Marbled Pug, 225. *Plate* 93
Marbled White-Spot, 57. *Plate* 21
March Moth, 294. *Plates* 122, 125
Marsh Carpet, 172. *Plate* 68
Marsh Oblique-barred, 96. *Plate* 36
Marsh Pug, 244. *Plate* 98
May Highflyer, 214. *Plates* 86, 87
Melanthia procellata, 204. *Plate* 82
Mellinia gilvago, 22, *Plate* 10 ; *ocellaris,* 22, *Plate* 10
Mesogona acetosellæ, 9
Mesoleuca albicillata, 202, *Plates* 76, 82 ; *bicolorata,* 204, *Plate* 82 ; *ocellata,* 203, *Plate* 82
Mesotype virgata, 146. *Plate* 54
Metrocampa margaritaria, 270. *Plates* 106, 108
Minoa murinata, 146. *Plate* 55
Mocha, 138. *Plates* 51, 53
Mother Shipton, 75. *Plates* 26, 30
Mottled Beauty, 307. *Plates* 131, 132, 134
Mottled Grey, 186. *Plates* 73, 75
Mottled Pug, 248. *Plate* 99
Mottled Umber, 293. *Plates* 122, 125
Mullein, 36. *Plates* 15, 18
Mullein Wave, 125. *Plate* 49
Mysticoptera. See *Lobophora*

NARROW-BORDERED Five-Spot Burnet, 339. *Plates* 145, 147
Narrow-winged Pug, 247. *Plate* 99
Nemoria viridata, 106. *Plates* 43, 44
Netted Carpet, 163. *Plates* 61, 64

Netted Mountain Moth, 322. *Plate 141*

Netted Pug, 227. *Plates 92, 93*

New Forest Burnet, 336. *Plates 146, 148*

Ni, 70. *Plates 26, 28*

Nonconformist, 30. *Plate 13*

Northern Spinach, 166. *Plate 63.*

Northern Winter-Moth, 157. *Plate 58*

November Moth, 188. *Plates 76, 78*

Numeria pulveraria, 268. *Plates 106, 108*

Nyssia lapponaria, 297, *Plate 126; zonaria*, 298, *Plates 124, 126*

OAK Beauty, 300. *Plates 127, 128*

Oak-tree Pug, 248. *Plate 99*

Oblique Carpet, 257. *Plate 102*

Oblique Striped, 146. *Plate 54*

Ochreous Pug, 226. *Plate 96*

Ochria aurago, 18. *Plate 10*

Ochyria. See Coremia.

Odezia atrata, 147. *Plate 55*

Olive, 9. *Plate 4*

Olive Crescent, 88. *Plate 36*

Omphaloscelis lunosa, 11. *Plate 7*

Ophiusa stolida, 77

Opisthograptis luteolata, 283. *Plate 117*

Oporabia autumnata, 189, *Plate 78; dilutata*, 188, *Plates 76, 78; filigrammaria*, 190, *Plate 77*

Orange Moth, 280. *Plates 117, 118*

Orange Sallow, 17. *Plate 10*

Orange Swift, 361. *Plates 157, 159*

Orange-tailed Clearwing, 353. *Plate 156*

Orange Underwing, 97. *Plates 38, 39*

Orange Upperwing, 22. *Plates 6, 10*

Orrhodia erythrocephala, 23, *Plate 11; ligula*, 25, *Plate 11; rubiginea*, 26, *Plates 6, 11; vaccinii*, 24, *Plate 11*

Ortholitha bipunctaria, 145, *Plates 52, 54; cervinata*, 143, *Plates 52,* 54; *limitata*, 144, *Plates 52, 54; mœniata*, 145; *plumbaria*, 143, *Plate 54*

Orthosia. See Amathes.

Ourapteryx sambucaria, 282. *Plates 117, 118*

PACHYCNEMA hippocastanaria, 318. *Plates 137, 140*

Pachys betularia, 301, *Plates 128, 129; strataria*, 300, *Plates 127, 128*

Pale Brindled Beauty, 295. *Plates 122, 126*

Pale-lemon Sallow, 22. *Plate 10*

Pale Oak Beauty, 309. *Plate 135*

Pale Pinion, 29. *Plate 12*

Pale Shoulder, 53. *Plate 19*

Parascotia fuliginaria, 86. *Plate 36*

Peacock, 287. *Plate 119*

Pease Blossom, 47. *Plate 17*

Pechypogon barbalis, 91. *Plate 35*

Pelurga comitata, 254. *Plate 102*

Peppered Moth, 301. *Plates 128, 129*

Percnoptilota fluviata, 258. *Plate 102*

Perconia strigillaria, 332. *Plate 144*

Perizoma affinitata, 205, *Plate 83; albulata*, 208, *Plates 83, 84; alchemillata*, 206, *Plate 83; blandiata*, 210, *Plate 83; bifasciata*, 208, *Plate 83; flavofasciata*, 207, *Plate 85; minorata*, 209, *Plate 83; tæniata*, 211, *Plate 85*

Phasiane petraria, 327. *Plate 143*

Phibalapteryx lapidata, 255, *Plate 102; polygrammata*, 256, *Plate 102; tersata*, 257, *Plate 102; vitalbata*, 256, *Plate 102*

Phigalia pedaria, 295. *Plates 122, 126*

Philereme. See Scotosia.

Phœnix, 164. *Plates 63, 67*

Phragmatæcia castaneæ, 349. *Plate 153*

Pimpinel Pug, 228. *Plate* 95
Pine Carpet, 176. *Plates* 70, 71
Pinion-spotted Pug, 226. *Plate* 96
Pinion-streaked Snout, 95. *Plate* 36
Pink-barred Sallow, 19. *Plates* 6, 10
Plain Golden Y, 69. *Plate* 24
Plain Pug, 237. *Plates* 94, 97
Plain Wave, 119. *Plates* 46, 47
Plastenis retusa, 9, *Plate* 4 ; *subtusa*, 9, *Plate* 4
Plusia bractea, 67, *Plate* 24 ; *chrysitis*, 65, *Plate* 22 ; *chryson*, 66, *Plate* 24 ; *festucæ*, 68, *Plate* 24 ; *gamma*, 72, *Plate* 26 ; *interrogationis*, 73, *Plates* 26, 28 ; *iota*, 69, *Plate* 24 ; *moneta*, 64, *Plates* 22, 27 ; *ni*, 70, *Plates* 26, 28 ; *pulchrina*, 70, *Plate* 24
Portland Ribbon Wave, 118. *Plate* 46
Pretty Chalk Carpet, 204. *Plate* 82
Pretty Pinion, 210. *Plate* 83
Prothymnia viridaria, 61. *Plates* 21, 25
Pseudophia lunaris, 77. *Plate* 29
Pseudoterpna pruinata, 101. *Plates* 38, 41
Psodos coracina, 321. *Plate* 139
Ptychopoda. See *Acidalia*
Purple Bar, 203. *Plate* 82
Purple-bordered Gold, 109. *Plate* 45
Purple Marbled, 55. *Plate* 21
Purple Thorn, 276. *Plates* 112, 113
Pylarge fumata, 131. *Plate* 5c
Pyrrhia umbra, 47. *Plates* 17, 20

RANNOCH Brindled Beauty, 297. *Plates* 126, 134
Rannoch Looper, 327. *Plate* 143
Red-belted Clearwing, 356. *Plate* 155
Red Carpet, 180. *Plate* 72
Red-green Carpet, 173. *Plate* 68
Red-headed Chestnut, 23. *Plate* 11
Red-line Quaker, 12. *Plates* 5, 7
Red Sword-grass, 35. *Plates* 8, 14

Red-tipped Clearwing, 357. *Plates* 155, 156
Red Twin-spot Carpet, 182. *Plate* 72
Red Underwing, 80. *Plates* 31, 33
Reed Leopard, 349. *Plate* 153
Rest Harrow Moth, 101. *Plate* 38
Rhagades globulariæ, 342. *Plate* 147
Riband Wave, 120. *Plates* 46, 47
Ringed Carpet, 304. *Plate* 130
Rivula sericealis, 60. *Plates* 21, 23
Rivulet, 205. *Plate* 83
Rosy Marbled, 59. *Plates* 21, 25
Rosy Wave, 128. *Plate* 49
Royal Mantle, 216. *Plate* 88
Ruddy High-flyer, 215. *Plate* 86
Rumia cratægata, 283. *Plate* 117
Rusty Wave, 111. *Plate* 45

SALLOW, 20. *Plates* 6, 10
Sandy Carpet, 207. *Plate* 85
Satellite, 27. *Plate* 12
Satin Carpet, 306. *Plates* 132, 138
Satin Wave, 117. *Plate* 45
Satyr Pug, 239. *Plate* 96
Scalloped Hazel, 278. *Plates* 114, 115
Scalloped Oak, 280. *Plates* 114, 116
Scallop Shell, 160. *Plates* 60, 62
Scarce Blackneck, 84. *Plate* 32
Scarce Bordered Straw, 52. *Plates* 19, 20
Scarce Burnished Brass, 66. *Plate* 24
Scarce Forester, 342. *Plate* 147
Scarce Pug, 238. *Plate* 97
Scarce Silver Y, 73. *Plates* 26, 28
Scarce Tissue, 159. *Plate* 60
Scarce Umber, 291. *Plates* 120, 125
Sciadion obscurata, 319. *Plates* 139, 140
Sciapteron tabaniformis, 351. *Plate* 154
Scodiona fagaria, 329. *Plates* 142, 144
Scoliopteryx libatrix, 63. *Plates* 22, 25
Scopelosoma satellitia, 27

Scorched Carpet, 263. *Plates* 105, 107

Scorched Wing, 282. *Plate* 117

Scoria lineata, 330. *Plate* 144

Scotch Annulet, 320. *Plate* 139

Scotch Burnet, 335. *Plate* 146

Scotosia rhamnata, 162, *Plate* 60 ; *vetulata*, 161, *Plate* 60

Selenia bilunaria, 274, *Plate* 112 ; *lunaria*, 276, *Plates* 112, 113 ; *tetralunaria*, 276, *Plates* 112, 113

Selidosema ericetaria, 325. *Plates* 142, 143

Semiothisa alternata, 288, *Plates* 119, 123 ; *liturata*, 288, *Plates* 61, 119, 123 ; *notata*, 287, *Plate* 219

September Thorn, 273. *Plate* 134

Seraphim, 155. *Plate* 57

Sesia andrenæformis, 353, *Plates* 1, 156 ; *chrysidiformis*, 359, *Plate* 155 ; *culiciformis*, 357, *Plate* 155 ; *formiciformis*, 357, *Plates* 155, 156 ; *ichneumoniformis*, 358, *Plate* 155 ; *muscæformis*, 359, *Plate* 155 ; *myopæformis*, 356, *Plate* 155 ; *scoliæformis*, 352, *Plates* 154, 156 ; *spheciformis*, 353, *Plate* 154 ; *tipuliformis*, 354, *Plates* 154, 156 ; *vespiformis*, 355, *Plate* 155

Sesiidæ, 350

Shaded Broad-bar, 144. *Plates* 52, 54

Shaded Pug, 242. *Plate* 97

Shark, 40. *Plate* 16

Sharp-angled Carpet, 199. *Plate* 82

Sharp-angled Peacock, 288. *Plates* 119, 123

Shoulder Stripe, 217. *Plates* 88, 89

Silky Wave, 116. *Plate* 45

Silver Barred, 57. *Plate* 21

Silver-ground Carpet, 193. *Plate* 80

Silver Hook, 58. *Plate* 21

Silver Y, 72. *Plate* 26

Single Dotted Wave, 121. *Plates* 46, 47

Six-belted Clearwing, 358. *Plate* 155

Six-spot Burnet, 340. *Plates* 145, 147, 148

Slender Pug, 245. *Plate* 98

Slender-striped Rufous, 255. *Plate* 102

Sloe Carpet, 264. *Plate* 107

Small Argent and Sable, 198. *Plate* 81

Small Autumnal Carpet, 190. *Plate* 77

Small Blood-vein, 129. *Plates* 48, 49

Small Brindled Beauty, 296. *Plates* 124, 126

Small Dark Yellow Underwing, 44. *Plate* 17

Small Dusty Wave, 112. *Plate* 45

Small Emerald, 103. *Plates* 40, 44

Small Fan-foot, 88. *Plates* 34, 35

Small Fan-footed Wave, 121. *Plate* 46

Small Grass Emerald, 106. *Plates* 43, 44

Small Marbled, 56. *Plate* 21

Small Phœnix, 162. *Plate* 63

Small Purple Barred, 61. *Plates* 21, 25

Small Rivulet, 206. *Plate* 83

Small Scallop, 133. *Plate* 50

Small Seraphim, 156. *Plate* 58

Small Waved Umber, 256. *Plate* 102

Small White Wave, 220. *Plates* 90, 91

Small Yellow Underwing, 46. *Plate* 17

Small Yellow Wave, 220. *Plate* 91

Smoky Wave, 131. *Plate* 50

Snout, 93. *Plates* 35, 37

Speckled Beauty, 310. *Plate* 134

Speckled Yellow, 286. *Plates* 61, 119

Spectacle, 74. *Plate* 22

Spinach Moth, 167. *Plates* 65, 67

Spotted Clover, 49. *Plate* 19

Spotted Sulphur, 62. *Plate* 21

Spring Usher, 290. *Plate* 120

Square Spot, 315. *Plates* 137, 138

Star-wort, 39. *Plates* 15, 18

Sterrha sacraria, 141. *Plate* 54

Straw Belle, 330. *Plate* 144
Straw Dot, 60. *Plate* 21
Streak, 150. *Plates* 56, 57
Streamer, 219. *Plates* 88, 89
Strenia clathrata, 328. *Plate* 143
Striped Lychnis, 38. *Plates* 15, 18
Striped Twin-spot Carpet, 186. *Plates* 73, 75
Sub-angled Wave, 127. *Plate* 49
Suspected, 7. *Plate* 4
Swallow-tailed, 282. *Plates* 117, 118
Sword-grass, 34. *Plate* 14
Synopsia abruptaria, 303, *Plates* 130, 133, 134

TARACHE lucida, var. *albicollis,* 53, *Plate* 19; *luctuosa,* 54, *Plates* 19, 23
Tawny-barred Angle, 288. *Plates* 61, 119, 123
Tawny Pinion, 28. *Plate* 12
Tawny-speckled Pug, 241. *Plate* 97
Tawny Wave, 130. *Plate* 50
Tephrosia bistortata, 312, *Plates* 136, 138; *consonaria,* 315, *Plates* 137, 138; *luridata,* 314, *Plate* 137; *punctularia,* 316, *Plate* 137
Thalera fimbrialis, 108
Thalpochares ostrina, 55, *Plate* 21; *parva,* 56, *Plate* 21; *paula,* 56; *Plate* 21
Thamnonoma wauaria, 326, *Plates* 142, 143; *brunneata,* 327, *Plate* 143
Thera cognata, 176, *Plate* 70; *firmata,* 176, *Plates* 70, 71; *juniperata,* 177, *Plate* 70; *variata,* 175, *Plates* 70, 71
Tholomiges turfosalis, 96. *Plate* 36
Thrift Clearwing, 359. *Plate* 155
Thyme Pug, 229. *Plate* 95
Timandra amata, 134. *Plate* 50
Tissue, 158. *Plates* 60, 62
Toadflax Pug, 224. *Plate* 93
Toxocampa craccæ, 84, *Plate* 32; *pastinum,* 83, *Plate* 32
Transparent Burnet, 334. *Plates* 145, 146

Treble-bar, 149. *Plate* 55
Treble Brown Spot, 122. *Plate* 46
Triangle, 346. *Plates* 149, 153
Trichopteryx. See *Lobophora*
Triphosa dubitata, 158. *Plates* 60, 62
Triple-spotted Pug, 236. *Plate* 97
Trochilium apiformis, 350, *Plate* 154; *crabroniformis,* 351. *Plate* 154
Twin-spot Carpet, 187. *Plate* 77

VALERIAN Pug, 243. *Plate* 98
Venilia maculata, 286. *Plates* 61, 119
Venusia cambrica, 190. *Plate* 78
Vestal, 141. *Plate* 54
V-moth, 326. *Plates* 142, 143
V-Pug, 251. *Plates* 99, 100

WATER Betony, 37. *Plate* 15
Water Carpet, 178. *Plates* 72, 74
Waved Black, 86. *Plate* 36
Waved Carpet, 221. *Plate* 91
Waved Umber, 303. *Plates* 130, 133, 134
Weaver's Wave, 109. *Plate* 45
Welsh Clearwing, 352. *Plates* 154, 156
Welsh Wave, 190. *Plate* 78
White-barred Clearwing, 353. *Plate* 154
White-line Snout, 94. *Plate* 36
White-pinion Spotted, 265. *Plate* 107
White-spotted Pinion, 4. *Plates* 2, 3
White-spotted Pug, 234. *Plates* 92, 97
Willow Beauty, 305. *Plates* 130, 131
Winter Moth, 156. *Plate* 58
Wood Carpet, 196. *Plates* 79, 81
Wormwood, 42. *Plate* 16
Wormwood Pug, 231. *Plate* 95

XANTHIA aurago, 18, *Plate* 10; *citrago,* 17, *Plate* 10; *flavago,* 19, *Plates* 6, 10; *fulvago,* 20, *Plates* 6, 10; *gilvago,* 21, *Plate* 10; *lutea,*

19, *Plates* 6, 10; *ocellaris*, 22, *Plate* 10

Xantholeuca croceago, 22. *Plates* 6, 10

Xanthorhoë fluctuata, 194, *Plates* 61, 80; *galiata*, 195, *Plates* 79, 81; *montanata*, 193, *Plate* 80; *picata*, 200, *Plate* 82; *rivata*, 196, *Plates* 79, 81; *sociata*, 197, *Plates* 79, 81; *tristata*, 198, *Plate* 81; *unangulata*, 199, *Plate* 82

Xylina. See *Lithophane* and *Graptolitha*.

Xylocampa areola, 33. *Plates* 8, 12

YELLOW Belle, 331. *Plates* 142, 144

Yellow-barred Brindle, 153. *Plate* 58

Yellow-legged Clearwing, 355. *Plate* 155

Yellow-line Quaker, 13. *Plate* 7

Yellow-ringed Carpet, 192. *Plate* 80

Yellow Shell, 212. *Plates* 61, 84, 85

ZANCLOGNATHA emortualis, 88, *Plate* 36; *grisealis*, 88, *Plates* 34, 35; *tarsipennalis*, 87, *Plates* 34, 35

Zeuzera pyrina, 348. *Plates* 152, 153

Zygæna achilleæ, 335, *Plate* 1; *exulans*, 335, *Plate* 146; *filipendulæ*, 340, *Plates* 145, 147, 148; *loniceræ*, 339, *Plates* 145, 147; *meliloti*, 336, *Plates* 146, 148: *purpuralis*, 334, *Plates*, 145, 146; *trifolii*, 337, *Plates* 145, 146, 148

Zygænidæ, 333

MOTHS.—Series II.

OLD EDITION.		NEW EDITION.
For *Dyschorista fissipuncta*	read	*Sidemia fissipuncta*
„ *Lithomoia solidaginis*	„	*Cloantha solidaginis*
„ *Hapalotis fasciana*	„	*Lithacodia fasciana*
„ *Erastria venustula*	„	*Monodes venustula*
„ *Pseudophia lunaris*	„	*Minucia lunaris*
„ *Lygris reticulata*	„	*Eustroma reticulata*
„ *Epione advenaria*	„	*Cepphis advenaria*

SPECIAL INDEX.

—◆—

abbreviata (*Eupithecia*), 248
abietaria (*Eupithecia*), 306, 312
abrotani (*Cucullia*), 43
abruptaria (*Hemerophila*), 303
absinthiata (*Eupithecia*), 231
absinthii (*Cucullia*), 42, 43
acetosellæ (*Mesogona*), 9
achilleæ (*Zygæna*), 334
Acidaliinæ, 109
adæquata (*Perizoma*), 210
adustata (*Ligdia*), 263
advenaria (*Cepphis*), 285
advenaria (*Epione*), 285
Ægeriadæ, 350
ærosa (*Eustroma*), 164
æstiva (*Selenia*), 276
æstivaria (*Hemithea*), 108
æscularia (*Anisopteryx*), 294
affinis (*Calymnia*), 3
affinitata (*Perizoma*), 205
agrotoides (*Omphaloselis*), 12
albicillata (*Mesoleuca*), 202
albicollis (*Acontia*), 53
albidaria (*Scodonia*), 329
albilinea (*Lithacodia*), 57
albipunctata (*Eupithecia*), 234
albistrigalis (*Hypenodes*), 94
albocrenata (*Cidaria*), 170
albulata (*Perizoma*), 208
alchemillata (*Perizoma*), 206
alchymista (*Catephia*), 78
allantiformis (*Trochilium*), 354
alniaria (*Ennomos*), 272
alternata (*Semiothisa*), 288
alternata (*Xanthorhoë*), 198
amata (*Timandra*), 134
amniculata (*Xanthorhoë*), 199
ancilla (*Naclia*), 333
andrenæformis (*Sesia*), 333
angelicata (*Eupithecia*), 234, 239
angularia (*Cleora*), 310
angustifasciata (*Perizoma*), 211

annosata (*Entephria*), 191
annulata (*Ephyra*), 138
Anthrocera, 333
apiciaria (*Epione*), 284
apiformis (*Trochilium*), 350
approximata (*Cabera*), 267
æthiops (*Anarta*), 45
arceuthata (*Eupithecia*), 239
arctaria (*Perizoma*), 211
areola (*Xylocampa*), 33
argentula (*Bankia*), 57
argillacearia (*Gnophos*), 319
armigera (*Heliothis*), 52, 53
artemisiæ (*Cucullia*), 43
arundinis (*Macrogaster*), 349
avellana (*Limacodes*), 346
asella (*Heterogenea*), 346
asiliformis (*Ægeria*), 351
asiliformis (*Sesia*), 355
assimilata (*Eupithecia*), 230
associata (*Lygris*), 167
asteris (*Cucullia*), 39
atlantica (*Camptogramma*), 212
atomaria (*Ematurga*), 86, 324
atraria (*Eupithecia*), 233
atrata (*Odezia*), 147
atrifasciaria (*Sterrha*), 141
aurago (*Ochria*), 18
aurago (*Xanthia*), 18
aurantia (*Xanthia*), 20
aurantiago (*Cirrhia*), 17
aurantiaria (*Hybernia*), 291
auroraria (*Hyria*), 109
autumnaria (*Ennomos*), 270
autumnata (*Oporabia*), 188
aversata (*Acidalia*), 118, 120

badiata (*Anticlea*), 217
badiofasciata (*Calymnia*) 4
bandanæ (*Eupithecia*), 228
barbalis (*Pechipogon*), 91
basalis (*Zygæna*), 237

belgiaria (*Scodiona*), 329
bembeciformis (*Trochitium*), 351
berberata (*Anticlea*), 218
betularia (*Pachys*), 301
biangulata (*Euphyia*), 200
bicolorata (*Mesoleuca*), 204
bidentata (*Gonodontis*), 278
bifasciata (*Perizoma*), 208
bilineata (*Camptogramma*), 212
bilunaria (*Selenia*), 274
bimaculata (*Bapta*), 265
biobsoleta (*Ephyra*), 138
bipunctaria (*Ortholitha*), 145
bisetata (*Acidalia*), 121
bistortata (*Tephrosia*), 312
biundularia (*Tephrosia*), 312
blandiata (*Perizoma*), 210
blomeri (*Asthena*), 222
Boarmiinæ, 259
boreata (*Cheimatobia*), 157
borealis (*Amathes*), 16
bractea (*Plusia*), 67
brassicæ (*Plusia*), 71
Brephidæ, 97
brightoni (*Ephyra*), 137
brumata (*Cheimatobia*), 156
brunnea (*Calocampa*), 35
brunnea (*Eupsilia*), 27
brunneata (*Hemerophila*), 303
brunneata (*Thamnonoma*), 327

cærulescens (*Catocala*), 81
cæsiata (*Entiphria*), 191
calceata (*Gnophos*), 319
callunaria (*Eupithecia*), 239
cambrica (*Venusia*), 190
campanulata (*Eupithecia*), 233
candidata (*Asthena*), 220
carbonaria (*Fidonia*), 322, 324
carpinaria (*Ennomos*), 271
carpinata (*Lobophora*), 153
carthami (*Thalpochares*), 55
castaneæ (*Phragmatæcia*), 349
castigata (*Eupithecia*), 237
cauchyata (*Eupithecia*), 240
chærophyllata (*Odezia*), 148
chamomillæ (*Cucullia*), 40
christyi (*Oporabia*), 188
chrysanthemi (*Cucullia*), 41
chrysanthemi (*Zygæna*), 340
chrysidiformis (*Sesia*), 359
chrysitis (*Plusia*), 65
chryson (*Plusia*), 66
cineræ (*Eupithecia*), 245
cineraria (*Mniophila*), 322
cinerascens (*Cloantha*), 32
cinereata (*Hydriomena*), 213
cinerata (*Triphosa*), 158

cinctaria (*Boarmia*), 304
circellaris (*Amathes*), 14
circellaris (*Orthosia*), 14
circellata (*Acidalia*), 113
circuitaria (*Acidalia*), 111
citrago (*Cirrhia*), 17
citrago (*Xanthia*), 17
citrina (*Zygæna*), 339
centrago (*Cirrhœdia*), 10
centumnotata (*Cidaria*), 170
cerago (*Xanthia*), 20
cervinata (*Eucosmia*), 159
cervinata (*Ortholitha*), 143
clathrata (*Chiasmia*), 328
clathrata (*Strenia*), 328
coarctata (*Coremia*), 181
coarctata (*Mesoleuca*), 203
coarctata (*Perizoma*), 210
Cochlidiidæ, 344
cognata (*Thera*), 176
comitata (*Pelurga*), 254
commanotata (*Cidaria*), 170
concinnata (*Cidaria*), 170
conformis (*Xylina*), 30
confusa (*Zygæna*), 336
congener (*Dyschorista*), 7
conjunctaria (*Phibalapteryx*), 256
consignata (*Eupithecia*), 227
consobrinaria (*Boarmia*), 305
consonaria (*Tephrosia*), 312, 315
consortaria (*Boarmia*), 309
constrictata (*Eupithecia*), 229
contiguaria (*Acidalia*), 109, 111
conversaria (*Boarmia*), 307
coracina (*Psodos*), 321
corculata (*Coremia*), 182
cordigera (*Anarta*), 44
coronata (*Chloroclystis*), 251
corticea (*Dyschorista*), 8
corusca (*Calymnia*), 2
corylaria (*Angerona*), 280
corylata (*Cidaria*), 169
Cossidæ, 347
cossus (*Cossus*), 347
costæstrigalis (*Hypenodes*), 95
costovata (*Xanthorhoë*), 194
crabroniformis (*Trochilium*), 351
craccæ (*Toxocampa*), 84
cratægata (*Rumia*), 283
crepuscularia (*Tephrosia*), 312
cribralis (*Herminia*), 90
cribrumalis (*Herminia*), 90
croceago (*Hoporina*), 22
croceago (*Xantholeuca*), 22
cucullata (*Anticlea*), 216
culiciformis (*Sesia*), 357
cuneata (*Geometra*), 102
curzoni (*Eupithecia*), 236

Cyclophora, 136
cydoniata (*Chloroclystis*), 252
cynipiformis (*Sesia*), 355
cythisaria (*Pseudoterpna*), 101
cytisaria (*Pseudoterpna*) 101
cytisi (*Zygæna*), 340

dartfordi (*Ennomos*), 271
dealbata (*Scoria*), 330
debiliata (*Chloroclystis*), 253
decolorata (*Perizoma*), 207
decoraria (*Ephyra*), 140
defoliaria (*Hybernia*), 293
degeneraria (*Acidalia*), 118
degenerata (*Xantherol*), 197
delamerensis (*Tephrosia*), 313
deleta (*Hypena*), 93
delphinii (*Chariclea*), 47
delunaria (*Selenia*), 276
demolita (*Eulype*), 201
denotata (*Eupithecia*), 232
derivalis (*Herminia*), 89, 90
derivata (*Anticlea*), 219
designata (*Coremia*), 183
destrigaria (*Boarmia*), 307
diffinis (*Calymnia*), 4
dilutaria (*Acidalia*), 114, 116
dilutata (*Oporabia*), 188
dimidiata (*Acidalia*), 121
dipsacea (*Heliothis*), 48
disparata (*Eupithecia*), 240
distinctaria (*Eupithecia*), 229
dodoneata (*Eupithecia*), 248
dolabraria (*Eurymene*), 282
doubledayaria (*Pachys*), 301
dubitata (*Triphosa*), 158

eboracea (*Zygæna*), 339
eburnata (*Dosithea*), 110
effusaria (*Cidaria*), 170
electa (*Catocala*), 79
elinguaria (*Crocallis*), 280
elutata (*Hydriomena*), 212
emarginata (*Ania*), 133
emortualis (*Sophronia*), 88
emortualis (*Zanclognatha*), 88
emutaria (*Acidalia*), 128
ericetata (*Perizoma*), 209
ericetaria (*Selidosema*), 325
erosaria (*Ennomos*), 273
erythrocephala (*Conistra*), 23
erythrocephala (*Orrhodia*), 23
exalbidata (*Eupithecia*), 241
exanthemata (*Cabera*), 267
excelsa (*Plusia*), 68
exiguata (*Eupithecia*), 248
exoleta (*Calocampa*), 34
expallidata (*Eupithecia*), 230

extensaria (*Eupithecia*), 238
exulans (*Zygæna*), 335

fagaria (*Scodiona*), 329
fasciana (*Erastria*), 57
fasciana (*Lithacodia*), 57
fasciata (*Ephyra*), 137
fasciata (*Gnophos*), 319
fasciata (*Lobophora*), 153
ferrea (*Amathes*), 16
ferrugata (*Coremia*), 182
ferruginago (*Dicycla*), 1
ferruginea (*Amathes*), 14
ferruginea (*Cidaria*), 172
festucæ (*Plusia*), 68
filigrammaria (*Oporabia*), 190
filipendulæ (*Zygæna*), 336, 340
fimbrialis (*Thalera*), 108
fimbriolata (*Acidalia*), 121
firmata (*Thera*), 176
fissipuncta (*Dyschorista*), 8
fissipuncta (*Sidemia*), 8
flava (*Zygæna*), 336, 340
flavago (*Xanthia*), 19
flavescens (*Bupalus*), 325
flavescens (*Xanthia*), 20
flavicinctata (*Entephria*), 192
flavofasciata (*Perizoma*), 207
flexula (*Laspeyria*), 85
fluctuata (*Xanthorhoë*), 194
fluviata (*Percnoptilota*), 258
fontis (*Bomolocha*), 92
formicæformis (*Sesia*), 357
fraxinata (*Eupithecia*), 247
fraxini (*Catocala*), 78
fucata (*Ochria*), 18
fuliginaria (*Parascotia*), 86
fulvago (*Xanthia*), 20
fulvata (*Cidaria*), 169
fumata (*Acidalia*), 131
fumata (*Fidonia*), 323
fumosa (*Mesoleuca*), 204
fumosæ (*Eupithecia*), 227
furcata (*Hydriomena*), 213
furcifera (*Graptolitha*), 29
furcifera (*Xylina*), 29
fusca (*Prothymnia*), 61
fuscantaria (*Ennomos*), 273
fuscaria (*Thamnonoma*), 326
fuscata (*Hybernia*), 292
fusconebulosa (*Hepialus*), 362
fusco-undata (*Hydriomena*), 213
fuscovenosa (*Acidalia*), 114

galiata (*Xanthorhoë*), 195
gallicus (*Hepialus*), 362
gamma (*Plusia*), 71, 72
gelata (*Entephria*), 191

gemmaria (Boarmia), 305
Geometridæ, 99
Geometrinæ, 101
germana (Cloantha), 33
geryon (Ino), 342, 343
gilvago (Mellinia), 21
gilvago (Xanthia), 21
gilvaria (Aspilates), 330
glabra (Orrhodia), 23, 24
glabraria (Cleora), 311, 317
glaciata (Entephria), 191
globularia (Ino), 342
glycirrhizæ (Zygæna), 337
glyphica (Euclidia), 76
gnaphalii (Cucullia), 41
Gonopterinæ, 63
goodwini (Asthena), 221
goossensiata (Eupithecia), 231
gracilis (Plastenis), 9
grisealis (Zanclognatha), 88
grisearia (Aspilates), 332
griseata (Lithostege), 148
grossulariata (Abraxas), 260
gueneata (Oporabia), 189

halterata (Lobophora), 155
hastata (Eulype), 201
hastulata (Eulype), 201
haworthiata (Eupithecia), 142
hazeleighensis (Abraxas), 260
hebudium (Eupithecia), 223
hebudium (Perizoma), 208
hecta (Hepialus), 363
helveticaria (Eupithecia), 239
helvola (Amathes), 15
Hepialidæ, 360
herbariata (Acidalia), 111
herefordi (Pachys), 301
hethlandica (Coremia), 180
hethlandica (Hepialus), 360
hibernica (Camptogramma), 213
hippocastanaria (Pachycnema), 318
hippocrepidis (Zygæna), 341
hirtaria (Lycia), 299
hispidaria (Apocheima), 296
holosericata (Acidalia), 114, 116
humidalis (Hypenodes), 96
humiliata (Acidalia), 115
humilis (Omphaloscelis), 12
humperti (Boarmia), 309
humuli (Hepialus), 360
Hydriomeninæ, 141
hyemata (Cheimatobia), 157
Hypeninæ, 85

ichneumoniformis (Sesia), 358
imbutata (Carsia), 150
imitaria (Acidalia), 129

immanata (Cidaria), 171
immorata (Acidalia), 126
immutata (Acidalia), 124
impluviata (Hydriomena), 214
indigata (Eupithecia), 226
infuscata (Camptogramma), 212
infuscata (Hydriomena), 213
innotata (Eupithecia), 246
inornata (Acidalia), 119
inscripta (Plusia), 69
insigniata (Eupithecia), 226
insulata (Eustroma), 162
insulicola (Lygris), 165
interbata (Eupithecia), 246
interjectaria (Acidalia), 114
intermedia (Asthena), 221
interrogationis (Plusia), 73
interrupta (Zygæna), 334
iota (Plusia), 69
irriguata (Eupithecia), 225
isogrammaria (Eupithecia), 243
isolata (Camptogramma), 213

jasoneata (Eupithecia), 233
jubata (Cleora), 311
juliaria (Selenia), 274
juncta (Plusia), 65
juniperata (Thera), 177

knautiata (Eupithecia), 232

labda (Sterrha), 141
lactearia (Iodis), 107
lacticolor (Abraxas), 262
lacticolor (Opisthographis), 283
lamda (Graptolitha), 30
lamda (Xylina), 30
lapidata (Phibalapteryx), 255
lapponaria (Nyssia), 297
laricaria (Tephrosia), 312
lariceata (Eupithecia), 236
latericolor (Xantholeuca), 22
latifasciata (Oporabia), 188
leucomelas (Noctua), 78
leucophæaria (Hybernia), 290
libatrix (Scoliopteryx), 63
lichenaria (Cleora), 310
lignata (Coenocalpe), 256, 257
ligniperda (Cossus), 347
ligniperda (Trypanus), 347
ligula (Conistra), 25
ligula (Orrhodea), 25
limacodes (Cochlidion), 345
Limacodidæ, 344
limbaria (Fidonia), 323
limitata (Ortholitha), 144
linariata (Eupithecia), 224
linearia (Ephyra), 137

lineata (Scoria), 330
litura (Orthosia), 16
liturata (Semiothisa), 288
lonicera (Zygæna), 239
lota (Amathes), 12
lota (Orthosia), 12
lucida (Acontia), 53
lucida (Tarache), 53
luctuosa (Acontia), 54
luctuosa (Tarache), 54
lunaria (Selenia), 276
lunaris (Minucia), 77
lunaris (Ophiodes), 77
lunosa (Anchocelis), 11
lunosa (Omphaloscelis), 11
lupulina (Hepialus), 263
luridata (Tephrosia), 314
lutea (Abraxas), 260
lutea (Xanthia), 19
luteata (Asthena), 220
luteolata (Opisthograptis), 283
lutescens (Zygæna), 237
lychnidis (Amathes), 16
lychnidis (Orthosia), 16
lychnitis (Cucullia), 37, 38

macilenta (Amathes), 13, 14
macilenta (Orthosia), 13
maculata (Venilia), 286
mancuniata (Acidalia), 117
margaritaria (Metrocampa), 270
marginata (Lomaspilis), 262
marginata (Pyrrhia), 258
marginepunctata (Acidalia), 125
marmorata (Cidaria), 172
marmorinaria (Hybernia), 290
maritima (Heliothis), 49
mathewi (Nemoria), 106
melana (Oporabia), 188
melanopa (Anarta), 45
melanozona (Abraxas), 261
meliloti (Zygæna), 336
merularia (Hybernia), 290
mi (Euclidia), 74
miata (Cidaria), 174
minoides (Zygæna), 237
minorata (Perizoma), 209
minos (Zygæna), 334
minutata (Eupithecia), 232
mixta (Orrhodia), 24
mneste (Catocala), 82
moeniata (Ortholitha), 145
monacharia (Phigalia), 296
moneta (Plusia), 64
montanata (Xanthorhoë), 193
monticola (Perizoma), 210
multistrigaria (Malenydris), 186
mundata (Gnophos), 319
nunitata (Coremia), 180

muraria (Boarmia), 307
muricata (Hyria), 109
murinata (Minoa), 146
musauaria (Lygris), 166
muscæformis (Sesia), 359
myopæformis (Sesia), 356
myricaria (Cheimatobia), 157
myrillata (Gnophos), 320
myrtilli (Anarta), 44

nadeja (Plusia), 65
nanata (Eupithecia), 247
neapolisata (Xanthorhoë), 194
ni (Plusia), 70
nigra (Calymnia), 5
nigra (Malenydris), 187
nigrescens (Dyschorista), 7
nigricarius (Bupalus), 325
nigricata (Boarmia), 307
nigristriata (Entephria), 191
nigrofasciaria (Anticlea), 219
nigrofasciaria (Lomaspilis), 263
nigrofulvata (Semiothisa), 289
nigropuncta (Chloroclystis), 253
nigroroseata (Ephyra), 140
nigrosericeata (Chloroclystis), 252
niveata (Perizoma), 208
nostromata (Chiasmia), 310
notata (Macaria), 287
notata (Semiothisa), 287
notha (Brephos), 98
nubiginea (Zygæna), 334
nubilata (Malenydris), 187
nubilata (Eupithecia), 227

obeliscata (Thera), 175
obfuscaria (Gnophos), 320
obliterata (Ecubæca), 219
obliterata (Hydriomena), 213
obliterata (Thera), 175
oblongata (Eupithecia), 222
obscurata (Catocala), 81
obscurata (Entephria), 192
obscurata (Gnophos), 319
obscurata (Hybernia), 203
obscurata (Oporabia), 188
obscurata (Xanthorhoë), 198
obscuriorata (Gnophos), 319
obsitalis (Hypena), 93
obsoleta (Ephyra), 138
obsoleta (Percnoptilota), 258
obsoletaria (Ematurga), 324
ocellaris (Mellinia), 21, 22
ocellaris (Xanthia), 22
ocellata (Mesoleuca), 203
ochracæ (Eupithecia), 228
ochrata (Acidalia), 132
ochrea (Calymnia), 3
ochreago (Xanthia), 19

ochrearia (*Aspilates*), 331
ochrearia (*Pachys*), 302
ochroleucata (*Malenydris*), 187
olivacea (*Percnoptilota*), 258
olivata (*Amoebe*), 184
oo (*Dicycla*), 1
operaria (*Charissa*), 320
orbicularia (*Ephyra*), 139
orcadensis (*Eupithecia*), 228
ornata (*Acidalia*), 123
ornithopus (*Graptolitha*), 31
ornithopus (*Xylina*), 31
orobi (*Zygæna*), 237
osseata (*Acidalia*), 114, 115
ostrina (*Thalpochares*), 55
oxydata (*Eupithecia*), 241

paleacea (*Cosmia*), 5
palleago (*Mellinia*), 21
pallida (*Heliothis*), 50
pallidaria (*Acidalia*), 133
pallidaria (*Angerona*), 281
paludata (*Carsia*), 150
pantaria (*Abraxas*), 259
papilionaria (*Geometra*), 102
parallelaria (*Epione*), 284
parthenias (*Brephos*), 97
parva (*Thalpochares*), 56
parvilunaria (*Selenia*), 277
parvula (*Mesoleuca*), 204
pastinum (*Toxocampa*), 83
pastoraria (*Acidalia*), 125
paula (*Thalpochares*), 56
pedaria (*Phigalia*), 295
peltigera (*Heliothis*), 50
pendularia (*Ephyra*), 139
pennaria (*Himera*), 279
percontationis (*Plusia*), 69
percontatrix (*Plusia*), 70
perfumaria (*Boarmia*), 305
perfuscata (*Cidaria*), 170
pernotata (*Eupithecia*), 240
perochraria (*Acidalia*), 133
petraria (*Lozogramma*), 327
phegea (*Syntomis*), 333
phlogophagus (*Heliothis*), 49
picata (*Euphyia*), 200
piceata (*Lampropteryx*), 178
picketaria (*Angerona*), 281
pictaria (*Aleucis*), 264
pilosellæ (*Zygæna*), 334
pimpinellata (*Eupithecia*), 228
pinetaria (*Thamnonoma*), 327
piniaria (*Bupalus*,), 325
piperata (*Eupithecia*), 242
pistacina (*Amathes*), 16
plagiata (*Anaitis*), 149
plumaria (*Selidosema*), 325

plumbaria (*Ortholitha*), 143
plumbata (*Mesoleuca*), 204
plumbea (*Toxocampa*), 84
plumbeolata (*Eupithecia*), 244
polita (*Orrhodia*), 25
pollutaria (*Lomaspilis*), 262
polycommata (*Lobophora*), 152
polycommata (*Trichopteryx*), 152
polygrammata (*Phibalapteryx*), 256
populata (*Lygris*), 166
porata (*Ephyra*), 135
porrittii (*Lampropteryx*), 178
prasinaria (*Ellopia*), 269
probosidalis (*Hypena*), 93
procellata (*Melanthia*), 204
promissa (*Catocala*), 82
prosapiaria (*Ellopia*), 269
prospicuata (*Entephria*), 191
pruinata (*Pseudoterpna*), 101
prunaria (*Angerona*), 280
prunata (*Lygris*), 164
pulchellata (*Eupithecia*), 223
pulchrina (*Plusia*), 70
pulveraria (*Numeria*), 268
pumilata (*Gymnoscelis*), 250
punctaria (*Ephyra*), 136
punctularia (*Tephrosia*), 316
punica (*Amathes*), 15
purpuralis (*Zygæna*), 334, 336
purpuraria (*Lythria*), 142
pusaria (*Cabera*), 266
pusillata (*Eupithecia*), 225
pustulata (*Comibæna*), 104
pustulata (*Euchloris*), 104
pygmæata (*Eupithecia*), 244
pyraliata (*Cidaria*), 168
pyralina (*Calymnia*), 2
pyrina (*Zeuzera*), 348
pythonissata (*Cidaria*), 172

quadrifasciaria (*Coremia*), 179
Quadrifinæ, 64
quadrimaculata (*Venilia*), 286
quadripunctaria (*Fidonia*), 323
quercinaria (*Ennomos*), 271, 274

radiata (*Chiasmia*), 328
radiatalis (*Hypena*), 94
ramburi (*Zygæna*), 340
rebeli (*Boarmia*), 305
rectangulata (*Chloroclystis*), 252
remutaria (*Acidalia*), 124
renago (*Dicycla*), 1
repandata (*Boarmia*), 307
recticulata (*Eustroma*), 163
retusa (*Plastenis*), 9
rhamnata (*Scotosia*), 162
rhomboidaria (*Boarmia*), 305

ribeata (*Boarmia*), 307
rivata (*Xanthorhoë*), 196
roboraria (*Boarmia*), 308
rosea (*Plusia*), 73
rosea (*Xylocampa*), 33
rostralis (*Hypena*), 94
rotundaria (*Cabera*), 267
ruberata (*Hydriomena*), 215
rubidata (*Anticlea*), 218
rubiginata (*Acidalia*), 130
rubiginata (*Mesoleuca*), 204
rubiginea (*Dasycampa*), 26
rubiginea (*Orrhodia*), 26
rubricata (*Acidalia*), 130
rufa (*Amathes*), 17
rufa (*Calymnia*), 5
rufata (*Chesias*), 151
rufescens (*Anarta*), 44
rufescens (*Bomolocha*), 92
rufescens (*Xylina*), 29
rufifasciata (*Gymnoscelis*), 250
rufina (*Amathes*), 15
rupestralis (*Anarta*), 45
rupicapraria (*Hybernia*), 289
rusticata (*Acidalia*), 110
sacraria (*Sterrha*), 141
sagittata (*Cidaria*), 172, 173
salicalis (*Madopa*), 89
salicaria (*Coremia*), 183
salicata (*Malenydris*), 186
sambucaria (*Ourapteryx*), 282
sanbergi (*Oporabia*), 189
sanguinaria (*Sterrha*), 141
satellitia (*Eupsilia*), 27
satellitia (*Scopelosoma*), 27
saturata (*Gnophos*), 319
satyrata (*Eupithecia*), 239
scabiosata (*Eupithecia*), 242
scoliæformis (*Sesia*), 352
scotica (*Thera*), 175
Scopula, 123
scrophularia (*Cucullia*), 37
scutosa (*Heliothis*), 49
scutulata (*Acidalia*), 121
semibrunnea (*Lithophane*), 28
semibrunnea (*Xylina*), 28
sepiaria (*Tephrosia*), 322
sericeata (*Chloroclysta*), 252
sericealis (*Rivula*), 60
sericearia (*Alcis*), 306
serrina (*Amathes*), 16
Sesiidæ, 350
sexalisata (*Lobophora*), 156
shetlandica (*Xanthorhoë*), 193
signatipennis (*Crocallis*), 280
silaceata (*Eustroma*), 162
simulata (*Thera*), 176
sinuata (*Anticlea*), 216
siterata (*Cidaria*), 173

smaragdaria (*Euchloris*), 105
sobrinata (*Eupithecia*), 249
socia (*Lithophane*), 28, 29
sociata (*Xanthorhoë*), 196, 197
sodorensium (*Boarmia*), 307
solaris (*Acontia*), 53
solidaginis (*Cloantha*), 32
somniculosa (*Xylina*), 30
sordidata (*Hydriomena*), 213
spadicea (*Orrhodia*), 24
spadicearia (*Coremia*), 183
sparsata (*Collix*), 254
spartiata (*Chesias*), 150
spangbergi (*Angerona*), 281
specciformis (*Sesia*), 353
spinachiata (*Lygris*), 167
spoliata (*Acidalia*), 120
sponsa (*Catocala*), 82
statices (*Ino*), 342, 343
Sterrha, 133, 142
stevensata (*Eupithecia*), 249
stentzii (*Zygæna*), 336
straminata (*Acidalia*), 113
strataria (*Amphidasys*), 300
strataria (*Pachys*), 300
strigata (*Hemithea*), 107
strigilaria (*Acidalia*), 127
strigillaria (*Perconia*), 332
strigularia (*Tephrosia*), 312
subærata (*Chloroclystis*), 252
subciliata (*Eupithecia*), 246
subfasciaria (*Perizoma*), 208
subfulvata (*Eupithecia*), 241
subfuscata (*Eupithecia*), 235
subhastata (*Eulype*), 301, 302
sublunaria (*Selenia*), 276
subnigra (*Orrhodia*), 25
subnotata (*Eupithecia*), 237
subochracea (*Zygæna*), 335
subroseata (*Acidalia*), 128
subroseata (*Ephyra*), 140
subsericeata (*Acidalia*), 117
subspadicea (*Orrhodia*), 25
subtusa (*Plastenis*), 9
succenturiata (*Eupithecia*), 240
suffumata (*Lampropteryx*), 178
suffusa (*Mesoleuca*), 202
suffusa (*Orrhodia*), 25
suspecta (*Dyschorista*), 7
sylvata (*Abraxas*), 259
sylvina (*Hepialus*), 361
syringaria (*Hygrochroa*), 277

tabaniformis (*Sciapteron*), 351
tænialis (*Hypenodes*), 94
tæniata (*Perizoma*), 211
tamariscata (*Eupithecia*), 247
tarsicrinalis (*Zanclognatha*), 87
tarsicrinatus (*Zanclognatha*), 87

tarsipennalis (*Zanclognatha*), 87
temerata (*Bapta*), 266
tempestivata (*Gymnoscelis*), 250
tenebraria (*Dasydia*), 322
tenebrata (*Heliaca*), 46
tentaculalis (*Pyralis*), 87
tenuiata (*Eupithecia*), 245
tersata (*Phibalapteryx*), 257
testaceata (*Asthena*), 221
testata (*Lygris*), 165
testudo (*Limacodes*), 346
tetralunaria (*Selenia*), 276
thingvallata (*Cidaria*), 172
thulensis (*Hepialus*), 360
thules (*Perizoma*), 208
thules (*Xanthorhoë*), 194
thymiaria (*Hemithea*), 108
tipuliformis (*Sesia*), 354
togata (*Eucymatoge*), 251
togata (*Xanthia*), 19
torvaria (*Dasydia*), 322
trabealis (*Emmelia*), 62
trapezaria (*Crocallis*), 280
trapezina (*Calymnia*), 4
trepidaria (*Psodos*), 322
trifolii (*Zygæna*), 337
trigeminata (*Acidalia*), 122
tripartita (*Abrostola*), 74
triplasia (*Abrostola*), 73
trisignaria (*Eupithecia*), 236
tristata (*Xanthorhoë*), 198
truncata (*Cidaria*), 170
turbaria (*Perizoma*), 205
turfosalis (*Tholomiges*), 96

ultimaria (*Eupithecia*), 249
umbra (*Pyrrhia*), 47
umbratica (*Cucullia*), 40
unangulata (*Xanthorhoë*), 199
uncula (*Hydrelia*), 58
undulata (*Eucosmia*), 160
unicolor (*Cirrhœdia*), 10
unicolor (*Hemorophila*), 303
unicolor (*Ochria*), 18
unicolor (*Orrhodia*), 24, 25
unicolor (*Dasycampa*), 26
unicolorata (*Ematurga*), 324
unicolorata (*Malenydris*), 186
unicolorata (*Perizoma*), 205
unicuba (*Catocala*), 81
unidentaria (*Coremia*), 181
unifasciata (*Perizoma*), 209
uniformata (*Gnophos*), 319

unilobata (*Xanthorhoë*), 195
upsi on (*Dyschorista*), 8

vaccinii (*Conistra*), 24
vaccinii (*Orrhodia*), 24
valerianata (*Eupithecia*), 243
vanadis (*Zygæna*), 335
variata (*Thera*), 175, 177
variegata (*Anarta*), 45
varleyata (*Abraxas*), 261
v-ata (*Chloroclystis*), 251
vau-nigraria (*Thamnonoma*), 326
velleda (*Hepialus*), 362
venosa (*Amathes*), 16
venosata (*Eupithecia*), 227
venustula (*Erastria*), 59
venustula (*Monodes*), 59
verbasci (*Cucullia*), 36, 38
vernaria (*Geometra*), 103
vespiformis (*Sesia*), 355
vespiforme (*Trochilium*), 351
vetulata (*Scotosia*), 161
vetusta (*Calocampa*), 35
viciæ (*Zygæna*), 336
viduaria (*Cleora*), 310
viretata (*Lobophora*), 153
virgata (*Cloantha*), 32
virgata (*Mesotype*), 146
virgaureata (*Eupithecia*), 235
virgularia (*Acidalia*), 112
viridaria (*Amoebe*), 185
viridaria (*Prothymnia*), 61
viridata (*Nemoria*), 106
vitalbata (*Phibalapteryx*), 256
vittata (*Coenocalpe*), 256, 257
vulgata (*Eupithecia*), 234

wauaria (*Thamnonoma*), 326
wiströmi (*Anarta*), 45
woodiata (*Gnophos*), 319

xerampelina (*Atethmia*), 10
xerampelina (*Cirrhœdia*), 10

ypsilon (*Dyschorista*), 8

zalmunna (*Catocala*), 79
zinckenii (*Xylina*), 30
zonaria (*Nyssia*), 298
zonata (*Lobophora*), 155
Zonosoma, 136
Zygænidæ, 333

A LIST OF THE
FAMILIES OF BRITISH MOTHS
DESCRIBED IN THIS VOLUME.

———

NOCTUIDÆ, 1–97
    TRIFINÆ (continued), 1–62
    GONOPTERINÆ, 63
    QUADRIFINÆ, 64–85
    HYPENINÆ, 85–97
BREPHIDÆ, 97, 99
GEOMETRIDÆ, 99–100
    GEOMETRINÆ, 101–108
    ACIDALIINÆ, 109–140
    HYDRIOMENINÆ, 141–259
    BOARMIINÆ, 259–333
ZYGÆNIDÆ, 333–344
COCHLIDIDÆ, 344 347
COSSIDÆ, 347–350
SESIIDÆ, 350–360
HEPIALIDÆ, 360–364

idæ—Families
inæ—Subfamilies

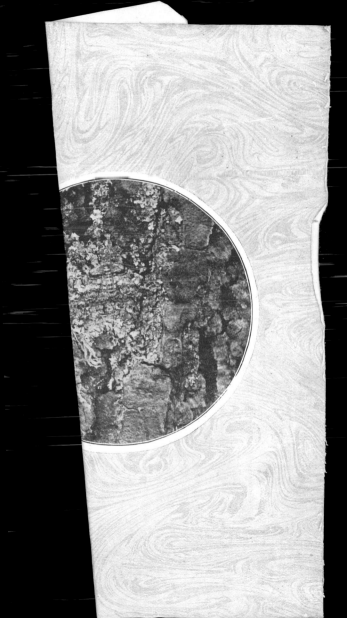